AFRICA

A Study in Tropical Development

AFRICA

A Study in Tropical Development

L. DUDLEY STAMP

Professor of Social Geography
University of London

JOHN WILEY & SONS, INC., NEW YORK
CHAPMAN & HALL, LIMITED, LONDON

Library of Congress Catalog Card Number: 53–5523

Printed in the United States of America

Preface

This book has grown indirectly from the course of lectures on the "Underdeveloped Lands" which I gave as Patten Foundation Lecturer at the University of Indiana in the spring of 1950. I was concerned to show that the word "underdeveloped" might have many meanings, and in the course of choosing examples I found myself referring again and again to the continent of Africa. The superficial judgment of anyone trained in the Western world or used to conditions which we loosely call "temperate" as opposed to "tropical" is likely to be very wide of the truth. Before we rush in, full of enthusiasm but lacking both knowledge and wisdom, to the salvation of Point IV areas we need a firmer foundation of factual information, and we need to apply ourselves seriously and humbly to its interpretation.

What I have tried to do in this book is quite dispassionately and objectively—and I hope with the complete elimination of any racial or political bias—to look at the continent of Africa: to consider its geographical background as an environment for human activity and to study the responses which have been evoked from its African inhabitants and those who, in the last few centuries, have penetrated its fastnesses and molded its fortunes.

This stock taking is what in naval parlance might be called "clearing the decks for action." To my mind it reveals how much in the way of careful detailed study and interpretation needs to be carried out. Not least among these needs are an accurate survey of the existing use (or, equally important, absence of use) of land and an honest attempt to evaluate the factors, whether they are geographical, historical, social or, more strictly, economic, which have led to the present stage in development. Such is the aim of the World Land Use Survey.

If the writing of this book has done nothing else, it has certainly clarified my own ideas on the African position, the part which that great continent plays in the world of today and its potential for the future.

v

The subject is vast, and I am conscious of many omissions in my book. In deciding what to include I have been influenced in the main by two considerations. The first is the need to keep in mind such factors as relief, climate and soil, which exercise a permanent and continuing influence on the past, present and future. The second is the desirability of dealing as far as possible with major problems rather than enlarging upon local details. This second consideration has prevented my referring to many places of interest and has necessitated my eliminating some systematic descriptions.

Any description of present economic developments is likely to become quickly out of date in an area where change is rapid. I have thus attempted to concentrate in the third part of the book on an account of the changing present together with latest available figures of population, production and trade. The reader may, as new figures become available, make the necessary additions and substitutions in Part 3.

For many years I have enjoyed the valued help of friends and colleagues who have drawn attention to errors and imperfections in my writings. I hope that they will extend to this book similar criticisms, which are always welcome.

L. D. S.

December 1952

Contents

The African Continent

CHAPTER

I

African Highlights

Africa is unique among the continents. Although each of the great continental masses of the earth's land surface has its own distinctive features, there are points of comparison between some of them. North and South America, for example, are broadly alike in build, with a great complex of mountain ranges trending from north to south in the west, vast plains in the center, and old mountain remnants and plateaus in the east. Australia repeats some of these features, though reversed—plateau in the west, central plains and mountains in the east. Asia with its huge arid mountainous heart is quite distinctive, but most mountain ranges in Asia trend from east to west, cutting off northern lands very sharply from southern. The same is true of Europe; the east-west central mountains, such as the Alps, cut off the north and northwestern European lands from the Mediterranean.

But Africa in all its major features stands alone. In the first place it lies fairly and squarely athwart the equator and projects almost equally into both the northern and the southern hemispheres. It is very roughly the same distance (2580 miles) from the equator to its northernmost point (Ras ben Sakka just west of Cape Blanco near Bizerta in Tunisia), which is in latitude 37°21′ North, as from the equator to its southernmost point in South Africa (Cape Agulhas), which is in latitude 34°51′ South (2400 miles). True, the continent is much broader in the north than in the south so that two-thirds of its area lies in the northern hemisphere, only one-third in the southern.

The bulk of its 11,700,000 square miles lies within the tropics— over 9,000,000 square miles in fact—so that it is Africa that is essentially the world's problem continent where development under tropical conditions is concerned. Africa's northern lands, cut off by the great Saharan deserts from the tropical parts, form worlds apart, fascinating in their own special problems and in their historical back-

3

grounds so different from the rest of the continent. In the extreme south of the continent the milder climatic conditions of lands again outside the tropics have combined with historical circumstances to give South Africa over the last 400 years a history very different from the history of the main mass.

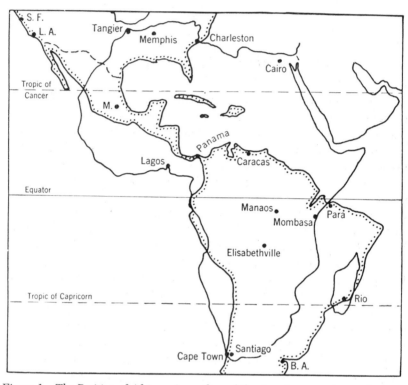

Figure 1. The Position of Africa. An outline of the Americas superimposed on an outline of Africa to show the relative position of some chief towns.

Africa is a remarkably compact land mass with no great gulf of the sea penetrating towards its heart. Figure 2 shows all those parts which are more than 250, 500, 750 and 1000 miles from the salt water of the oceans. This is in marked contrast to the North American continent. Yet the African continent has never really been a unit. The Mediterranean shoreland and the Barbary States of the northwest have always been part of the Mediterranean world cut off from what may be called Africa proper by the great Saharan desert. Egypt has been linked throughout its history with either its

Asiatic neighbors or the Mediterranean world. Off the west coasts the Azores and Cape Verde Islands are stepping stones along trans-Atlantic routes rather than African islands. The eastern shorelands of Africa have long been part of the Indian Ocean basin, indeed

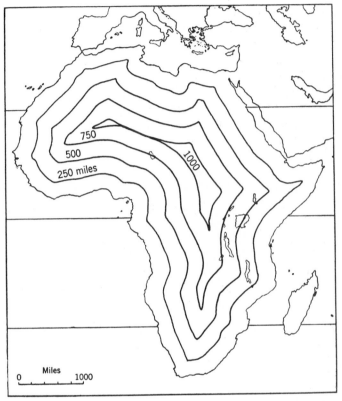

Figure 2. Africa, Showing Distances from the Heart of the Continent to the Coasts.

since the Hovas, allied racially with the peoples of southeast Asia, crossed the ocean and settled in Madagascar. The Arab traders and slavers for centuries ranged the East African coasts and penetrated considerable distances inland; they maintained the link with the other shores of the Indian Ocean and even imparted a veneer of Mohammedanism over the once extensive Sultanate of Zanzibar. Thus the "core" of Africa is intertropical Africa, south of the great deserts and away from the coasts. This, the true *Afrique noire*, has a considerable unity, even monotony of pattern. The absence of mountain barriers means that peoples and their cultures have flowed back and forth over its gently rolling plateau surfaces, and there is much to be said which remains true of east and west, north and south in this, the real Africa, the Africa of the pagan Negro.

Africa is not quite an island. Its link with Asia in the northeast is a narrow neck of flat desert land, less than 150 miles across, between the Mediterranean Sea and the Gulf of Aqaba, which joins the Red Sea. West of Sinai, between the Mediterranean and the Gulf of Suez, the Isthmus of Suez is even narrower, less than 100 miles. Yet this Isthmus of Suez has played a role throughout Africa's history out of all proportion to its inconspicuous appearance on the map. In the great days of world exploration in the fifteenth and sixteenth centuries it forced the explorers' ships that were seeking passage to the Indies to circumnavigate Africa, and incidentally to discover America. When the isthmus was cut by the Suez Canal in 1869, it focused world spotlight on the essential link in a new world trade chain. Eighty years later the control and the protection of the Suez Canal were still questions of high priority in world affairs.

Although, beginning with the voyage of Vasco da Gama from Portugal to India in 1497–1498, the continent of Africa had been continually circumnavigated, almost until the end of the nineteenth century Africa the unknown remained the Dark Continent. Books with such titles as *In Darkest Africa* served by those very titles to underline the remoteness and the isolation of lands which so long remained unknown and unexplored by Europeans.

That the whole vast extent of Africa south of the Sahara should thus have remained unknown to Europeans for more than three centuries after its shores were charted is due to an interesting and fundamentally important combination of circumstances. Inhospitable desert coasts are succeeded quite abruptly by almost equally forbidding swamps and forested shores. Except for temporary use as ports of call for running repairs, water supplies and the like on the route to India and the Far East, there was little to attract the European voyager. The scantily clad black inhabitants were all regarded simply as savages, and there were no fabulous cities with gold and silver treasure to attract *conquistadores* as in South America. Nor was there any reason why the native peoples should receive voyagers from afar with joy. For countless generations the foreigner had been identified with slave raiding; never had the stranger brought other than sorrow. Where, as on the east coast, alien traders—the

Arabs—were established, they were far from friendly towards possible rivals.

The prevalence of various tropical fevers added to the unattractiveness of tropical Africa, and where the adventurous sought to penetrate inland, natural obstacles presented themselves. In the first place the coastline of Africa is almost devoid of any major opening permitting penetration by sea into the heart of the land; indeed even harbors affording reasonable shelter are few. Along great stretches of the coast there are off-shore winds, and the great waves which break some distance out in a line of surf presented another formidable hazard. With no roads, often no tracks other than footpaths wandering from village to village, only human porters afraid to go far from their own village because of intertribal feuds, penetration by land was almost impossible. The obvious routes were up the few major rivers. It was found that in nearly all cases these routes were barred at no great distance from the sea by rapids and waterfalls which we now know to mark the descent of the rivers from the great African plateau. That great navigable stretches lay beyond these falls was not realized until much later.

Where the hinterland offered conditions more physically attractive in South Africa, the story of European interest and subsequent settlement and development, as we shall see later, has been very different. In tropical Africa there have been coastal trading posts and forts maintained by European nationals for the last five hundred years, but the "opening-up" of the interior and the partition of Africa among the European nations have taken place almost entirely within the last century. It was in 1855 that Livingstone discovered the Victoria Falls on the Zambezi; it was as recently as 1871 that H. M. Stanley set out to look for the missing Livingstone and found him lying ill at Ujiji on the shores of Lake Tanganyika.

The story of the development of Africa in the last hundred years is a complex one. It is sometimes depicted as one of exploitation of the African by the white man, and, although there are elements of exploitation to be found, a more dominant motive was the suppression of the age-old slave trade.

The opening-up of tropical Africa has brought a crop of problems, perhaps best described as the results of a clash of cultures. African tribal organizations and systems of law and justice have been brought up against Western concepts of democracy and European law. Jungle law—the survival of the fittest and might is right—may have been reflected in some aspects of the earlier European penetration but is incompatible with modern concepts.

Africa has other claims to urgent world attention. By Western standards much of the continent is underdeveloped, with resulting poverty and misery to its inhabitants and with a further consequence that resources of interest to the outside world in minerals, agricultural and forest products remain unused.

We find two consequences of this position. One is the awakened conscience of the Western world expressed most forcibly as Point IV of President Truman's address to Congress in January 1949. The other is Africa's own growth of political consciousness and move towards nationalism and self-determinism. On the whole, all those nations of Western culture which have an interest in Africa seek to guide the development of these legitimate ideals and aspirations, though clashes may result where there are different views concerning rate and type of progress. These are problems we shall try to examine in their geographical setting. Africa is the last remaining great colonial domain of the European powers. Here Britain, France, Belgium, Portugal and Spain have their chief colonial dependencies. Although each may be said to wish the progress of their African peoples, lines of development differ widely. In Africa it is a three-cornered struggle between nationalism, communism and Western interests.

Although there is, in parts of Africa, considerable pressure of population on land resources, the continent as a whole is still sparsely populated. In a number of territories no exact census has ever been taken, and in some instances, as in Uganda, where a first census was taken after the Second World War, earlier estimates were found to be very wide of the truth. In 1900 the population of the continent was estimated at 120 millions; in 1933 at 145; in 1940 at 158; and by the mid-century it had probably reached 170 millions. If, however, one excludes the Moslems of the Atlas lands, Egypt, and the white population of South Africa, the total population of Negro Africa in 1950 was probably of the order of 120 to 130 millions. Moreover, Africa has been steadily losing ground in its relative world position. If an estimate of 100,000,000 is accepted as the population in 1650, that figure would represent over 18 per cent of the world's population. By 1850, using Carr-Saunders' figures, an estimated population of 95 million would represent only 8 per cent of the world total.[1] Today

[1] A. M. Carr-Saunders, *World Population*, London, 1936.

Africa as a whole has about 7 per cent of the world's people, and Negro Africa about 5 per cent.

Although in some areas the population density may be the maximum supportable under existing conditions and existing economic systems, potential changes are enormous. The spread of the knowledge of medicine and hygiene means greatly increased survival rates and greater longevity. The conquest of such pests and diseases—so often described as the real rulers of Africa—as tsetse fly, locusts, yellow fever, malaria and hookworm means that enormous areas at present unusable may be thrown open to settlement and development. Increased control of water supplies will mean a maintenance of crop yields as well as an extension of irrigated areas; the spread of agricultural knowledge can only result in greater productivity. When cattle come to be regarded as sources of human sustenance rather than symbols of wealth, the carrying capacity of the lands in terms of human beings will be still further increased.

Some writers place the control of water as the foundation for all development, but others would echo the words of Lord Lugard: "The material development of Africa may be summed up in one word—transport."

All the signs are that Africa is on the threshold of a period of great population expansion coupled with economic and political development. The lesson of Africa, however, has been, over and over again, to "make haste slowly." The failure of some recent large schemes has served to emphasize this lesson.

The emphasis in this book is on Africa between the tropics. The monotony of the physical pattern over much of this vast area is matched by the sameness of human response. From the far west to the east coasts the African system of shifting cultivation is found with little variation. Yet there are contrasts, and Africa today may be divided into four regions: Mediterranean Africa, which is part of the Moslem world; western Atlantic Africa, which is tropical Africa *par excellence;* eastern Africa, affected by large-scale immigration by non-African peoples, notably Arabs, Indians and Europeans; South Africa, the white man's stronghold. Each has its own problems; each reacts upon the other. Not least among the problems is the contrast between the white settlers' outlook in South Africa and the attitude of the rest of the Western world.

From another point of view, Pierre Gourou in his *Pays tropicaux* draws a distinction between "tropical lands" with a rainfall exceeding 800 millimeters (16 inches) a year and "desert lands" occupying drier country, where the problems are different.   Here again, in this book, the emphasis is on tropical Africa.

BIBLIOGRAPHY

Books dealing comprehensively with the whole continent of Africa in its geographical setting are few.   First place must be given to the two volumes in the great French *Géographie universelle: Afrique septentrionale et occidentale* (Vol. XI, in two parts), by A. Bernard; and *Afrique équatoriale, orientale et australe* (Vol. XII), by F. Maurette (1937–1939).

In English, *Africa*, by Walter Fitzgerald (New York, First Edition, 1934, Seventh Edition, 1950), is a general geography emphasizing the physical background and especially the major regions.   There is still much of value in A. H. Keane's *Africa* (*Stanford's Compendium of Geography and Travel*, 2 volumes, Second Edition, London, 1907).   When the problems of Africa were coming markedly to the fore an administrator with wide experience was commissioned to make a comprehensive survey.   The result was Lord Hailey's *An African Survey* (Oxford, Second Edition, 1945).   It is not a geography but a mine of information. Later Lord Hailey followed this with a four-volume account of administration in the British Colonial territories.   Certain scientific and economic materials could not be included in the original survey but were published in E. B. Worthington's *Science in Africa* (Oxford, 1938).

For a valuable pictorial survey and careful commentary reference should be made to R. U. Light's *Focus on Africa* (American Geographical Society, 1944). For illuminating sidelights Julian Huxley's *Africa View* (London, 1931) may be noted.   Though dealing with the subject generally, R. J. Harrison-Church's *Modern Colonization* (London, Hutchinson, 1951) has much of relevance to African problems.   The same is true of the scholarly work of Pierre· Gourou, *Tropical Lands* (New York, 1953).   As the political development of Africa commands the attention of the world, books such as W. M. Macmillan's *Africa Emergent* (Revised Edition, Pelican Books, 1949) help greatly in the interpretation of the changing scene.   A survey of the main problems of British Africa in the years following the Second World War has been given in small compass by four authors in *Attitude to Africa* (Penguin Books, 1951).   At the same time economic and industrial developments have been taking place at an ever-increasing rate, and a valuable survey has been given in the United Nations publication, *Review of Economic Conditions in Africa* (1951).

CHAPTER
2

Unrolling the Map
of Africa

The sea in the midst of the lands, the Mediterranean, if not the cradle of mankind, has seen around its shores the birth, growth and decay of many great civilizations. Its Asiatic, African and European shorelands have all shared in this early history—Babylonia, Assyria, Phoenicia, Israel and later the Ottoman Turks in Asiatic lands; Greece and Rome in Europe, and Minos on the Island of Crete. But perhaps the greatest of all these early civilizations was in Egypt, on African soil. Egyptian civilization flourished for some four millennia before the birth of Jesus Christ. In the great days of Rome, Carthage, founded by the Phoenicians in the ninth century before Christ and also in North Africa, was more than once a serious contender for world supremacy. In the eighth and ninth centuries of the Christian era when Mohammedanism swept across North Africa, Moorish or Arab domains extended from Egypt across to Morocco and thence into Iberia.

Thus the long well-documented history of North African lands is in complete contrast to the almost history-less story of most of the rest of the continent. What was the barrier which separated two worlds so utterly in contrast? It was, as it still is, the greatest arid waste on the earth's surface, the Sahara Desert, stretching unbroken from the Atlantic coasts to the shores of the Red Sea, and nowhere less than a thousand miles wide.

The one natural routeway across the desert waste would appear to be the River Nile. But sailing up the Nile beyond Upper Egypt is impossible, for no less than six series of cataracts obstruct navigation between Assuan and Khartoum. Above Khartoum another obstacle exists in the form of great masses of floating vegetation, or sudd.

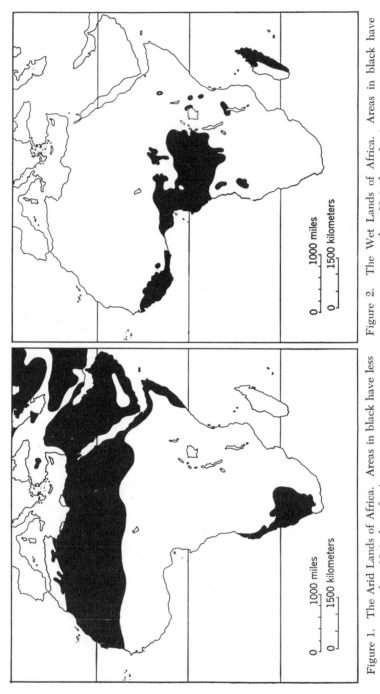

Figure 2.   The Wet Lands of Africa.   Areas in black have more than 60 inches of rain a year.

Figure 1.   The Arid Lands of Africa.   Areas in black have less than 10 inches of rain a year.

Thus for thousands of years those who dwelt within reach of the Mediterranean had no direct knowledge of the lands which lay to the south of the great wastes. The nomadic tribesmen who knew the secrets of its waterholes took care to keep their knowledge to themselves for their livelihood depended upon the transport of a few rare commodities cheaply obtained in the south which the northerners valued.

In the Christian era the spread of Mohammedanism only intensified the barrier; the Christian who attempted to penetrate the barrier took his life in his hands.

For many centuries, indeed millennia, Negro Africa, as we may call those parts of the continent south of the Sahara, yielded but one product of major interest to the outside world. That product was slaves. Slavery would seem to be indigenous in Negro Africa itself. There were Negro slaves in ancient Egypt; Ethiopian and Negro slaves were by no means unknown in Greece and Imperial Rome— Arab slave traders brought them across the northern deserts; Arab slave ships called in at ports down the east coast. It was about 1442 that the first Negroes were brought from West Africa by the Portuguese to work in Spain and Portugal, and it was from there that they were introduced into the New World—some to Haiti as early as 1502. In 1517 Bartolomé de las Casas, the celebrated Bishop of Chiapa, sought to relieve the sufferings of the native Indians of Haiti working in the mines by securing a license to import slaves. This was really the beginning of the systematic slave trade between Africa and America.

When the Portuguese were allotted by the Pope's Line the Brazilian shores of South America they did not find there the sophisticated Inca cities with stores of gold and silver such as lured the Spaniards in the western parts of the continent. They found instead land which could yield abundantly if only labor were available. This constituted another large demand for slave labor in the New World. Though the English Admiral John Hawkins, at war with Spain and Portugal, captured slaving ships and then sold the slaves to the Spanish settlements as early as 1562, it was not till 1620 that a Dutch ship sailed for Jamestown in Virginia and sold the first slaves to a British American settlement. As sugar plantations became established in the West Indies and cotton plantations in the American South, Britain developed the notorious "triangular traffic." Ships left Liverpool, Bristol or Lancaster in Britain with cotton goods, cheap jewelry and other merchandise or gold as the price of slaves.

They took on their human cargo along the "Slave Coast" as parts of West Africa were long known, sailed across the Atlantic, sold the slaves and returned to Britain with cargoes of sugar and raw cotton. Bad as were the conditions on the slave ships the hardly won cargo was too valuable to lose, and the survival rate was high, about 85 per cent. On the coasts of East Africa conditions in the slave trade were infinitely worse; it has been said that sometimes only 10 per cent of the cargo of some Arab slave ships survived. The West African trade reached its height just before the War of American Independence when 192 slave ships, with a capacity of 47,000 Negroes, were sailing from these British ports. In 1790, during the revival of slave trade after the war 75,000 slaves were landed in America by the British, French, Portuguese, Dutch and Danes.

The slave trade conferred one lasting benefit on Africa. For the purpose of feeding the slaves herded together in the coastal barracoons awaiting shipment to the Americas and also for feeding the same slaves en route, the Europeans, especially the Portuguese, introduced many exotic food plants since local foodstuffs were either too scarce or too perishable. In this way corn, peanuts, manioc, sweet potatoes, coconuts, bananas and citrus fruits were introduced into Africa. The long-term results on African diets have been almost as revolutionary as the introduction into the Americas by the Spaniards of such European animals as the horse and cattle or such grains as wheat.

It may seem strange that this trade in Negro slaves continued for so many centuries. Why, for example, did not the Africans band themselves together to prevent it? It is necessary to form a picture of a continent inhabited by warring tribes. The hunters who depended for their existence on the chase wanted vast tracts of land in which to hunt; they resented any intruders. The nomadic cattle keepers and herdsmen needed vast open grasslands for their animals and resented any enclosures, though their animals appreciated succulent crops stolen from sedentary cultivators. Those who had adopted the settled life and systems of shifting cultivation were at pains to keep off the cattlemen. Almost any one of these groups would view the selling of an enemy as a slave a more profitable solution to his problem than killing him. Over this continent-wide pattern of incompatible economic elements were the ambitious empire builders, gaining wealth and power by selling their captives or betraying enemies. The Moslems from the north brought Islam to the Negroes along the Saharan borders but made little impression on the vast tribes of pagans, and it was clearly in accord with the will of Allah to rid the world of the infidels. So great was the drain on the continent that it is probable that its overall population was actually reduced from the sixteenth to the nineteenth centuries.

Mention of the early Portuguese participants in the slave trade brings us to consider the European exploration of African coastlands. The Carthaginian Hanno claims to have made a voyage about 470 B.C. through the Pillars of Hercules (Strait of Gibraltar) and along the west coast of Africa, with the object of founding colonies. He probably reached south of the Gambia River, but for many centuries his discoveries were forgotten. It was only after the decline of the Moorish power in Spain and the rise of Spain and Portugal to front rank among the nations that European exploration by sea of the African coasts was undertaken in earnest.

Prince Henry the Navigator (1394–1460) was the fourth son of King John (João) I of Portugal and his French bride Philippa, daughter of John of Gaunt. He discovered the fertile island of Madeira, and his ships sailed on past the inhospitable Saharan coasts of the mainland to the green lands beyond, hence the name Cape Verde (or "Green Cape") and Cape Verde Islands. Prince Henry established a school for navigation and an observatory.

Before the voyages of Columbus, the Portuguese had sailed along the coasts of Guinea, and Bartholomeu Diaz (1455–1500), without realizing it, had rounded the south of Africa into the Indian Ocean in 1486. It was the strong easterly winds which drove him back to the Cape of Storms, afterwards renamed by the King of Portugal, the Cape of Good Hope.

These probing voyages of the Portuguese were prompted by a desire to reach the spice lands of the Far East by an all-water route instead of having to rely on the uncertain and expensive supplies brought to Europe overland.

Although the shores of Greenland, Labrador and other parts of North America were undoubtedly known to early Norse voyagers and others from northwestern Europe, the discovery of America is normally understood to mean the first sighting of land by Christopher Columbus in the Bahama group in 1492. The voyage of Columbus the Genoese, financed by Spain, had been undertaken, it is generally believed, to find a westward route to the Spice Islands of the East Indies. There are, however, those scholars who consider that the North American continent had been discovered some years earlier by Portuguese sailors and that when Columbus sailed he already knew that his way to the west would be barred by a great continent. At a time when there was intense rivalry, indeed mortal enmity, between Spain and Portugal it is difficult to understand why Columbus on his return voyage called at the Azores—Portuguese territory—and then went straight to Lisbon. It is difficult to believe that he was such a bad navigator that he struck Lisbon in Portugal accidentally instead of Cadiz, or some other part of Spain. In Lisbon he was certainly granted an interview with the King of Portugal and then allowed to depart unhindered for Spain, instead, as one might have thought, of being imprisoned or even executed. Was King John of Portugal his secret master? Was the object of the intrigue to draw the attention of Spain to the New Lands of the New World while Portugal consolidated her interests in India and the Far East by seeking the Cape route? If so, it succeeded to an amazing degree, and we have fully explained the lack of Spanish interest in the early exploration and development of Africa.

If those are right who believe the Portuguese knew of the existence of the American continent before Columbus sailed on his first voyage, we have a reason for the ready acceptance by the Portuguese of the Treaty of Tordesillas in 1493. It will be recalled that this treaty gave lands discovered west of 60° West to Spain; lands east of that line to Portugal. Though this treaty is normally considered as applying to the Americas—it gave Brazil to Portugal before land in that area was even discovered—it clearly gave authority to Portuguese claims to *any* lands east of the 60° West meridian, that is, to all Africa. While Columbus and the Spaniards were concentrating on the New World, Portugal was certainly active in the search for the sea route to India. Vasco da Gama rounded the Cape of Good Hope in 1497 and landed on the well-watered forested coasts farther to the northeast on Christmas Day; hence the name Natal which he gave to the area, and which has remained to this day. He reached what is now Lourenço Marques on Delagoa Bay on March 1, 1498, but farther north he was not welcomed by the Arab traders and settlers in the coastal towns. As it turned out, this was fortunate for he secured a pilot who directed him across to India and he landed at Calicut, previously visited by Cavilhao traveling via Egypt in 1486. The way to India was won. The great spice trade was soon firmly in Portuguese hands, and the Spaniards could have America. A settlement was established at Mozambique in 1505; a fortified factory was built at Calicut in 1510 and established as a Portuguese settlement and trading post; Goa was occupied in 1510; the coasts of Ceylon were settled in the next few years, and Malacca on the coast of Malaya was captured in 1511. A little later, in 1557, Portuguese settled on the island of Macao off the south of China.

While the Spanish Conquistadores were busy with the northern coastlands of South America, the Portuguese Cabral, taking advantage of the northeast Trades on his way to India, found himself carried too far westward and off the coasts of Brazil. This was in 1500, and the land was promptly claimed by Portugal. In the following year, 1501, the King of Portugal sent out Amerigo Vespucci to follow up Cabral's discovery. He probably (though there is some doubt about his achievements) traversed the whole coast of South America from Cape San Roque to the Plate estuary, and then sailed on to South Georgia. Portugal thus gained interests on both sides of the South Atlantic, but it was the sea route to India which was of immediate importance. It is said that Algoa Bay (on which Port Elizabeth now stands) was the resting place "on the way to Goa," while Delagoa Bay in what later became Portuguese East Africa was the most convenient port of call "on the way from Goa."

In the meantime the Portuguese had penetrated well into the Gulf of Guinea. They observed the frequent thunderstorms around the norite mass which forms the Peak in what is now Sierra Leone and likened the noise to the constant roaring of lions, hence the name Lion Mountains or Sierra Leone. They founded their first permanent station at Elmina on the Gold Coast as early as 1481. The small quantities of alluvial gold brought down from the interior and exchanged for manufactures by the tribes of the coast originally made these lands of interest to Europeans. African ivory had long been famous, but it was slave trading that soon became most important. The Portuguese established a string of forts to guard their interests in the trade. British traders visited the West African coasts from 1530 onward, and it was as early as 1554 that the famous Captain Thomas Wyndham died in the creeks of the Oil Rivers, or Niger Delta. It was not until the early seventeenth century that the British established their first trading post, a fort on the Gambia River. That century witnessed the ousting of the Portuguese by the Dutch, but the Dutch found themselves sharing interests with the British while Denmark and Brandenburg also had forts along the coast. France was also interested in the far eastern trade. French interests in Senegal (West Africa) date from 1637, and the capital, Saint-Louis, was founded in 1658. In the Indian Ocean the French have held Réunion since 1643 and were masters of Mauritius (Île de France) from 1715 to 1810, and Pondicherry, the oldest French Indian settlement, was founded in 1674.

It was not until towards the end of the eighteenth century that a profound change took place in the European (and by this time American) attitude towards Africa. On the one hand was the growth

Figure 3. The Old Danish Fort of Christiansborg Castle, Accra. It is now used as the official residence of the Governor of the Gold Coast. (British Official Photograph.)

of the movement for the abolition of slavery: on the other hand, the urge towards exploration of the unknown African interior.

In Britain the abolitionists found a champion in William Wilberforce. Born in 1759, he was elected to Parliament at the age of 21 and was soon known for his forceful advocacy of many philanthropic causes. In 1787 he took on the leadership of the abolitionists and fought doggedly for 20 years before his dreams were realized. In 1807 the British Parliament passed a measure for the abolition of the slave trade. This was, of course, an entirely different matter from the abolition of slavery and the emancipation of slaves, but Wilberforce lived to see this ideal realized too. He died in 1833, the year in which slavery was abolished throughout the British Empire. Even in the early days the abolitionists were not inactive. In 1787 they formed the Sierra Leone Company, with a trading charter from the British crown, but with the avowed object of resettling freed slaves in Africa. It was impossible to return the slaves to their native places because these places were unknown. A tract of land, therefore, was ceded to the Company by its native ruler in Sierra Leone. The task was a difficult one, but after early troubles progress was made, especially after the founding of Freetown in 1792. However, the Company was glad to transfer its responsibilities to the British crown in 1808. Though it was not the oldest of the British Colonies in Africa, the origin of Sierra Leone as one of the oldest as a home for freed slaves should not be forgotten.

American interests in tropical Africa have a similar origin. In 1821 the American Colonization Society selected Cape Mesurado (now Monrovia) as an area to which freed slaves could be sent, and the American-Negro colony was founded between 1822 and 1828 by the white American Jehudi Ashmun, some 30 years after the founding of Freetown. The name Liberia was given to the settlement in 1824 by the Reverend R. R. Gurley. Another settlement, like Liberia a republic, named Maryland existed until the two were joined in 1857. Curiously enough, the United States did not recognize the new republic until 1862.

The early years of the nineteenth century were the days of Britain's struggle with Napoleon of France, a struggle which did not cease until the decisive victory at Waterloo in Belgium in 1815 and Napoleon's exile to St. Helena. Even then, the traditional British-French rivalry persisted. The abolition of slavery in 1807 rendered the West African forts of little value. By 1821 the number of British stations was reduced from twelve to four despite many requests from the Africans that Britain should take over the whole coast from Gambia to the Congo. By 1820 the forts, however, assumed a new importance as bases from which the British navy could operate against the remaining slave traders. The handful of traders who refused to leave the coast when Britain proposed to evacuate the whole area turned the scales towards a new growth of real trade.

Turning to exploration, we have an important name in the Scottish doctor, Mungo Park, who set out from the mouth of the Gambia in 1795 to find the great river known to exist inland and called the Niger. He traveled almost due east, and passed through country where he found strong, well-built Negroes engaged in cattle rearing and in burning the grass· of the savanna lands in the dry season,

which they believed improved the growth of succulent shoots later.
When he entered the country of the Mohammedan emirates he found
hostility but persisted—as a Christian in danger of his life—northeast-

Figure 4. Reproduction of a Map of Africa, 1821. This map shows the large
areas of the interior then remaining unknown, including the Congo and Zambezi
rivers, the true course of the Niger and the source of the Nile. (From *A New
and Comprehensive System of Modern Geography*, by Thomas Myers, London,
1822.)

wards to the Saharan margins, where wandering pastoralists were still unfriendly. He reached the Niger at Segu and traveled down it some fifty miles before he decided to return. Despite great hardships (it was the rainy season), he had, on his return, a burning desire to solve the riddle of the Niger. In 1805 he set out again on a similar route. He was never again seen alive by white men; he was drowned at the falls of Bussa (now in the heart of Nigeria) after an attack by local tribesmen. So the outlet of the Niger remained a mystery until 1830, when R. L. Lander proved the "Oil Rivers" to be the delta of the Niger.

It is interesting to turn for comparison to South Africa, where the story of European interest and penetration was very different. In general terms the climatic conditions around the Cape of Good Hope are comparable to those in the pleasantest parts of California. The winters are milder, and the summers are less scorching than in Mediterranean Europe, but there is abundant sunshine in the well-watered coastal plains and valleys. Furthermore, there are some reasonably good natural harbors, especially the harbor of Cape Town under the shelter of Table Mountain. Though known to and used by the Portuguese ships en route to the Indian Ocean, Cape Town came into being as a regular halfway house when the Dutch ousted the Portuguese in the Far Eastern trade. Though the Dutch East India Company was sternly against the establishment of a colony, it was convenient to allow old servants of the Company to retire there and grow produce and rear cattle for the benefit of ships which called to re-water and re-victual. Naturally farms were established at increasing distances from the coast, and the settlers came into collision with the native Hottentots against whom the Dutch Company had neither men nor materials to defend Dutch nationals. The British occupied the Cape during the Napoleonic Wars to protect the sea route to India, and by the Peace Treaty of 1814 they retained the territory. By this time the Dutch farmers or "Boers" (*boer* = farmer) had become well established, but, as they expanded farther into the interior, they met increasing resistance not only from the Hottentots but also from the Kaffirs. This was not altogether the fault of the Kaffirs for they were being pressed southward by the war-like Bantu tribes sweeping southward from central Africa. The Boer farmers relied on slave labor, taking the frontiersman's view that when there were signs of trouble a dead Kaffir was safer than a live one.

The British, on the other hand, had abolished slave trading and were seeking to abolish slavery altogether. They sought to replace the frontiersman's methods by peaceful settlements. Disagreement between the Boer farmers and the British Government came to a head in 1833 when slavery was abolished and the Boers received eventually somewhat inadequate compensation for the loss of their slaves. In 1836 the Great Trek began; the Boer settlers set off with their great lumbering ox wagons, each with a "span" of sixteen oxen, into the interior. They crossed the Orange River and later set up the Orange Free State (Orange Vrij Staat). Others crossed the Vaal River, fought the Matabele, and established what later became the Transvaal Republic. In 1837 Piet Retief crossed the scarp of the Drakensberg into country occupied by the Zulus, but he and other leaders were murdered by the Zulu king in February 1838. Though the Zulus were defeated later the same year, the Boers found a British colony already established at Fort Natal. After a period of friction Natal was declared a British Colony (1843), and the Boers left.

The British Government was in a difficult position when the Great Trek took place. Should it try to follow the trekkers and attempt both to control and protect them, thus involving itself in a possibly endless war? Or should it let them go and risk their being overcome by the hostile Kaffir tribes? In 1852 the decision was made by recognizing the Transvaal as an independent republic, provided there should be no slavery. The trekkers of the Orange Free State were more doubtful about accepting independence if it involved losing protection. Nevertheless, the Orange Free State was declared formally independent in 1854. Thus in broad lines the four countries which eventually became provinces of the Union of South Africa were established by 1854.

By this time the work of exploration from South Africa associated with the name of Dr. David Livingstone was already well advanced. David Livingstone, the son of a poor Scot, was born in 1813. Though he was working in a cotton mill at the age of 10, he had a burning desire to become a medical missionary to China. The London Missionary Society sent him instead to South Africa. He arrived at Cape Town early in 1841, proceeding at once to the mission station established by Robert Moffat at Kuruman in southern Bechuanaland. In 1844 he married Mary Moffat, who (sometimes with young children) accompanied him on many of his journeys until her death at Shupanja in 1862. In 1849 he discovered Lake Ngami, which has since partly dried up. In 1850 he reached the Upper Zambezi with

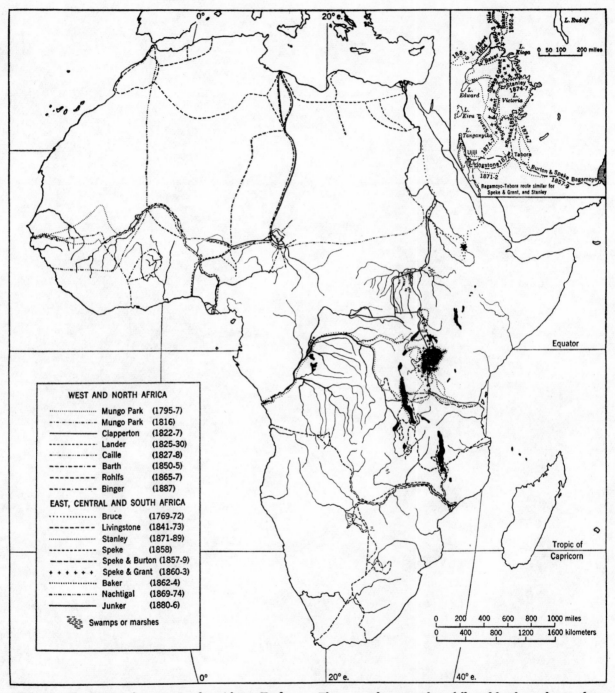

WEST AND NORTH AFRICA

··········	Mungo Park	(1795-7)
·—·—·—	Mungo Park	(1816)
————	Clapperton	(1822-7)
— — — —	Lander	(1825-30)
·····—·····—	Caille	(1827-8)
— ·· — ·· —	Barth	(1850-5)
— — — —	Rohlfs	(1865-7)
— · — · —	Binger	(1887)

EAST, CENTRAL AND SOUTH AFRICA

··············	Bruce	(1769-72)
— — — —	Livingstone	(1841-73)
··············	Stanley	(1871-89)
— — — —	Speke	(1858)
— — — —	Speke & Burton	(1857-9)
+ + + + +	Speke & Grant	(1860-3)
··············	Baker	(1862-4)
— ·· — ·· —	Nachtigal	(1869-74)
————	Junker	(1880-6)
〰️	Swamps or marshes	

Equator

Tropic of Capricorn

0 200 400 600 800 1000 miles
0 400 800 1200 1600 kilometers

Figure 5. The Routes of Certain Leading African Explorers. The routes shown are those followed by the explorers whose work is mentioned in the text, together with others who added greatly to the knowledge of the interior of the continent prior to 1850.

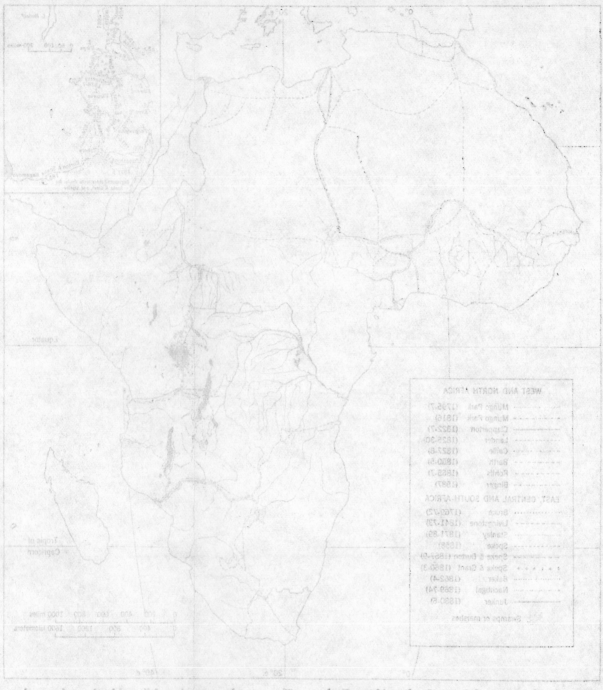

Figure 5. The Routes of Certain Leading African Explorers. The routes shown are those followed by the explorers whose work is mentioned in the text, together with others who added greatly to the knowledge of the interior of the continent prior to 1850.

his wife and children, but they fell sick and he sent them back to Cape Town (incidentally they took nearly two years on the journey). From the Upper Zambezi he went north and west up the Liba to Lake Dilolo, arriving, exhausted from fever and ill nourished, at Loanda on the west coast on May 31, 1854. Nothing daunted, he returned in 1855 to the interior determined to follow the Zambezi to its mouth. On this journey he discovered the Great Falls, which he named in honor of Queen Victoria, in 1855 and reached the mouth of the Zambezi the following May. After a sojourn in England he set off in 1858 on a second journey to Africa with his brother Charles and John Kirk. The expedition started up the Zambezi and its tributary the Shiré, met the inevitable rapids, but on a second attempt light canoes were carried to the navigable upper reaches. The party had many other troubles, but when he returned in July 1864 Livingstone had explored the Shiré River, discovered Lakes Shirwa and Nyasa and opened the eyes of the world to the horrors of the slave trade which still existed. Although Livingstone declared that he found exploring easier than writing, his diary [1] is fascinating reading. On his 1849 journey to Lake Ngami he spent some time among the Bushmen. By showing them how to irrigate their crops in this dry Kalahari country from wells in the dry season and streams in the precarious wet season he did much to ameliorate their hard life. In his 1855 journey he met with suspicion as well as demands for bribes from the native chiefs. He learned also of the many plagues of Africa: heat and drought; mosquitoes which were sometimes only annoying, at other times dangerous carriers of fever; the tsetse fly, which caused havoc among his cattle and pack animals and was capable also of bringing the dread sleeping sickness to man. Travel by canoe involved the hazards of attack by crocodiles and by the floating logs which resolved on approach into hippopotami capable of capsizing the canoes if only in play. Living entirely on the country meant killing antelopes in the savanna lands and subsisting on nuts and fruits in the forests.

In 1865 he started on his last journey with the object of finding the source of the Nile, an old problem. It cannot be said that he was treated overgenerously. The British Government granted him £500 (then about $2500), and the Royal Geographical Society a like amount. While he wandered over vast tracts of country from Lake Nyasa to Lake Tanganyika he was lost to the world, and his fate for five years was unknown.

[1] *Missionary Travels and Researches in South Africa*, London, 1857.

The exploration of Dr. Livingstone and his revelations of the horrors of the slave trade which still existed had aroused intense interest in the United States, where slavery had been finally abolished in 1864. Mr. Gordon Bennett of the *New York Herald* translated into deeds the popular demand by sending Henry Morton Stanley with a well-equipped expedition to search for Livingstone. Stanley was an Englishman born in North Wales in 1841, who emigrated to New Orleans at the age of fifteen and sought adventure as a roaming journalist. Having already accompanied Lord Napier's Abyssinian expedition in 1867–1868 as special correspondent for the *New York Herald*, he was the obvious person to send in search of Livingstone. Reaching Zanzibar in 1871, later in the year, he came upon Livingstone, ill with fever but indomitable as ever, at Ujiji on the shores of Lake Tanganyika. Livingstone refused to return and, partly recovered in health, he and Stanley explored the northern end of Lake Tanganyika together. When Stanley reluctantly left him, Livingstone set off once again to seek the source of the Nile. His health deteriorated, and on May 1, 1873, his followers found him dead. He was at Chitambo's village on the Molilamo, actually one of the headstreams of the Congo. The love and confidence he had inspired in his African followers were well shown in the devotion with which they carried his body a thousand miles to Zanzibar, whence it was conveyed to England and buried in Westminster Abbey.

Before we review the later work of Stanley we must look at some of the earlier exploration in East Africa. Little is known of the early contacts between Egypt and the peoples to the south, including the ancient Empire of Ethiopia or Abyssinia. The Abyssinians proper or Amharas were converted to Christianity in the fourth century, and connection has been maintained continuously with the Coptic Church of Alexandria since the Abuna or Chief Bishop of Ethiopia had (until the Second World War) always been a Copt and appointed by the Coptic Patriarch of Alexandria. This did not, however, result in any direct contacts between Europe and Ethiopia. The first written record of a land exploration by a European is that of the Portuguese missionary, Father Lobo, who reached Ethiopia in 1622. Although he saw the deep valleys whose waters feed the Blue Nile he did not realize the connection, and it was not until 1770 that the Scottish explorer, James Bruce (1730–1794), in the course of five years' journeying in Ethiopia, solved the riddle by following the Blue Nile down until it joined the main river, the White Nile, at Khartoum. Nearly a century was to pass before Speke solved the riddle of the source of the White Nile.

Exploration in East Africa was hindered, even along the coastlands, by the jealousy of Arab seamen and traders. Richard Francis Burton, born in England, educated in France, Italy and at the University of Oxford, served as a young man in the Indian Army and as a surveyor before he made his famous journey to Mecca in 1853 disguised as an Indian Pathan. He then turned his attention to Africa and was the first white man to enter the Somali capital of Harrar. He had time to serve in the British Army though never actually reaching the front in Crimea before joining John Hanning Speke (1827–1864) when they set off in June 1857 from Zanzibar westward. They crossed the high grassy plateau abounding in game in what is now Tanganyika until they overlooked that great rift in the earth's crust, the East African Rift Valley, with the long narrow Lake Tanganyika at their feet. This was in 1858, and they reached the settlement of Ujiji where thirteen years later Stanley was to find the sick Livingstone. Burton was already seriously ill, and, leaving him at Tabora, Speke went on northwards alone. He discovered the great inland sea, which he named in honor of Queen Victoria, before returning to Burton. With Burton's later journeys in West Africa, South America and elsewhere we are little concerned, but Speke, accompanied by J. A. Grant, set off on a second expedition with the help of the Royal Geographical Society in 1860. They reached and were detained in the capital of the prosperous land of Uganda but were later released. Finding that the waters of Lake Victoria poured out over the Ripon Falls, they realized that at last they had found the source of the Nile. To confirm what must have been virtually certain they followed the river northwards until they had the good fortune to meet S. W. Baker (1863), who had journeyed up the White Nile through the Sudd Region. Speke published his findings in 1863, but his old companion Burton was not fully convinced. Speke accidentally shot himself the very day he was to meet Burton and defend his momentous discoveries. Samuel White Baker (1821–1893), after eight years in Ceylon attempting to form an agricultural settlement on the English model, started his explorations of the Nile Basin in 1861. He explored the Atbara and Ea tributaries and, after meeting Speke, went on to find Albert Nyanza (1864), which he showed contributed an important part of the waters of the Nile. In 1870 he was actually appointed Governor-General of the Nile Equatorial Districts by the

Khedive Ismael to suppress the slave trade and open up the area to trade. In this post he laid the foundation for the work of General Charles George Gordon, his successor.

We must now return to H. M. Stanley, who set out on his second journey in 1874 with the main object of solving some of the great problems which the death of Livingstone had left unsolved. He circumnavigated Lake Victoria, passed down the Lualaba to where it becomes the Congo and then down that great river to the sea. It was Leopold II, King of the Belgians, who realized the enormous potential value of this navigable highway penetrating into the heart of Africa. On his behalf Stanley headed an expedition in 1879 which resulted in the establishment of the "Congo Free State" five years later. For many years, indeed until 1907–1908, this enormous area in the heart of Africa remained the personal possession of the King of Belgium. With its establishment the "scramble for Africa" may fairly said to have begun. It was precipitated by the activities of the German explorer, Karl Peters (1856–1918). Peters founded the German Colonization Society at Berlin in 1884 and in the same year made an expedition to East Africa.

The chief ruler in East Africa had long been the Sultan of Zanzibar. After the abolition of slavery in the British Empire in 1833, Britain's policy was to influence this powerful ruler against slavery and to persuade him to undertake the necessary reforms, and to help him to do so. The first British Consul at Zanzibar was appointed in 1840, but it was not until Sir John Kirk was appointed in 1873 and occupied himself with great skill for fifteen years that slavery was actually brought to an end and replaced by legitimate trading. At first the closing of ports to the Arab slavers drove them inland, then Britain supported the Zanzibar Sultan Barghash with arms and ammunition and the sultanate began to grow into a real state. But Karl Peters had gained access to East Africa with three companions, all in disguise and using false names. They traveled around the country, obtaining concessions for the German Colonization Society from chieftains who were in fact under the Sultan of Zanzibar's suzerainty. In 1885 the German Government backed up the claims based on these treaties with local chieftains and sent a fleet to anchor off Zanzibar, which they threatened to bombard. The British Government weakly instructed Kirk to advise the Sultan to submit, with the result that he lost the bulk of his mainland territory, and German East Africa came into existence.

But for two circumstances the whole of East Africa might have become German. One was an Arab revolt which, though suppressed

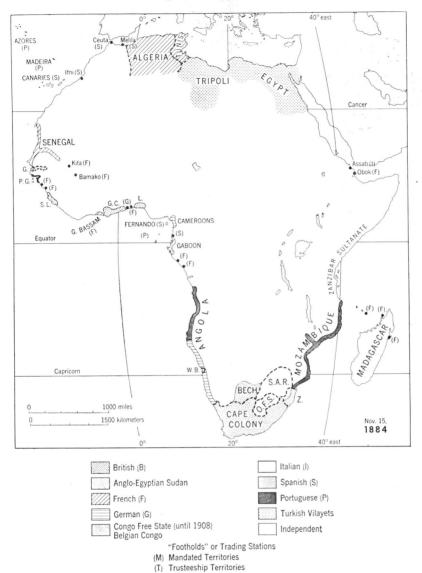

British (B)

Anglo-Egyptian Sudan

French (F)

German (G)

Congo Free State (until 1908)
Belgian Congo

Italian (I)

Spanish (S)

Portuguese (P)

Turkish Vilayets

Independent

"Footholds" or Trading Stations
(M) Mandated Territories
(T) Trusteeship Territories

Figure 6.   Africa, November 15, 1884.   This map shows the spheres of influence of the various European powers prior to the Berlin Conference.   It indicates also the footholds or trading stations.   With the exception of two French trading stations in Senegal, European influences were entirely restricted to the coast.

Note.   Figures 6 to 13 show the partition of Africa among European and other powers.   Each of these maps has been drawn on the same scale and with the same key and indicates the rapid partition of Africa and the very small part of the continent (indicated by unshaded areas) which remained under African control.

in 1889, occupied the attention of the German administration. The other was the formation of the British East Africa Company in 1888 with the primary aim of rousing British public opinion to a realiza-

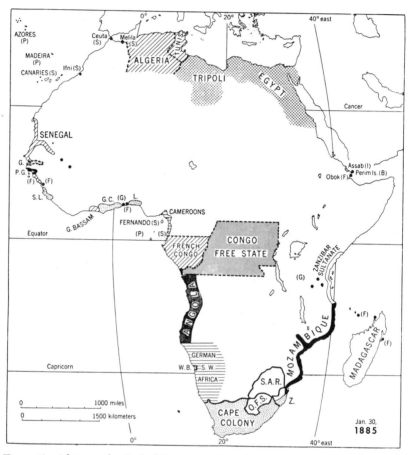

Figure 7.   Africa at the End of January, 1885, after the Berlin Conference.   The broad claim of the French to the French Congo is indicated by broken lines and the approximate area laid down for the Congo Free State.

tion of the importance of East Africa and to act as an agent of civilization and good government in the regions entrusted to it.   The Company successfully contended the claim of Peters to Uganda until the British Prime Minister, Gladstone, was forced by public opinion against his own will to take over responsibility in 1893.   The Company similarly looked after the destiny of the territory, later known as Kenya, until it surrendered its charter in 1895. British East Africa became a protectorate under the British crown, and the

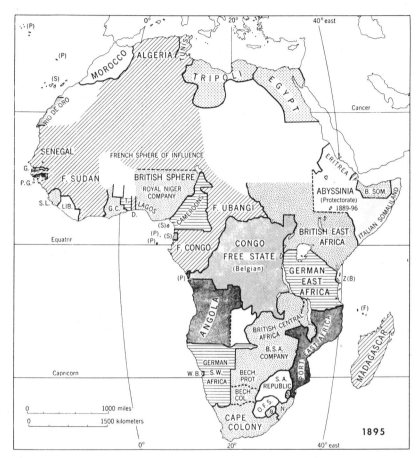

Figure 8. Africa at the End of 1895. This map contrasts very sharply indeed with the preceding one and indicates that practically the whole of Africa had within the short space of the ten years from 1885 to 1895 been partitioned among the leading European powers. 1895 was before the outbreak of the war between the British and the Boer settlers whose two independent Republics, the Orange Free State and the South African Republic, are shown unshaded.

construction of the Kenya-Uganda railway dealt a final blow to the slave trade. Zanzibar became a British protectorate in 1890.

The revival of French interest in West Africa was an indirect result of France's defeat by Germany in 1870–1871 and the loss of

Alsace-Lorraine. To restore her prestige and self-esteem she turned her attention to West Africa, and had secured a firm hold by the time Germany became active in the same area. Various British trading

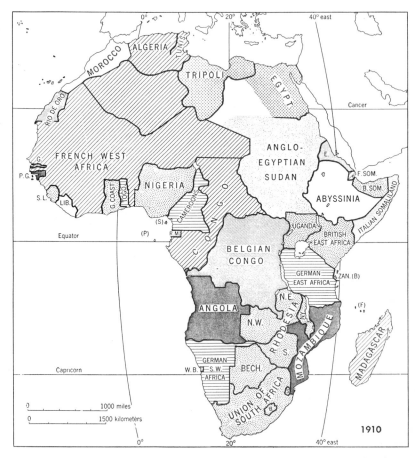

Figure 9. Africa in 1910. This was the year in which the four South African Colonies united to form the Union of South Africa. The Congo Free State had been annexed to the Belgian Crown as the Belgian Congo and the Anglo-Egyptian Sudan had been established for more than ten years.

interests had consolidated themselves as the United African Company in 1879, which became the Royal Niger Company in 1886. The vigorous policy of the Company's chief, George Taubman Goldie, secured trading places and agreements with Negro authorities, thus forestalling the activities of Herr Flegel, who attempted the same

methods as Karl Peters was using in East Africa. By the Berlin Conference of 1884–1885 (the "General Act" was signed on February
26, 1885) Great Britain's paramount interest in Nigeria was con-

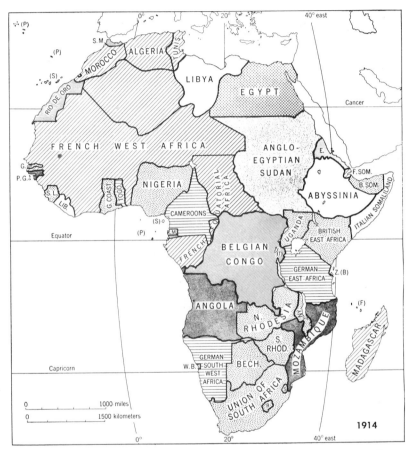

Figure 10. Africa in 1914. This was at the outbreak of the First World War,
and it will be noted that the Germans had so far extended their territory of the
Cameroons as to split French Equatorial Africa into two separated portions.

firmed. German claims were restricted to the Cameroons and Togoland, both of which may be regarded as becoming German in 1884.
It was also in 1884 that Germany annexed Southwest Africa.

Both Germany from the west and Portugal, occupying Mozambique
on the east and Angola on the west, had plans for stretching inland
across the whole of the southern part of the continent, which Portu-

gal claimed but had neither explored nor annexed. But a strong man arose in the person of the British Cecil John Rhodes. In 1887

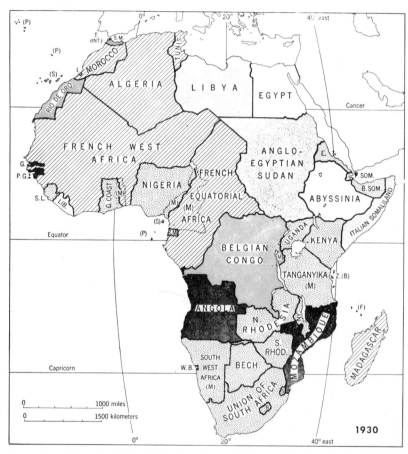

Figure 11. Africa in 1930. With the defeat of Germany in the First World War, German territory in Africa disappeared. Former German territory is shown as held under mandate from the League of Nations by Britain, France, Belgium and South Africa. As a reward for Italian efforts, Italian Somaliland was increased in area by the addition of the country around the Juba River. (M = Mandated Territories.)

Portugal attempted to close the Zambezi, announcing that the interior belonged to her. Rhodes retaliated by securing in 1888 from Lobengula, the King of the Matabele, exclusive rights to work minerals in his territories, which lay north of the Transvaal. In

1889 he formed the British South Africa Company for the purpose. In 1891 the limits of the Portuguese and British spheres of influence being agreed upon, Nyasaland became a British Protectorate whereas

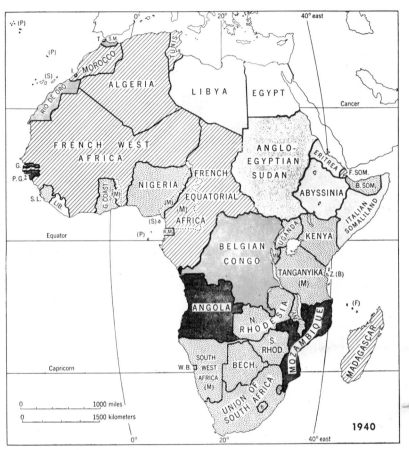

Figure 12. Africa in 1939 to 1940. At the outbreak of the Second World War the Italian Empire had come to include Abyssinia as well as Eritrea and Italian Somaliland, together with the enlarged and redefined Libya. Only two countries in the whole of Africa are shown in this map as independent, Egypt and Liberia.

the bulk of the heart of the country was handed over to Rhodes's company, afterwards becoming Northern and Southern Rhodesia.

In the meantime French interests in West and Equatorial Africa had been consolidated. In Equatorial Africa (long called French Congo) acquisition began on the Gabun River in 1841, and Libreville was founded in 1849. The coastal possessions extended along the coast for 200 miles to include Cape Lopez. Everywhere the story

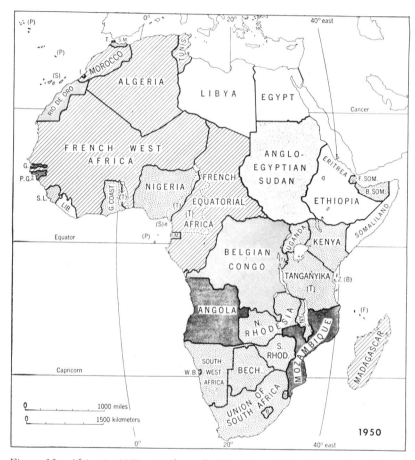

Figure 13. Africa in 1950. At the end of the Second World War the old mandated territories became trusteeships under the United Nations. The growth of nationalism in Africa is indicated by the reappearance of the independent Ethiopian Empire, now including Eritrea, and by the appearance of independent Libya, together with the old independent countries of Egypt and Liberia. (T = Trusteeship Territories.)

is the same; coastal settlements followed much later by extension inland. In West Africa, the British failed to respond to requests— a natural result of the British Anti-Slavery Law of 1807—to take the whole coast under protection and so left the field open to the French.

However, there was little activity by France till she recovered from the Napoleonic Wars. The French obtained rights on the Ivory Coast about 1842 but did not actively and continuously occupy the territory till 1882. In Dahomey the footing on the coast dates from 1851, but not till 1894 was the whole Kingdom of Dahomey annexed.

Along the Guinea Coast fragments remained to Portugal (Portuguese Guinea; the islands of São Tomé and Príncipe) and to Spain (Spanish Guinea and the islands of Fernando Po and Annobón). Although many boundaries were not defined until much later, it may be said that by 1891 practically the whole of tropical and South Africa had been parceled out between Britain, France, Belgium, Germany, Portugal and Spain. Even the Republic of Liberia was alien and not African.

The story over the north of the continent was somewhat different. The Atlas lands of the northwest, long called the Barbary States from their Berber inhabitants, had formed part of the dominion of Carthage. Carthage itself was near the modern Tunis. After the fall of Carthage in 146 B.C. the Atlas lands continued to flourish under Roman rule; many cities were built and the land provided much food for the Roman Empire as a whole. After the fall of Rome the Moorish or Arab Empire extended right over North Africa, and in turn the Barbary States became nominally part of the Turkish or Ottoman Empire, which extended from Egypt to the Atlantic. Conditions were worst in Algeria, where Turkish and other renegades terrorized both inhabitants and traders, and along the coasts became notorious as the Barbary Pirates from 1650 onward. English, Dutch, French, Spaniards and Americans all failed successively to check piracy until in 1830 the French bombarded Algiers into submission. Thus began the French regime in Algeria, now administered with certain differences as part of France. Success was not immediate, and troubles lasted until 1883. Tunis is a kingdom whose ruler, the Bey, is descended from one who, a native of Crete, made himself master of the country in 1705 while acknowledging the suzerainty of the Sultan of Turkey. The obvious need of the French to protect law and order recently established in neighboring Algeria led to invasion in 1881 and the placing of Tunis under the protection of France. Morocco, lying west of Algeria, remains nominally an independent Empire, an absolute monarchy in which the reigning Sultan exercises both supreme religious and civil authority. The establishment of "zones" of protection by France (the bulk) and Spain in 1912 and the subsequent recognition of the "International

Zone" of Tangier by agreement with Britain in 1923 were closely connected with the threat by Germany to occupy the country.

Between the Atlas lands and Egypt lies the country, largely desert, known as a whole as Libya. Part of the Turkish or Ottoman Empire, despite a certain measure of Arab autonomy, the area was a Turkish vilayet from 1835 to 1911. In the latter year a quarrel between Italy and Turkey, then the "Sick Man of Europe," led to Italian annexation.

The story of Egypt is much more complex. For long a part of the Turkish Empire, Egypt was at least nominally a vassal state of Turkey until the outbreak of the First World War. Since the latter part of the eighteenth century Great Britain has had special interest in Egypt. The old route from Britain to India was by ship to Egypt, thence up the Nile to a point where the desert was crossed to the Red Sea, and so by ship again to Indian ports. Egypt was thus a vital link in a vital Empire chain, and the strategic importance of Egypt's position was emphasized rather than diminished when the Suez Canal was opened in 1869.[1] The protection of the Canal became of first importance to Britain. In 1882 internal disorders led to British military intervention and the stationing of British troops in the country. When the First World War broke out in 1914, with Turkey ranged amongst the enemies, a British protectorate over Egypt was declared, thus ending its status as a Turkish vassal. The protectorate ended in 1922, when Egypt became an independent Kingdom.

We turn now to the vexed and complicated question of the Sudan and northeastern Africa. Between Khartoum and Aswan the Nile follows a long course interrupted by successive rapids across 500 miles of waterless desert, effectively dividing the habitable parts of Egypt from the Sudan. The Nile water is the life blood of Egypt so that there is an obvious importance in considering the water problems of the Nile Basin as a whole. From about 1820 onward, the Egyptians began to extend their control over the Sudanese peoples and to claim the newly discovered Equatorial lands. The Khedive Ismael of Egypt relied largely on collaboration with the British, and in 1870, as we have already seen, S. W. Baker was appointed governor of the Equatorial Provinces to deal with the suppression of the slave trade. The British General Charles George Gordon (1833–1885) was governor of the Sudan from 1873 to 1880, when he resigned after dealing successfully with the slave trade.

[1] See below, page 221. Incidentally, the strategic value of Aden, the islands of the Red Sea such as Perim and the ports opposite on African shores was also enhanced.

Two years later came the great revolt of the Sudanese under Mohammed Ahmed, who declared himself the Mahdi. It was decided to abandon the Sudan, and General Gordon was sent in 1884 to undertake the difficult task of evacuating the Egyptian population. With only one English officer he and his faithful Egyptian Moslem band were surrounded and besieged in Khartoum for 5 months. There was fatal delay in sending a relief party, which reached Khartoum eventually on January 28, 1885, 2 days after Gordon had been put to death. There followed 13 years of tyrannically cruel despotic rule by the Mahdi and his successor, the Khalifa. In 1896 an Anglo-Egyptian army commenced operations for the recovery of the lost provinces, culminating in the overthrow of the Khalifa in 1898 and his death in 1899. The convention between the British and Egyptian Governments signed at Cairo on January 19, 1899, provided for the administration of the territory jointly by Egypt and Britain as a condominium.

Among other foreigners in the service of the Egyptian Government in the expansionist days of the seventies was a German, Eduard Schnitzer, who had been a medical officer under General Gordon, and who was appointed Governor of the Equatorial Province. Known as Emin Pasha, he was isolated by the rebellion in which Gordon was killed, and no news of him caused anxiety. So Stanley, having founded the Congo Free State, was sent to search for him. Because access via Egypt was impossible Stanley determined to travel up the Congo, and had a very difficult journey both by river and through the forest. He discovered Emin Pasha at Lake Albert in April 1888, happy and comfortable with his men and disinclined to leave Uganda for Europe. Emin's real object was to remain and to claim Uganda for his fatherland Germany. A little later, while exploring, he was killed by Arab slave traders; otherwise the story of East Africa might have been very different.

Lying east of the great knot of Abyssinian mountains are the arid plains of Somaliland occupying the "Horn of Africa" with shores along the Indian Ocean, Gulf of Aden and Red Sea. Near the entrance to the Red Sea the French acquired the port of Obok in 1862 but did not undertake its active occupation until 1884, when the territory was extended. In 1888 the French created the port of Jibuti and later constructed the Jibuti-Addis Ababa railway, the one main outlet of Ethiopia. The Somali Coast farther east was administered by Egypt until 1884, when their control collapsed and the British Indian Government administered the territory as a pro-

tectorate. Italian interest in these coastlands dates from the establishment of a colony in Eritrea whose boundaries were defined in
1889–1891. In 1892 the Sultan of Zanzibar leased certain Somali
ports to Italy, selling them outright in 1905 when Italy assumed
control of Italian Somaliland.

Between the momentous decade of 1880–1890 and the outbreak
of the First World War in 1914 changes in Africa were mostly of the
character of consolidation of interests (as of the French in North
Africa), further exploration, definition of boundaries, organization
of administration and administrative units, construction of railways,
roads, ports and administrative centers and the development of
agriculture, commerce and trade. There were inevitable clashes
and minor wars. The one serious conflict involving two peoples of
European stock was the Anglo-Boer War of 1899–1902, which will
be considered under the Union of South Africa. The political map
of Africa as it was in 1914 is shown in Fig. 10.

With the outbreak of hostilities in August 1914 between Britain
and Germany things began to happen in Africa. German Southwest
Africa surrendered to the forces of the Union of South Africa on July
9, 1915. Togoland surrendered unconditionally to British and French
forces in August 1914; the Cameroons in February 1916. German
East Africa, renamed Tanganyika, was conquered in 1918. Britain,
France, Belgium and South Africa all accepted the jurisdiction of
the League of Nations. Southwest Africa was entrusted under mandate to the Union of South Africa. This was a Class C mandate,
which laid down that the territory should be administered as an
integral part of the territory of the mandatory power, but made
the mandatory power responsible for promoting the moral and material welfare of the peoples. Togoland was divided between Britain
and France as a Class B mandate. Part became joined to the Gold
Coast, part to Dahomey. The Cameroons (Class B) were similarly
divided between Britain (Nigeria) and France (French Equatorial
Africa). An important though small strip of German East Africa
(Ruanda-Urundi) passed to Belgium, also under Class B mandate,
and was added to the Belgian Congo; the main part became a
Class B mandate under Britain as Tanganyika. It was laid down
that Class B mandates should be separately administered, but again
making the mandatory power responsible for promoting the moral
and material welfare of the peoples. After the Second World War
all these mandated territories passed under the trusteeship scheme
of the United Nations.

Figure 11 shows the political map of Africa as it appeared shortly after the end of the First World War.

The period between the World Wars was marked by much economic activity—the building of railways and roads, the opening up of mineral deposits especially in the Katanga and the development of air transport, which has made such a tremendous difference to

Figure 15. The Supreme Court at Accra, Gold Coast. Typical of the permanent work of the European powers since the partition of Africa. (British Official Photograph.)

the accessibility of the heart of Africa. The British Colonial Office, following the tenets laid down especially by Lord Lugard after his experience in Nigeria, did much to develop indirect rule—to encourage the Africans to perfect their own administration based on tribal customs and laws under British guidance so that the British officers interfered only when African customs were found to be directly opposed to Western ideas of right and justice.

To this interwar period belongs the story of Italian expansion. With a restricted and overpopulated homeland their need for elbow room was great. Libya, acquired in 1911, though large, was mainly desert; Somalia was no better. Eritrea had some good land but had nothing compared with the undeveloped resources of the ancient kingdom of Ethiopia. So Ethiopia, or Abyssinia, was invaded and conquered in 1935–1936. With Eritrea and Somalia it was reorganized to form Italian East Africa (Africa Orientale Italiana) by the Act of June 1, 1936, under the dictatorship of Benito Mussolini. Italy declared war on Britain on June 11, 1940. British Imperial forces invaded Ethiopia, and by November 1941 the country was cleared of Italian forces and the Emperor Haile Selassie restored to his throne.

After the Second World War Libya, Eritrea and Somalia were governed until 1950 under British Military Administration, replaced later by a British Civil Administration. Libya was then granted independence, taking effect formally on January 1, 1952. Eritrea became an autonomous state under the Ethiopian crown, and Italy was allowed, in 1950, to re-enter and administer Somalia.

BIBLIOGRAPHY

The partition of Africa as it took place in the crucial years 1880 to 1895 is well shown and well illustrated by maps in the *Partition of Africa,* by J. Scott Keltie (London, 1895).

Later changes are shown in *The Map of Africa by Treaty,* by Sir E. Hertslet (London, His Majesty's Stationery Office, 1909; 3 volumes and atlas).

Reference should also be made to articles in the *Encyclopaedia Britannica* and to *Philip's Historical Atlas,* by Ramsay Muir and George Philip (George Philip, London).

The Physical Background

Geography and Man

Throughout much of Africa, especially tropical Africa, the course of man's life is still dictated in large measure by the physical environment. Even where the weapons of modern Western science have been introduced, the physical factors are so strong that their influence is everywhere clearly seen in the pattern of population distribution. The focal points of modern Africa's industrial development are clearly associated with sources of minerals and power and are thus related to the age-old geological structure of the continent. That population density in rural areas is primarily related to climatic conditions, especially rainfall, has long been clear, but the subtle and intimate relationships between the form of the land surface, drainage, soils and land use are only now being slowly appreciated. It is because of the paramount influence which they exert that the various physical features of Africa will now be examined in detail.

Structure and Earth History

Throughout the many millions of years of the earth's geological history there have always been areas of relative stability separated by belts of instability. Although at the present time the earth is enjoying in the geological sense one of its quiet periods, so that earthquakes disturb the surface but rarely and volcanic activity is at a minimum, it is still true that there are certain earthquake belts and certain lines of crustal weakness with which volcanoes are associated. In times past the belts or regions of orogenic or mountain-building movement have fluctuated in position and so have the position and the shape of the stable blocks between. Those stable blocks are sometimes wrongly referred to as the great "unfolded" masses of the earth's surface—an entirely false concept because they usually consist of rocks which have been most intensely folded, broken, recemented and worn down by long ages of denudation and erosion. The important fact is that they are blocks which underwent their evolution in the early days of the earth's history since when they have acted as rigid masses not directly affected by later folding movements.

Unique in so many other aspects, Africa is again unique in that the whole continent save the extreme north (Barbary States or French North Africa) and the extreme southwest (in the Cape Province of South Africa) consists of one great rigid block of ancient rocks which has remained little changed in its essential geology since the days—perhaps 200,000,000 years ago—when the Karroo Beds of South Africa were laid down.

The great Alpine storm, as it has been called, of middle Tertiary time which caused the rise of the Alps and most of the great present-day mountain chains of Europe to the north affected only the northwest of Africa, where the Atlas and associated ranges are of this age. The picturesque ranges of the Cape of Good Hope with their folded sedimentary rocks belong to an earlier period of mountain building.

We get thus a mental picture of the huge continental mass of Africa consisting essentially of an ancient rigid earth block. In its general characteristics and the nature and composition of its rocks, it closely resembles other ancient earth blocks, but notably those of Brazil to the west, peninsular India to the northeast and the western half of Australia to the east. Indeed the resemblances between these different areas are so strong that we are tempted to wonder whether they may not once have formed part of a single continental mass. The more closely they are studied, the more evidence is forthcoming of similarities. The question obviously arises, were these earth blocks, now widely separated, once part of a single continent? Associated with the masses of South Africa, peninsular India and western Australia, there are beds roughly of the same age as the coal-bearing beds of Europe and North America; there are sediments, shales and sandstones, resting on the ancient rocks, which must have been deposited in shallow basins on their surface. These rocks are often coal-bearing, and among the plants which contributed to the formation of the coal remains of a remarkable genus *Glossopteris* are dominant. Although this *Glossopteris* flora is common to the basins of the ancient blocks mentioned, it is absent from the Coal Measure beds of Europe and North America. The argument is accordingly that the ancient blocks of Africa, India and Australia, perhaps also of South America, were part of an ancient continent to which the name Gondwanaland has been given. *Glossopteris* and its allies flourished all over this continent, but a wide ocean separated Gondwanaland from northern land masses where an entirely different assemblage of plants was in existence.

There are many other pieces of evidence to support the existence of Gondwanaland. At a stage in its history it was subjected to one

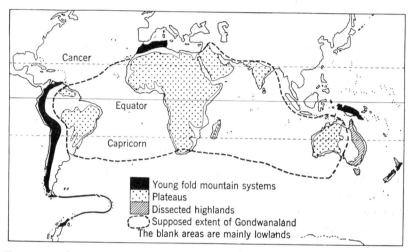

Figure 1. The Main Structural Elements in the Southern Continents. The interrupted line encloses the fragments of former Gondwanaland.

or more glaciations so that ancient boulder clays or tills of glacial origin exist. But the *Glossopteris* flora of the swamp forests of Gondwanaland flourished over 200,000,000 years ago. What has happened in the meantime? There are at least three possibilities:

(1) The seas may have denuded away the former land connections.

(2) The old continent of Gondwanaland may have been fractured by great rifts or faults, some sections remaining above sea level, cthers sinking so as to be covered by sea.

(3) The present-day masses may represent fragments which have drifted away from one another.

Evidence has been adduced to show that the specific gravity of the rocks underlying the continents is lower than the specific gravity of rocks found beneath the great ocean basins. On this evidence it has been postulated that the continental masses may be regarded as blocks having the approximate composition of granite resting on a lower layer having the approximate composition of basalt. The lighter continental rock material has been given the name sial from the dominant elements silicon and aluminum, while the heavier layers have been given the name sima from the dominant elements silicon and magnesium. It is of course known that there is a rapid rise in temperature as the earth's crust is penetrated and that at no great distance from the surface extremely high temperatures occur, so that if it were not for extreme pressure the rocks would be molten. It is quite possible that these lower layers of the earth's crust are at least in a plastic condition. Having gone so far, we find that it is not difficult to go further and to believe that the continental masses of sial, floating, as it were, on a plastic layer of sima, are able to move, to split into sections, to drift apart or to be pushed closer together.

The general concept of the lateral movement of continental masses is by no means new, but worked out in detail it has become associated with the name of George Wegener, as Wegener's Hypothesis of Continental Drift. Thus the position may have been that the South American, African, Indian and Australian sections of Gondwanaland formed one whole continent which has split up, and the constituent sections drifted apart. Gondwanaland, however, existed some 200,000,000 years ago. There has been ample time for the drifting apart of the separate sections. Biologists who note the similarity between the present-day floras and faunas in the three southern continents, and especially between the existing land animals in these areas, are helped by the Wegener hypothesis only if the drifting apart of the continental masses has taken place within, say, the last million years or so.

In between these two extremes it would seem to be quite clear that the great continental mass of Africa drifted, or was pushed, northwards, for it is on this basis and almost on this basis alone that we can explain the intense folding of the Alps and associated Alpine ranges in Europe, including the Atlas ranges of North Africa. These movements were at their height in Miocene times, let us say 20 million years ago. Many attempts have been made in recent years to detect actual present-day lateral movements of the continental masses but without any direct positive results.

The geologist on the available evidence would therefore be justified in saying that the northward movement of the continental mass of Africa took place in middle Tertiary times, and ceased when the Alpine earth movements ceased. There is no direct evidence of later movement so that the geologist is not in a position to help the biologist to explain the present distribution of the fauna and the flora of the southern continents. There is certainly no justification for attempting to fit the present details of the coastline of South America into the coastline of West Africa. In any case, it is the edges of the continental shelves which should fit into one another and not the existing coastlines.

In broad outline both the geological structure and the geological history of the African continent are relatively simple, however much remains—and very much does remain—to be investigated in detail.

The ancient crystalline basal complex is exposed over very large areas. In some sections the dominant rocks are granites, or granitic rocks, which show varying degrees of alteration, and fall into the groups known as ortho-gneisses and para-gneisses. Elsewhere the dominant rocks are very highly metamorphosed—schists and gneisses of varied character which may originally have been sediments.

In consisting of these two main groups the ancient African mass resembles in general the other ancient earth masses, such as the Canadian Shield or the Brazilian Plateau. Certain parts of the complex are highly mineralized, and Africa is of course a repository of a number of extremely valuable mineral deposits. For reasons which will appear later there are considerable possibilities of new discoveries. Resting on these very ancient metamorphosed rocks, often with basal conglomerates, are sedimentary rocks, for the most part comparatively little altered, some of which are also believed to be pre-Cambrian in age; others are early Paleozoic. These too may be economically very important because of the association of gold and other metallic ores with them. The gold of the Rand comes from pre-Cambrian conglomerates; the copper of the Katanga from rocks of early Paleozoic age.

The ancient earth block from its establishment in earliest times to the present day has been subjected to vertical movement of elevation and depression, but only to relatively slight subsequent folding. Consequently there are considerable areas of its surface covered by older Paleozoic rocks of marine origin, little altered, for the most part nearly horizontal though sometimes gently folded. Where these Paleozoic rocks are folded it is claimed that the folds can be termed broadly Hercynian, and in West Africa, for example, the gentle Hercynian folds trend from northeast to southwest. It should be noted that the older marine Paleozoic sediments are succeeded by rocks of Carboniferous and Permian ages, with which are associated the coal seams of Africa's one important coal field, in South Africa.

The post-Paleozoic sedimentary rocks in Africa were either de-

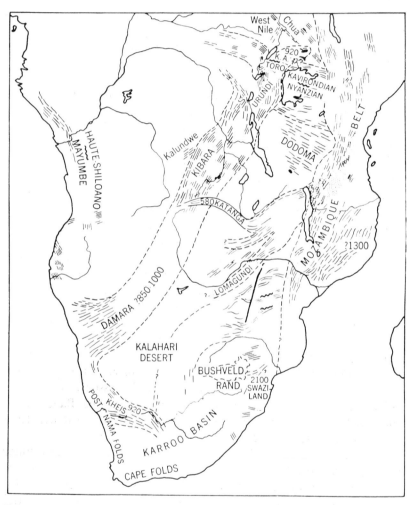

Figure 2.   Provisional Map of Ancient Mountain Belts in South and Central Africa. This map is intended to show that the very ancient rocks of the African mass, like those of the Canadian shield, were intensely folded and erected into great mountain chains which were later worn down to a common level.   The figures are estimated ages in millions of years.   (After Arthur Holmes, *Report of the 18th International Geological Congress of 1948*, Vol. XIV, 1951.)

posited in shallow seas which locally invaded the continental mass and occupied extensive gulfs as in parts of West Africa, or were laid down in broad shallow basins on the surface under fresh or brackish water conditions. The large stretches of sandstone and other sediments, so important in North Africa, called broadly Nubian Sandstones, are of later Mesozoic or early Tertiary age.

With the absence of folding and the long-continued exposure of huge tracts to atmospheric weathering the surface of Africa was reduced to an almost level surface, referred to below as the Miocene Peneplane. This ancient surface has since been raised many thousand feet above sea level, and in the process three important things have happened.

In the first place the great rigid block of Africa gave way under the strain, and great fractures developed from north to south on the eastern side of the continent and locally elsewhere. Thus from the Red Sea in the north, almost to the borders of the Transvaal in the south, were formed those gigantic troughs, or *graben*, the famous rift valleys of East Africa, since occupied in part by the East African lake system. The general position of the East African rift valley system is shown in Fig. 3.

In the second place, volcanic activity was also associated with this faulting or cracking of the rigid masses. There are enormous areas covered with flows of lava in Ethiopia, there are other lava-covered areas in East Africa, and a number of magnificent volcanic cones as reminders of this volcanic activity. Mount Kenya, Mount Kilimanjaro and Mount Elgon are three outstanding examples. More localized fracturing in the west is associated with the great volcanic peak of Cameroon Mountain. Incidentally it may be noted that the Rift Valley area of East Africa is still an area of relative instability and hence appears as one of the earthquake belts of the world of today. In both southern and eastern Africa old volcanic necks or pipes became plugged with a consolidated lava of very basic composition which is the source rock of most of Africa's diamonds.

In the third place broad shallow basins in the uplifted surface gave rise to vast inland seas or lakes which have since disappeared or have left but small remnants. In them were deposited huge stretches of Quaternary and recent alluvium, hence the Quaternary lake basins of the Upper Niger, of the Lake Chad region and of the Central Congo. The rivers of today meander across these old basins before tumbling over the edge of the plateau to reach the present sea coast.

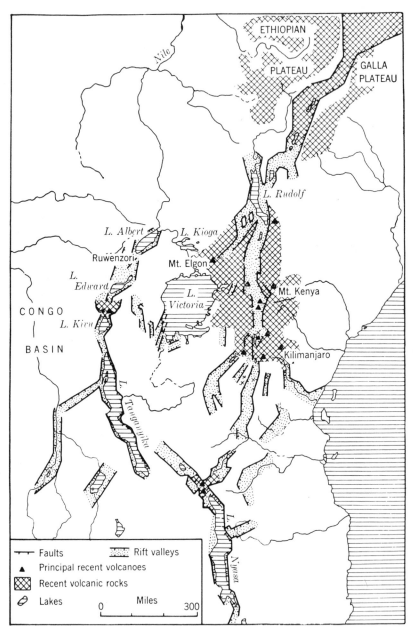

Figure 3. The Rift Valleys of East Africa. A simplified version is shown in Chapter 17. This map is after Maurette.

Elsewhere the older rocks are still hidden by a mantle of aeolian deposits, the wind-borne sands of the great Sahara and other wastes.

The Plateau Surfaces

From the foregoing description we see that the interest of the geographer lies often in the geomorphology rather than the geology of Africa.

One of the most striking features of the African landscape is the vast extent of level or gently undulating surfaces. At high levels on the plateau we have the illusion of traveling over a lowland plain, often monotonous in the extreme. Such plains occur at different levels and are erosion surfaces which may be found up to heights of 8600 feet (as in the Basuto Highlands) above the present sea level. They have been discussed briefly by Dr. F. Dixey,[1] who points out that, since the widespread movements of late Karroo or post-Karroo times (Permo-Carboniferous), central and southern Africa have been a stable land mass subject to periodical uplift. The main periods of uplift have been separated by intervals long enough for possibly three important erosion cycles to have run their course and for resulting peneplains to have developed. There are also certain incompleted cycles, whereas the whole has been modified at a late stage by the rift faulting of East Africa, accompanied by volcanic activity, and the related gentle warping of regions to the south and southwest.

One well-marked high-level erosion surface is found in a number of widely separated plateau remnants—at 7000 to 8000 feet on the Cape ranges where it is quite independent of the folding of the rocks, at 8000 feet in southwest Africa and rather higher in the Basuto Highlands, at 7000 to 7500 feet in the Nyika Plateau. This peneplanation is ascribed to the late Jurassic and indicates that the rise of the African continental mass has been of the order of 7000 to 8000 feet since that time.

At lower levels there are remnants of other surfaces. In early Cretaceous times troughs were opened and later filled with sediments (as in the Nyasa trough), but a really well-marked erosion surface is that at about 4500 feet, ascribed to the Miocene or mid-Tertiary. It may seem surprising that so much of this surface is preserved, but the major rivers such as the Congo, Zambezi (with the Luangwa, Shiré and Lake Nyasa), Limpopo and Orange have

---

[1] "African Landscapes," *Geog. Rev.,* XXXIV, July 1944, pp. 457–467.

carved out for themselves great valleys in troughs floored by the Karroo sediments of low resistance. It is on the weaker sediments and on Cretaceous beds filling the Nyasa and Luangwa troughs that

Figure 4. The African Plateau and the Zambezi Gorge. Vast stretches of Africa are savanna-covered plateau. Here the Zambezi plunges over Victoria Falls into a zigzag gorge cut out of great cracks in the plateau surface. (Courtesy the late Major Cochran-Patrick.)

the Pliocene or late Tertiary erosion surface at 2500 to 4000 feet has been developed.

Dr. Dixey finds it unnecessary to postulate warping of the Miocene surface or block faulting to explain the higher plateau surfaces as others have done. He considers that the low divides between the great river basins, such as between the Congo and Zambezi, are features of the old Miocene peneplained surface—legacies from the past.

It is almost certain that vast areas of Africa have been exposed to atmospheric weathering for many millions of years. On the old Miocene peneplain surfaces, therefore, the solid rocks may have been disintegrated to a very considerable depth, but the soils which have been formed have been formed in situ, and their mineral particles consist of comminuted fragments of underlying rocks. Not infrequently it is possible to trace a vein of quartz from the underlying rock through into the subsoil and to find abundance of fragments of the shattered quartz in the surface soil, a feature of the utmost significance in determining the nature and usability of African soils.

The Geological Map of Africa

We are now in a position to interpret the geological map of Africa. The continent is far from mapped in detail, but the broad lines of its rock formations are now known.

Rocks of the ancient pre-Cambrian mass, the whole comparable in character to the Canadian Shield except for the weathering of the surface, reach the surface and so are "exposed," that is, they are not covered by later rocks, over approximately a third of the whole of Africa. It must be remembered that large parts have been subjected to the action of the atmospheric elements for many millions of years so that the solid rocks themselves may be obscured by many feet of laterite and other products of weathering. This superficial mantle makes the search for ore bodies particularly difficult, and there is little wonder that spectacular finds are still being made and are almost certain to be made far into the future, especially as modern methods of prospecting, such as geophysical methods, are applied. Mineralization of the rocks and consequent occurrence of metallic ores are always irregular, but deposits are widely distributed in Africa. The present share of the continent in world production of certain mineral products is discussed in Part 3 of this book.

It must be borne in mind that the rocks of the ancient complex underlie nearly the whole of Africa and that metalliferous deposits may lie buried, but not too deeply for future exploitation, where sediments cover the old mass. The sands of the deserts, the alluvium of the old lake basins, perhaps some of the flows of lava may one day be penetrated to reach ore bodies hidden below.

The older sedimentary rocks, especially the shales and sandstones of Karroo (Permo-Carboniferous) Age, are important in two ways. They have their seams of coal in South Africa, the Rhodesias and Tanganyika. In the second place the beds are usually almost hor-

izontal, and weathering has given rise to those mountains of cir-
cumdenudation, the flat-topped mesas, which are such a characteristic
feature of the landscape in so many parts of Africa. This is especially true in South Africa, where resistant volcanic rocks are inter-
bedded with the sediments.

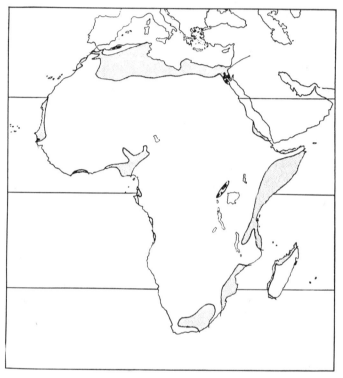

Figure 5. Sedimentary Basins in Africa. Showing possible areas for the occurrence of oil. Dots show existing oil fields in Egypt and Algeria. (Adapted
from the *World Geography of Petroleum*, American Geographical Society, 1951.)

The younger sedimentary rocks of marine and brackish water
origin represent incursions of the sea at times when the whole continental surface was lower than at present. Broadly, they are
confined to the margin of the continent as shown in Fig. 5, which
is based on the map of "sedimentary basins" published by the American Geographical Society in *World Geography of Petroleum* (1950).
This map may be interpreted as indicating the areas where occur-
rences of mineral oil are possible, though in most cases unpromising.

Apart from the fields along the shores of the Gulf of Suez in Egypt, and a small yield from three tiny fields in Algeria and four in Morocco, Africa has no oil. The conditions favoring the accumulation of oil in quantity, in folds among sedimentary rocks on the margins of great sedimentary basins, do not exist in Africa.

The superficial sands and alluvia which occupy very large areas in some parts of Africa represent the wind-deposited debris of weathering in the deserts and the floors of once extensive though shallow lakes. The interest of such areas is in agricultural development, given water, rather than in minerals.

The Relief Map of Africa

The common generalization that Africa consists of a gigantic plateau bordered, except on the northwest where the Atlas ranges occur, by narrow coastal plains may now be stated more exactly. In fact Africa consists of a succession of plateau surfaces at varying elevations, generally higher in the south and lower in the north, often with abrupt edges. On the surface of the plateaus are shallow depressions, some forming basins of inland drainage, others drained by rivers which pass over cataracts or through gorges as they leave the plateau surfaces to reach the coastal plains.

In the south of the continent the average elevation is over 3000 feet, and the magnificent scarp of the southeastern edge known as the Drakensberg usually exceeds 10,000 feet. Rising from the plateau surfaces flat-topped mesas are common features; rocky hills with "tors" are features of the old rocks where granites occur. The divides between the broad open river basins are usually inconspicuous, and the ridges between tributary valleys are so little developed that the water partings can be detected only by careful leveling.

The lofty plateau of East Africa is complicated in several ways. The great north-south trenches of the rift valleys (Fig. 3) are deeply incised in its surface, and the section between the two main rifts has collapsed in the center, which is occupied by the huge but shallow Lake Victoria over 26,200 square miles in area and the world's third largest lake (after the Caspian Sea and Lake Superior). From the surface of the plateau rise the great volcanic piles of Kilimanjaro (19,321 feet), Kenya (17,040), Ruwenzori (16,800), Elgon (14,140) and many others. Northward a large part of the mountain complex of Ethiopia is over 4000 feet in elevation.

The great basin in the heart of equatorial Africa is that of the Congo and its tributaries. From an average elevation of rather over

1000 feet in the center of the basin the land rises gently to 3000 and 4000 feet around the rim. The whole is indeed like a shallow saucer. The plateau surfaces and basins to the north of the Congo are at generally lower elevations, and parts of the Sahara actually sink

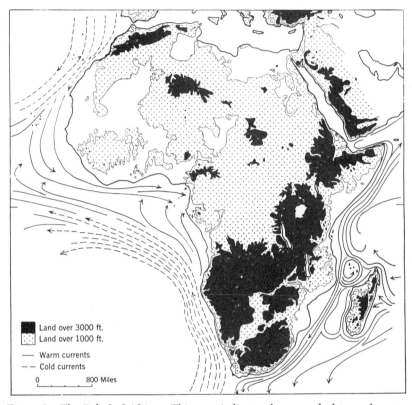

Figure 6. The Relief of Africa. This map indicates the general plateau character of the continent. The ocean currents influencing climatic conditions are also indicated.

below sea level. There are areas characterized by mesas; there are some rock-edged highlands, notably the Futa-Jallon-Liberian massif, and the Tibesti Mountains tower to snow-covered heights in the midst of the Sahara. The volcanic pile of Cameroon Mountain (13,350 feet) repeats in the west some of the features of East Africa, being associated with fault lines trending northeast to southwest.

Utterly in contrast are the Tertiary fold ranges of the Atlas and Anti-Atlas ranges, with the elevated plateaus of the Shotts which lie between.

The coastal plains between the edge of the main plateau and the sea vary in character, as well as in width. Sometimes there are steps up to the plateau, sometimes a belt of foothills between a coastal plain and the plateau edge. Only in parts of northern Africa does the plateau edge tend to disappear or become inconspicuous.

Figure 7. The Edge of the African Plateau—Drakensberg Mountains of Natal. This shows clearly the horizontal beds of sandstone here making up the plateau. (Copyright Aircraft Operating Company of Africa.)

African Rivers and River Basins

It may be said that two-thirds of the surface of Africa is drained by seven or eight major rivers; much of the remainder is occupied by basins of inland drainage with no outlet to the sea.

THE ORANGE RIVER BASIN. In southern Africa the plateau slopes in general from the high eastern edge (the Drakensberg) to the west. Nearly all the surface is drained by the Orange River, the chief tributary of which is the Vaal. The southern half of the Kalahari Desert in Bechuanaland lies in the same basin, but the water courses are nearly always dry. True to the African type, the Orange passes over the Great Falls on its way to the Atlantic Ocean, but its bed is usually dry before the ocean is reached through the coastal desert belt of the

Namib. Even in the damper parts of the High Veld the streams are frequently non-perennial so that the whole system has no use for navigation and but limited use (discussed under South Africa) for irrigation.

Yet the Orange in flood can be an impressive sight, and the same is true of the Kunene, a considerable stream marking for part of its

Figure 8. Flying over the Highest Point of the African Continent. The snow-capped Kilimanjaro in Tanganyika reaches over 19,500 feet and is an extinct volcano. This picture shows the view looking into the old crater. (Courtesy British Overseas Airways Corporation.)

course the boundary between Southwest Africa and Angola. Consequently exaggerated claims have been made for the value of this river as a potential source of irrigation water.

THE LIMPOPO BASIN. For much of its course the Limpopo forms the boundary between the Transvaal on the south, Bechuanaland and Southern Rhodesia on the north. It is one of Africa's lesser rivers, but it drains well-watered country eastward to the Indian Ocean, and its basin includes lands of much economic importance.

THE ZAMBEZI BASIN. In many ways the Zambezi is a "typical" African river. Its upper course drains a huge shallow basin, floored with alluvial deposits, in the heart of the African plateau. Those headstreams which drain the drier western lands are non-perennial streams, but the main river is constant and navigable by native craft over much of its plateau course. Then the great river cas-

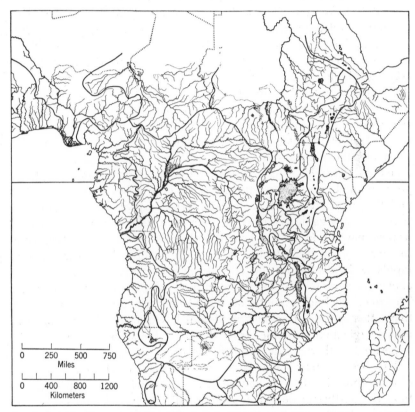

Figure 9. The Rivers and River Basins of the Heart of Africa. This map shows that the great river basins have little relation to political units, the boundaries of which are indicated by fine dotted lines.

cades over the world-famed Victoria Falls (343 feet high compared with 165 feet of Niagara) and passes through a narrow zigzag gorge excavated in the crushed rock of successive fault lines. There are long navigable stretches in the lower courses before the river is joined by the Shiré draining the waters of Lake Nyasa to the sea. Thus in common with the greater African rivers the headstreams of the Zambezi could be used for local irrigation, but little such use is made of them. The plateau courses are navigable over large stretches, the main falls provide an enormous potential source of power, the lower reaches are valuable for navigation though interrupted by gorges and rapids, but only a relatively minor port (Chinde) has grown up on the delta—not on the main stream. Immediately below the Victoria Falls the Zambezi gorge is spanned by a railway and road bridge completed in 1904 (see Fig. 4), but the 900 miles from this point to the sea forms a very serious obstacle to north-south communications. The Lower Zambezi Bridge was accordingly built where the river is 3775 yards wide and can claim on this basis to be the longest bridge in the world.

THE CONGO BASIN. Even more than the Zambezi, the Congo is the river of tropical Africa. It also has a great shallow basin on the surface of the plateau, but the whole is cut by the equator and so enjoys the higher and better-distributed rainfall characteristic of equatorial latitudes. As a result all its main stream and tributaries are perennial, most are navigable for long stretches by country boats and the main river and major tributaries, except for rare interruptions, are navigable by river steamers. Although Stanley Falls interrupt navigation in the heart of the basin, the main drop from the plateau to the Atlantic Ocean occurs through a succession of rapids and falls below the lake, known as Stanley Pool (800 feet above sea level), only 250 miles in a direct line from the open sea. The deep sheltered mouth of the Congo has proved more useful than other rivers. The port of Matadi has grown up at the head of ocean navigation (85 miles from the sea), Boma lower down on the opposite (northern) side and Banana on a delta distributary.

THE NIGER BASIN. The Niger repeats some of the main features of the Zambezi. It has a long plateau course with many· "tributaries" from the northern side which are normally dry water-courses, a main stream valuable for navigation until the chief rapids and falls a long way from the ocean are reached. Below the falls there are again long navigable stretches; the important tributary, the Benue, invites comparison with the Shiré. The main headwaters of the Niger are in the very wet Futa-Jallon highlands of the Sierra Leone border less than 200 miles from the Atlantic Ocean, but the river transports this water 2600 miles before discharging it into the ocean. In so doing, it swings in a great loop into the arid Sahara lands and so confers an immensely valuable gift of irrigation water on land well suited to receive it—in the neighborhood of the so-called inland Niger delta above Timbuktu.

THE NILE BASIN. With a total length of about 4000 miles the Nile rivals the Mississippi and Amazon for its sheer length, but in other ways it has features which are unique. The main stream, the White Nile, is a relatively constant river because it receives the well-distributed equatorial rainfall collected in the natural reservoir of Lake Victoria, from which it spills over in the Owen Falls. Uniting with the Albert Nile draining Lake Albert, its main navigable course begins below the Fola Rapids when it enters the great Bahr-el-Ghazal Basin. It may be said to pass out of that saucer-shaped hollow shortly before it is joined by the Blue Nile at Khartoum. Since the Blue Nile receives the Monsoon rain of the Ethiopian mountains, it is a fluctuating stream and so responsible for the annual rise of the united Nile as it passes over its six cataracts and enters its amazing 10-mile-wide cliff-bound trench through Egypt. Below Cairo the Nile Delta is the prototype of all deltas, the triangular shape of the delta resembling the Greek capital letter Δ, establishing the term for all time.

THE LAKE CHAD BASIN. This may be noted as one, indeed the largest, of the inland drainage basins of the great Saharan region. The proved diminution in the size of the lake since it was first seen by Europeans is of major interest in the study of the supposed "desiccation" of Africa, which will be discussed later (Chapter 13).

The African Coastline

One glance at a map of the continent shows that there are no deep bays or gulfs penetrating into the solid continental mass. There is literally nothing to compare with the Gulf of Mexico or Hudson Bay. Africa's rivers have deltas, not estuaries, and so there is nothing which compares with the mouth of the St. Lawrence or even with the Hudson, except perhaps the Congo. As far as shipping is concerned, both in sailing ship days and at the present, the word which is applicable to most of the African coastline is "inhospitable." Rocky headlands sheltering bays fit for anchorage are rare; the best examples are found in the ports of Dakar, Freetown, Cape Town and Simonstown. An island may offer shelter, Zanzibar and Mombasa, for example. There are a few well-protected bays or inlets such as Port Natal (Durban) or Lourenço Marques. River mouths may offer shelter though they are usually obstructed by a sand bar, for instance, Calabar on the Cross River or Duala on the Cameroon River. In general the coasts of Africa present to the approaching vessel a line of breakers through which small craft such as surf boats may make a precarious passage. Beyond the breakers, the shore is often sandy, but the sand bars and spits are cut off from the mainland by extensive though shallow lagoons, often with mangrove swamp-forests. In places the lagoons may form a valuable natural harbor where the entrance is adequate or, like Lagos, can be deepened. Elsewhere the shoreline may be sandy and shelving with desert or forest right to the beach; cliffs are rare. Exceptions to the latter statement are naturally found in southwest Africa around the Cape of Good Hope and in northwest Africa (Barbary States), where the structure of the terrain itself differs so much from the rest of Africa.

The absence of natural harbors along vast stretches of Africa's coastline has necessitated the construction of expensive artificial harbors before any marked development of foreign seaborne trade became possible. A good example is the Gold Coast. There Takoradi is entirely artificial and has now supplanted Sekondi and Tema is replacing Accra, where goods had to be landed by surf boats from ships anchored far offshore. Pointe Noire in French Equatorial Africa is another example.

The Continental Shelf

Ignoring the Mediterranean and the Red Sea basins, the continental shelf around Africa is everywhere narrow. The shelving shores on which the oceanic rollers break extend but a short distance from the coastline before the gentle submarine slope gives place to the abrupt edge of the continental shelf and the drop to oceanic depths of 2000 to 3000 fathoms. In the Atlantic Ascension, St. Helena and Tristan da Cunha are true oceanic islands—the tops of volcanic piles rising from great ocean deeps—and the same is true of Mauritius and Réunion in the Indian Ocean.

This fact has several important results. Where winds are offshore the main surface waters are replaced by cold oceanic waters welling up from those depths when temperatures remain about 34°F. The cold currents which lave the African shores—the Canaries and Benguela—not only flow from colder to warmer areas but also have their waters replenished in this way, with a correspondingly increased effect on the temperature of the air masses above them, and so on neighboring lands.

Because the shallow waters overlying the continental shelf around the Japanese or British islands are particularly favorable to breeding and growth of fish, these islands have great fishing industries. In Africa, where such favorable conditions are absent, there are no large commercial fisheries. Off South Africa the fishing industry which has been developed is closely associated with certain offshore "banks."

BIBLIOGRAPHY

A. Bernard, *Afrique septentrionale et occidentale,* Vol. XI, *Geographie Universelle,* Paris.

F. Maurette, *Afrique, equatoriale, orientale et australe,* Vol. XII, *Geographie Universelle,* Paris.

A. Wegener, *The Origin of Continents and Oceans* (translated by Skerl), London, 1922 (historical interest).

J. W. Gregory, *The Rift Valleys and Geology of East Africa,* London, 1921 (historical interest).

F. R. C. Reed, *The Geology of the British Empire,* London, 1921.

Bailey Willis, *East African Plateaus and Rift Valleys,* Washington (Carnegie Inst.), 1936.

E. B. and S. Worthington, *Inland Waters of Africa,* London, 1933.

F. Dixey, "African Landscapes," *Geog. Rev.,* XXXIV, 1944.

CHAPTER

4

African Climates
and the Water Problem

Africa lies between 35° North and 35° South, with the result that, excluding the lands associated with the lofty Atlas ranges in the north, the high plateau in the south and isolated mountainous areas elsewhere, the whole continent has average temperatures over the crucial figure for plant growth of 42°F. throughout the year. Despite the elevation of the plateau in East Africa, frost is practically unknown throughout humid intertropical Africa. Furthermore, violent fluctuations of temperature which are associated with the movements of fronts in the North American continent are absent. Thus plant life is assured of temperatures which permit of growth throughout the year; the farmer is assured of a regular temperature regime which, though it may scorch, is unlikely to wither by unexpected cold. In Africa climatic interest centers on rainfall rather than on temperature. For rainfall the story is very different. Viewed over the averages of a span of years the rainfall regimes may appear regular enough, but few places enjoy an "average" rainfall. Instead there are violent fluctuations from year to year, serious differences in the dates when the rains come, violent spasmodic downpours rather than steady falls. The key to the whole of Africa's development is control of water. Drainage and flood control are needed where rainfall is regularly or occasionally excessive; storage and irrigation are needed where rainfall is normally moderate both to guard against bad years and to extend the growing period; irrigation is essential where rainfall is low despite the fact that in a majority of years the rainfall may be sufficient for dry zone crops. Unless there is elaborate provision for the storage of food produced in excess in good years—which there is not in Africa—without irrigation the land can support only the population which it can support in the *bad* years.

62

Being situated in low latitudes and almost entirely surrounded by water, there is no immediate source of cold continental air to affect the continent. South Africa is separated by 2000 miles of ocean from Antarctica and, unlike South America, has few invasions of cold polar air from that direction. Though northern parts of Africa are affected by conditions in Euro-Asia and are more "continental" in the wide range of temperature, there is an approximately symmetrical distribution of climatic types north and south of the equator. The greatest differences are between the northeastern and southeastern segments of the continent. In the northeast the great African hot desert area continues across the Red Sea into Arabia, and Ethiopia comes within the ambit of the great Asiatic monsoon. In the southeast, on the other hand, Africa is open to the influences from over the open south Indian Ocean.

Gradual transitions from one type of climate to another are the general rule over the whole of Africa. There are no great mountain chains such as act as climatic divides in America or Asia, though the Atlas mountains in the north restrict good winter rains associated with Mediterranean cyclones to the coastlands. The elevation of the great African plateau, especially since its higher parts are in the east towards the windward, modifies both temperature and rainfall. The July temperatures of the East African plateau actually on the equator are 20 degrees lower than they would be at sea level and actually 10 degrees lower than those of the coastlands of the southeast, outside the tropics, at the same season. The moderate rainfall of the East African plateau is due in part to the lifting of rain-bearing winds so that the heavy equatorial rainfall and equatorial climate do not extend across the continent. The East African plateau, right on the equator, is thus suited to European settlement, and the equatorial rainforest is absent.

Climatic conditions around the African coasts are considerably influenced by oceanic currents. Along the west coast of northern Africa the cold Canaries current flows southward. The low sea temperatures are due partly to the northern origin of the water, partly to the upwelling of cold bottom water to replace the surface waters constantly propelled towards the southwest by the dominant northeasterly winds. Coastal fogs are frequent, but hot season temperatures are relatively low. With offshore winds, the coastlands are very arid. Similar effects are associated with the cold northward-flowing Benguela current off the shores of southwest Africa, where conditions resemble those of northern Chile. The Canaries and

Benguela currents both swing westwards while between them the eastward-flowing equatorial countercurrent or Guinea current brings very warm water to the Guinea or West African coast. Because the air currents are onshore the coastlands are constantly bathed by very warm and moist air masses, with a resultant heavy rainfall almost from Dakar to Libreville.

The east coast of Africa with its onshore winds driving warm surface currents towards the land is entirely different. South of the equator the island of Madagascar splits the main South Equatorial current of the Indian Ocean, and the Mozambique current flows southward from off Mombasa to about Lourenço Marques, where it merges into the Agulhas current. The presence of these warm surface currents results in sea-surface temperatures 15 to 20 degrees (Fahrenheit) higher than on the west coast, and the warm moist air masses associated with them afford a moderate to good rainfall along the coastlands. In the north Indian Ocean, circulation of waters is reversed according to the Asiatic monsoon. In the season of the northeast monsoon (November to April) the drift of water is from northeast to southwest along the coast—a cool current flowing *towards* the equator; in the season of the southwest monsoon the air movement is offshore, and the current is alongshore from southwest to northeast. Because neither condition favors precipitation the coast is arid from the equator northward.

Turning now to the main features of the atmospheric circulation over Africa, we see that the continent is dominated by the world distribution of pressure—the two extra-tropical high-pressure belts and the equatorial low-pressure belt. These so-called permanent belts move northward in the northern summer, lagging behind the overhead sun, and southward in the southern summer. For the month of January (northern winter, southern summer) the position is shown in Fig. 1. The Azores high-pressure system extends over the relatively cool Sahara, the south Atlantic high-pressure belt lies to the north of the continent and the equatorial low is south of the equator.

In July, as shown in Fig. 4, the January conditions are largely reversed. The Sahara, which has become extremely hot, gives rise to a huge low-pressure area whereas South Africa comes under the influence of the extra-tropical high-pressure belt. At this season conditions over northeastern Africa are complicated by the great Asiatic monsoon.

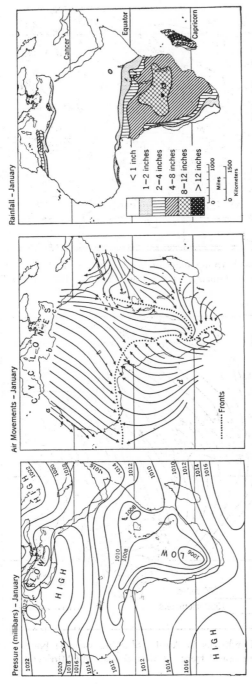

Figure 1. Climatic Conditions over Africa in January. (After Brooks and Mirrlees, "A Study of the Atmospheric Circulation over Tropical Africa," *Geophysical Memoirs*, Vol. VI, No. 55, 1932, London, Meteorological Office.)

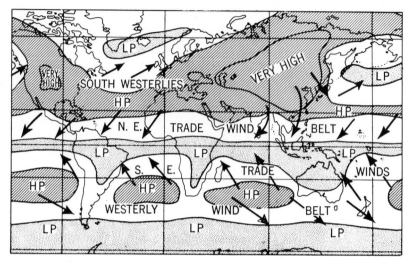

Figure 2.   Theoretical Arrangement of World Pressure Belts and Winds in Relation to Africa in January.   LP = Low Pressure;   HP = High Pressure.

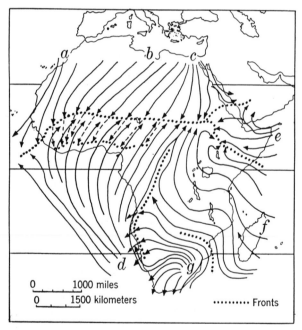

Figure 3.   Wind Conditions in April.   Showing variable position of the main
intertropical front.   (After Brooks and Mirrlees.)

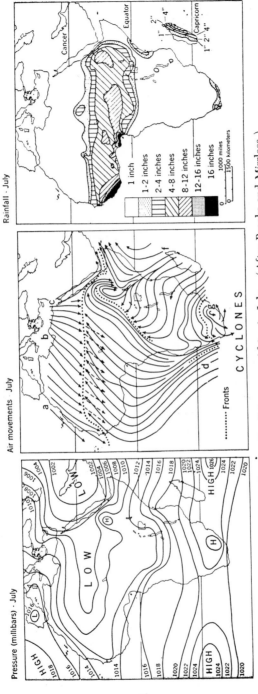

Figure 4. Climatic Conditions over Africa in July. (After Brooks and Mirrlees.)

67

These pressure systems give rise to the movements of air masses which are in turn responsible for the distribution of rainfall over the continent. Brooks and Mirrlees [1] distinguish seven air streams, as shown by arrows, lettered *a, b, c, d, e, f* and *g* in Figs. 1, 3 and 4. They may be compared with the theoretical arrangement of winds shown in Fig. 2. Two other air streams affect the extreme northwest and southeast of the continent. The air streams are:

(*a*) The Atlantic Northeast Trades blowing towards the southwest from the Azores high-pressure system.

(*b*) The Harmattan, the air stream blowing from the Saharan high-pressure belt across the Sudan and towards West Africa.

(*c*) The Egyptian air stream blowing up the Nile valley as a northerly wind and reaching as far south as Bechuanaland.

(*d*) The Atlantic Southeast Trades blowing towards the equatorial low-pressure belt from the high-pressure belt over the south Atlantic. On crossing the equator, which they do especially during the northern summer, these winds become southwesterly and produce a monsoon effect in West Africa, but penetrate in January only a short distance inland.

(*e*) The Arabian or Indian Northeast Trades blowing from the high-pressure system of southwest Asia in the winter months only, being eliminated and reversed by the monsoon currents for the other half of the year.

(*f*) The Indian Ocean Southeast Trades are the dominant influence over the southeast part of the continent.

(*g*) The Southeast Africa air is a dry mass.

(*h*) and (*i*) These air streams, also shown in Figs. 1, 3 and 4, though not studied by Brooks and Mirrlees, are the westerly air streams of midlatitudes. That over the Mediterranean is a cyclonic belt of alternating depressions and wedges of high pressure, responsible for the winter rainfall from Morocco to Egypt. That over the southern ocean is associated with strong, more regular winds, the Roaring Forties (so-called from their prevalence in the forties of south latitude), and is responsible for the winter rainfall of the Cape.

Since Brooks and Mirrlees prepared this illuminating analysis of the air circulation over Africa, climatologists have become accus-

[1] C. E. P. Brooks and S. T. A. Mirrlees, "A Study of the Atmospheric Circulation over Tropical Africa," London, Meteorological Office, *Geophysical Memoirs*, Vol. VI, No. 55, 1932.

tomed to think in terms of air masses. Thus Haurwitz and Austin [1] distinguish:

(*a*) *Tropical Maritime Air* (mT)—warm, moist air, originating over the ocean north and south of the equator.

(*b*) *Tropical Continental Air* (cT)—warm, dry air originating over the vast dry Sahara and also over the Kalahari.

Figure 5. A Pair of Giraffes on the East African Plateau. They are silhouetted against a heavy evening sky, which suggests the meeting of two air masses along a front. There are few natural climatic divides in Africa. (Courtesy British Overseas Airways Corporation.)

(*c*) *Polar Maritime Air* (mP)—invading the extreme northwest of the continent in the northern winter and a similar type invading the extreme southwest in the southern winter.

(*d*) *Polar Continental Air* (cP)—as already noted, such air does not reach Africa from the Antarctic, but during the southern winter the continental cooling tends toward the creation of a mild type of cP air over the highlands of south Africa.

The maps (Figs. 1 and 4) leave no doubt of the close association between the main air streams and rainfall. In January the North-

[1] B. Haurwitz and J. M. Austin, *Climatology*, New York, 1944, pp. 332–336.

east Trades (the Harmattan and Egyptian air streams [*b* and *c*]) blow from colder to warmer latitudes and are dry winds. The air stream from the South Atlantic (*d*) brings a small rainfall to the Guinea

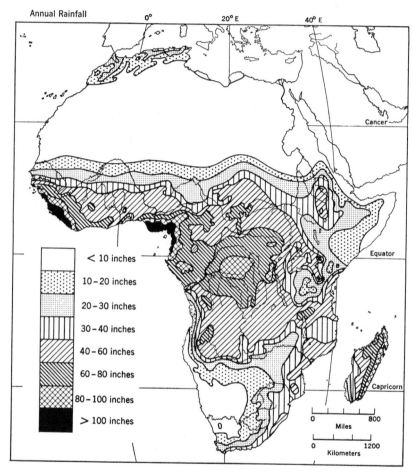

Figure 6.   Average Annual Rainfall.

coast, but farther south it blows from over the cold Benguela current to the heated land and no rainfall results. The effects of the Indian Ocean streams (*e* and *f*) are just what one would expect.

Similarly the position in July is easily explicable.

Of supreme importance to Africa is the intertropical front, shown in Figs. 1, 3 and 4. Over the plateau surface of Africa there are no outstanding physical features, no ranges of mountains to act as climatic divides or to help fix the intertropical front. Consequently its position at all seasons is ill-defined and varies not only with the seasons but noticeably also from one year to another. In the month of April, for example, the intertropical front may lie almost as near the West African coast as in January, and all lands away from the coast remain

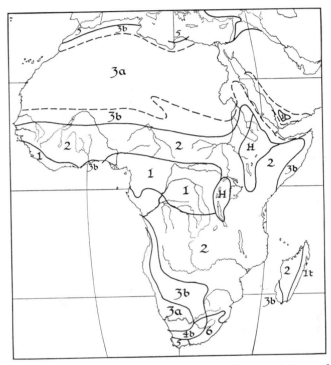

Figure 7. The Climatic Regions of Africa. (After Finch and Trewartha, *Atlas of World Maps*, Army Service Forces Manual, M 101, 1943.)

under the influence of the dry Harmattan. Or it may lie 500 miles farther north, and the same lands have welcome rains from moist tropical air. It is, in a few words, the irregular behavior of the intertropical front which is responsible for Africa's greatest curse, irregularity of rainfall.

Although Africa does not suffer from the destructive hurricanes which are so serious in parts of tropical and subtropical America, the cyclonic storms associated with the intertropical front produce very heavy and sometimes destructive falls of rain.

Despite the several systems of climatic classification in common use, the general picture in Africa is clear. The scheme shown in

Fig. 7 is derived from Finch and Trewartha—familiar from its use in the *Atlas of World Maps* (Army Service Forces Manual, M 101, 1943). It distinguishes:

A Tropical Rainy Climates	*A*

1 Tropical Rainforest Climate, better called the Equatorial Climate. This is limited to areas within 10° of the equator, but the similar 1t (Windward Coasts) characterizes the eastern coastlands of Madagascar.

Af

2 Tropical Savanna or Summer Rain Climate, covering more than a third of all Africa.

Aw

B Dry Climates	*B*

3 Low Latitude Dry Climates
   3*a* Desert
   3*b* Steppe

BW

4 Middle Latitude Dry Climates
   4*b* Steppe

BS

BSk

C Humid Mesothermal	*C*

5 Mediterranean
6 Humid Subtropical

Ca

Cfb

The symbols on the right hand are those of the well-known classification of Wilhelm Köppen, where *f* indicates no dry season; *w* is winter dry; *s* is summer dry; *k* is cold (mean annual temperature below 64.4°F.); *b* is mean temperature of warmest month below 71.6°F.

British geographers normally use simple climatic-vegetation regions modified but slightly from the scheme introduced by A. J. Herbertson in 1905.[1] In the original paper Herbertson distinguished very simply in Africa:

3. The warm temperate regions:
   (*a*) The western margin with winter rains (Mediterranean type)
      [= 5 of Finch and Trewartha]
   (*b*) The eastern margin with summer rain
      [= 6 of Finch and Trewartha]
4. (*a*) The west tropical deserts (Sahara type)
      [= 3 of Finch and Trewartha]
   (*b*) Intertropical tablelands (Sudan type)
      [= 2 of Finch and Trewartha]
6. Equatorial lowlands (Amazon type)
      [= 1 of Finch and Trewartha]

It is interesting that the two schemes of classification, in view of the different starting points, should prove to be practically identical.

[1] "The Major Natural Regions," *Geog. Jour.*, XXV, 1905, 300–312.

Pierre Gourou, the well-known French authority on tropical climates, draws a distinction between *pays tropicaux*, lands within the tropics having an annual rainfall exceeding 800 millimeters or 16 inches, and *pays désertiques*, where the annual rainfall drops below 16 inches.

The Equatorial or Tropical Rainforest Climate (1)

The keynote of the Equatorial climate is monotony. There are constant heat, constant humidity and constant rainfall. There is little or no seasonal rhythm, little relief at night from the heat of the day. Yet there are no great extremes: in lowland stations the thermometer remains around 80°F.; on the hottest day it rarely rises to much above 90°; in the coolest night it does not sink below 70°. With early morning mist there may be a feeling of chill, more apparent than real. As the sun climbs high at mid-day there is a sense of great heat, often dispelled by afternoon cloud and rain, giving place to clear starlit nights. Plant growth takes place throughout the year so that luxuriant vegetation is the rule. It is the absence of seasonal rhythm which constitutes the "unhealthy" aspect of a climate which has been described as a good servant but a bad master. H. J. Fleure characterized equatorial lands as regions of "constant endeavour."

Some stations have two rainfall maxima during the year; others (especially towards the margins) have a season rainier than the rest of the year, but typically there is no dry season. It is this feature which distinguishes the truly "equatorial" climate from the wettest parts of the tropical savanna or windward coasts. In many parts of the region, lying in the belt of equatorial calms or doldrums, the rainfall is convectional, and regular winds are absent. The heat of the sun causes evaporation from water surfaces and damp land. The heated, saturated air rises and is cooled by convection so that rain falls on almost the same area from which the moisture originated.

With increasing elevation the daily and monthly temperatures are lowered, and, although there is some increase in the daily range, there is little in the annual. With lowered temperatures rainfall is also less.

On the margins of equatorial regions and notably along the wet part of the West African coasts moisture-laden air masses moving in from the sea play a larger part.

In the tables which follow the first two stations may be called typical equatorial; the second two show stations modified by elevation; the third two show the wet margins.

Windward Coasts (1f)

In Africa Finch and Trewartha show this type of climate on the eastern coastlands of Madagascar, from latitude 12° to 25° South. This is in the belt of the Southeast Trades, but in January the equatorial doldrums belt of rising air affects the northern end of the island and this is the wettest season. But there is no dry season; the southeast winds rising to cross the mountains deposit at least 3 inches even in the driest months, September, October and November. Only some of the tropical cyclones which originate over the south Indian Ocean and affect Mauritius and Réunion, especially from January to April, reach Madagascar. The constant onshore winds prevent any violent daily fluctuations of temperature, and the annual range is also small. The figures for Tamatave illustrate the conditions.

In many ways the wetter coastal regions of West Africa—Sierra Leone and Liberia—belong to the "windward coasts" rather than the equatorial.

The Tropical Savanna (2)

This is *par excellence* the climate of tropical Africa, just as the varied forms of savanna which result are the dominant natural vegetation of the vast intertropical plateaus. Since the savanna stretches from the equatorial rainforest, on the one hand, to the desert margins on the other, the savanna climate must clearly vary greatly also. In fact the variation is primarily in the total amount of precipitation, commonly from 80 inches on the equatorial margins (but greatly exceeding this on exposed slopes) to 16 inches where it merges into the "low latitude steppes" of Finch and Trewartha. There is a consequent effect on temperature, but what is constant throughout is the rhythm of the seasons. A cool or at least relatively cool dry season (November to February in the northern hemisphere) gives place to a hot dry season so that in the northern hemisphere the hottest month is early in the year, commonly in April or May. The coming of the rains causes a lowering of the temperature except where the falls are too small to have this effect, and the rainy season is thus equivalent to our midlatitude summer. For reasons already indicated as related to the movement of air masses and the associated fronts over a continent where there are few physical barriers to air

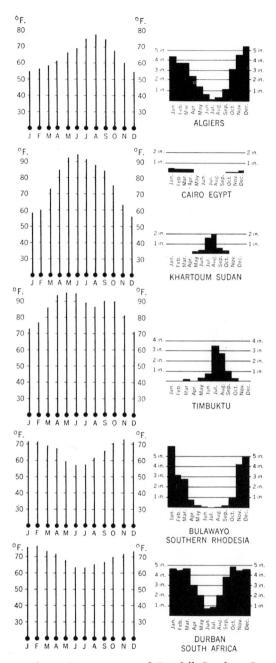

Figure 8. Some African Temperature and Rainfall Graphs. Over the vast bulk of Africa a rainfall, whether heavy or light, well-distributed throughout the year is unknown. The temperature graph showing a great range is characteristic of the heart of the Sahara.

movement, the break of the rainy season may be early in some years, greatly delayed in others. Annual totals show a wide variation from year to year whereas in any given year the incidence may show remarkable irregularities since the rain falls almost entirely as heavy

Figure 9. The "Hungry Season" in the Northern Gold Coast. This village is typical of the overworked poor lands on the drier margins of the tropical lands. The soil is thin, and the yam heaps poor. The children show signs of malnutrition, notably the bulging stomach. (British Official Photograph.)

showers or thundershowers. The irregularities between one month and another as well as from year to year increase as the average total fall decreases. Thus in one year a place with an "average" fall of 40 inches may have abundant moisture for a good harvest; the next year the fall may only total 20 inches, and famine conditions result. This is in addition to the so-called hungry season which occurs after all the crops of one harvest have been consumed and before the first crops from the new harvest are ready for consumption. A good example of the climatic vagaries is afforded by a station in the Gambia, where the rainfall totals for 18 successive years were as follows:

1901	45 inches	1910	44 inches
1902	29	1911	28
1903	57	1912	34
1904	38	1913	24
1905	66	1914	49
1906	64	1915	48
1907	34	1916	38
1908	44	1917	38
1909	57	1918	54

Taking individual months in the same place, we find that June showed a range from 2.24 inches in one year to 12.32 in another. Over the same period May ranged from nil to 1.90 inches, and October from 0.24 to 9.08 inches.

The figures for temperature show that plant growth is normally possible throughout the year. Though the day temperatures, especially in drier regions, greatly exceed those in the equatorial belt, they do not reach the extremes found in the great deserts. There is everywhere close correlation between daily and annual temperature ranges and the situation relative to the sea and to moist air masses. Bathurst on the coast in Gambia (13° North) has a range from 74°F. in January to 80°F. in July (when rainfall is 12 inches), but October when the rains have almost ceased (average 4 inches) is one degree hotter than July. Inland stations such as Kayes show a range from 77°F. in January to 96° in May.

Low-Latitude Deserts and Low-Latitude Steppes (3a and 3b)

Essentially deserts result from low precipitation. On the margins towards the equator it is difficult to say where "desert" fades into what Finch and Trewartha record as "steppe," and where the steppe gives place to tropical "savanna." For the savanna limit many would follow Gourou, using the 16-inch isohyet. On the poleward margins a lower rainfall limit may be taken to indicate where the steppe-lands fade into the Mediterranean. In the heart of the Sahara such rain as falls (as at Tamanrasset) comes in storms at irregular intervals; along the southern margins the "rainy season" is the hot season or summer; along the Mediterranean margins it is the winter—well exemplified by Alexandria.

Like all deserts, the African regions have great temperature extremes. The daily range in the heart of the desert is as much as

50° to 60°F.; the highest recorded temperatures on the surface of the earth are claimed by the Sahara. Shade recordings of 136°F. are said to have been made; the surface of the ground frequently exceeds 170°F. Most of the heart of the Sahara has a July mean exceeding 95°. The annual range is between 30° and 40°; in the north the coldest month has a mean of 50°F. so that frost is quite usual.

The mean annual cloudiness is normally less than 10 per cent so that cloudless skies are the rule—bright sunshine by day, starlight by night. The atmosphere is so dry that the wet-bulb thermometer may be 40 degrees lower than the dry. The air may be so dry as to inhibit plant life, and it has been claimed that a man needs to drink a minimum of 10 pints of liquid a day to maintain health.

Conditions in the corresponding area in southern Africa are much less severe. There the most arid strip is along the coast; the so-called Kalahari desert has in fact sufficient vegetation to be classed at worst as semi-desert only.

Middle Latitude Steppe (4b)

In Africa this is the climate of the damper parts of the South African High Veld. It owes its character in large measure to elevation which results in a lower temperature throughout the year. Although snow is not unknown and winter frosts occur during 3 to 6 months, the area is too near the moderating influence of the ocean to suffer from the climatic extremes of northern steppelands and prairies. Graaff Reinet shows a spring or early summer rainfall maximum and also one in the fall. This station is only 2500 feet above sea level; places like Bloemfontein have characteristically lower winter averages.

Mediterranean Climate (5)

The Mediterranean climate, deriving its name from the fact that it is characteristic of so many countries round the Mediterranean Sea, is one of the most distinctive of all climatic types. It shares its hot dry summers with the neighboring desert lands; its cool moist winters derive their rainfall from the westerly air streams which bring through a succession of depressions or lows the rain to lands nearer the poles. The rainfall may show a fall maximum (the "former rains" of the Bible) and a spring maximum ("latter rains") rather than a single winter maximum, but the fact that the supply of moisture coincides with the cool season results both in a slow formation of soil and a slow vegetative growth. In the long hot summer plants need to conserve their moisture, and, unless they tap deep-seated supplies by very long roots, they have reduced leaf surfaces with such protective devices as hairs (for example, olive

Figure 10. The Drakensberg above the Clouds of the Coastal Plain. This picture shows dramatically the contrast often to be found on the African plateau heights from the plains below. (Copyright Geographical Publications Limited.)

tree), waxed or leathery surfaces (laurels, evergreen oak, pines). The thick "cork" bark of the cork oak is another protection against loss of moisture. Cultivation of grain and herbaceous crops necessitates an early harvest before the scorching heat of late summer, or a dependence on irrigation.

The Mediterranean climate is found in the northwest and extreme southwest of the continent, where mountain ranges, deep valleys and coastal strips of varying exposure give marked and rapid local variations in temperature and rainfall. Rainfall (see Fig. 6) generally increases with elevation. Though rare at sea level, frost and even

THE EQUATORIAL OR TROPICAL RAINFOREST CLIMATE

Station	Jan.	Feb.	Mar.	Apr.	May	June	July	Aug.	Sept.	Oct.	Nov.	Dec.	Range	Year
Duala (Cameroons) (Debundja) (39 ft.) °F.	79.3	79.9	79.2	78.8	78.3	76.8	74.7	74.5	75.6	75.9	77.9	78.6	5.4	
Rainfall (in.)	8.0	10.9	17.1	17.3	24.8	59.7	64.4	57.7	65.2	45.2	26.6	15.1		412.0
New Antwerp, Belgian Congo (1230 ft.) °F.	79.2	80.1	79.2	78.1	79.2	78.4	76.5	76.3	77.0	77.4	77.9	78.1	3.8	
Rainfall (in.)	4.1	3.5	4.1	5.6	6.2	6.1	6.3	6.3	6.3	6.6	2.6	9.3		67.0
Entebbe, Uganda (3863 ft.) °F.	71.1	71.1	71.3	70.3	69.8	69.4	68.6	68.6	69.4	70.1	70.1	70.2	2.7	
Rainfall (in.)	2.6	3.6	5.8	9.7	8.5	5.1	2.9	3.1	3.1	3.5	5.0	5.1		58.0
Nairobi, Kenya (5450 ft.) °F.	63.8	64.7	65.2	63.9	63.4	61.6	58.5	59.3	61.6	64.8	61.0	62.3	6.7	
Rainfall (in.)	1.9	3.6	4.2	8.9	5.6	2.2	0.9	1.1	1.2	2.3	5.3	2.8		40.0
Freetown, Sierra Leone (223 ft.) °F.	81.3	82.3	82.4	82.4	81.5	80.3	78.6	77.9	79.1	80.1	81.2	81.4	4.5	
Rainfall (in.)	0.4	0.3	1.2	4.1	11.5	20.0	35.6	36.6	28.5	12.6	5.1	1.4		157.3
Lagos, Nigeria (25 ft.) °F.	80.9	82.2	83.3	82.5	81.8	79.3	78.0	77.7	78.4	79.5	81.4	81.5	5.6	
Rainfall (in.)	1.1	2.1	3.7	5.7	10.5	18.7	10.7	2.8	5.3	7.8	2.6	0.8		71.8

WINDWARD COAST (1*t*)

Tamatave, Madagascar (16 ft.)	°F.	79.3	80.6	78.3	76.5	72.5	69.3	68.4	69.3	71.2	73.8	76.5	78.6	12.2
	Rainfall (in.)	15.0	14.3	17.8	12.0	9.8	14.4	13.2	8.5	7.1	5.3	3.9	9.6	130.9

THE TROPICAL SAVANNA

Gorée (Dakar), French West Africa (20 ft.)	°F.	68.5	66.2	68.2	68.9	71.6	78.3	81.1	81.5	82.4	82.0	78.3	72.0	16.2
	Rainfall (in.)	0	0	0	0	0	0.9	3.6	9.9	5.2	0.7	0.1	0	20.4
Kayes, French West Africa (197 ft.)	°F.	77.2	80.8	88.7	94.1	96.4	90.5	83.7	81.7	82.2	84.5	83.1	77.2	19.2
	Rainfall (in.)	0	0	0	0	0.6	3.9	8.3	8.3	5.6	1.9	0.3	0.2	29.1
Mongalla, Sudan (1440 ft.)	°F.	80.4	81.7	82.6	81.0	79.0	77.4	75.9	75.7	77.2	78.1	79.0	79.2	6.9
	Rainfall (in.)	0.1	0.7	1.5	4.2	5.4	4.6	5.2	5.8	4.9	4.3	1.8	0.3	38.8
Luluabourg, Belgian Congo (2034 ft.)	°F.	76.1	75.7	76.3	77.0	76.6	76.3	76.5	76.3	75.9	76.3	76.6	77.2	1.5
	Rainfall (in.)	7.2	5.4	7.9	6.1	3.1	0.2	0.1	2.5	6.5	6.6	9.1	6.6	61.3

THE TROPICAL SAVANNA (*Continued*)

Station	Jan.	Feb.	Mar.	Apr.	May	June	July	Aug.	Sept.	Oct.	Nov.	Dec.	Range	Year
Salisbury, S. Rhodesia (4880 ft.) °F.	69.7	68.8	68.2	65.7	60.6	56.9	56.1	60.2	66.4	70.7	70.7	69.6	14.6	
Rainfall (*in.*)	7.5	7.4	4.5	1.0	0.5	0.1	0	0.1	0.3	1.1	3.7	5.8		32.0

LOW LATITUDE DESERTS AND LOW LATITUDE STEPPES

Station	Jan.	Feb.	Mar.	Apr.	May	June	July	Aug.	Sept.	Oct.	Nov.	Dec.	Range	Year
Alexandria, Egypt (105 ft.) °F.	56.1	57.2	60.1	63.7	68.5	73.4	77.0	78.1	76.3	73.0	66.4	59.4	22.0	
Rainfall (*in.*)	2.1	0.9	0.5	0.2	0	0	0	0	0	0.3	1.3	2.6		7.9
Khartoum, Sudan (1280 ft.) °F.	70.3	73.4	79.2	86.0	90.7	91.4	88.5	86.5	88.2	87.4	80.2	72.1	21.1	
Rainfall (*in.*)	0	0	0	0	0.1	0.3	1.6	2.2	0.7	0.2	0	0		5.1
In-Salah, Sahara (Southern Algeria) (919 ft.) °F.	54.7	59.4	67.8	76.1	85.6	94.3	99.3	97.0	91.6	80.1	68.2	57.7	44.6	
Swakopmund, S. W. Africa (20 ft.) °F.	62.6	63.1	63.3	59.9	60.6	58.5	56.5	54.9	56.1	58.1	58.6	61.5	8.4	
Rainfall (*in.*)	0	0.1	0.2	0	0	0	0	0	0	0.1	0	0.2		0.6

MIDDLE LATITUDE STEPPE

Location														
Graaff Reinet, Cape Province, South Africa (2500 ft.) °F.	71.8	72.3	68.2	61.8	56.5	53.0	51.0	53.8	59.0	63.8	68.5	71.5	21.3	15.3
Rainfall (in.)	1.7	1.4	2.7	0.9	1.2	0.4	0.2	0.7	1.3	0.9	2.5	1.4		

THE MEDITERRANEAN CLIMATE

Location														
Funchal, Madeira (82 ft.) °F.	59.4	59.2	59.7	61.2	63.5	67.1	70.2	72.1	71.4	68.4	64.4	61.2	12.9	27.1
Rainfall (in.)	3.4	3.6	3.4	1.9	1.1	0.4	0.1	0.1	1.2	4.0	4.7	3.2		
Algiers, Algeria (72 ft.) °F.	49.3	50.4	52.5	55.8	61.0	67.8	73.1	74.7	70.3	63.7	56.8	51.8	25.4	27.2
Rainfall (in.)	4.0	2.6	3.3	2.0	1.7	0.7	0.1	0.1	1.2	3.4	4.1	4.0		
Tunis, Tunisia (141 ft.) °F.	48.4	51.3	54.3	58.3	64.4	72.0	77.7	78.6	54.5	66.7	58.8	52.3	30.2	16.6
Rainfall (in.)	2.1	2.0	1.9	1.5	0.9	0.5	0.1	0.2	1.0	1.9	2.1	2.4		
Cape Town, Cape Province, South Africa (40 ft.) °F.	69.9	70.3	68.1	63.2	58.9	55.7	54.7	55.6	57.9	61.2	64.4	67.9	15.6	25.3
Rainfall (in.)	0.7	0.6	0.9	1.9	3.8	4.5	3.7	3.4	2.3	1.6	1.1	0.8		

The Humid Subtropical Climate

Station	Jan.	Feb.	Mar.	Apr.	May	June	July	Aug.	Sept.	Oct.	Nov.	Dec.	Range	Year
Durban, Natal, South Africa (260 ft.) °F.	76.3	76.8	74.9	71.8	67.8	64.8	64.3	65.8	67.6	69.5	72.0	74.6	12.5	
Rainfall (in.)	4.6	4.9	5.4	3.4	1.9	1.2	1.2	1.7	3.2	5.1	5.0	5.1		42.7
Pietermaritzburg, Natal, South Africa (2225 ft.) °F.	73.3	73.4	71.4	67.8	61.9	57.6	58.6	62.4	65.2	67.4	69.1	71.8	15.8	
Rainfall (in.)	5.1	6.2	5.1	2.6	1.1	0.3	0.1	0.8	1.8	2.5	5.3	5.0		35.9

snow occur at comparatively low elevations and are usual at greater heights.

The examples given on p. 83 include the island site of Funchal (Madeira), the coastal stations of Algiers and Tunis in the north, Cape Town in the south. Marrakesh, inland at a height of 1542 feet, though dry, shows a fall and a spring maximum.

Humid Subtropical Climate (6)

In Africa this is the climate of Natal and neighboring parts of the southeastern coasts of the continent about latitude 30 degrees. Durban shows the small range of temperature near the coast, increasing slightly inland as indicated in Pietermaritzburg. In neither place is the range as great as in areas like the southeastern United States.

Undifferentiated Highlands (H)

The whole of the African plateau exhibits climatic modifications due to elevation. In Nairobi on the equator, already mentioned, the modification is profound and is shared by the large area of highland in East Africa. There remain, however, parts of the continent, notably the mountain knot of Ethiopia, where rugged or varied relief results in a vertical zonation of climatic types; the same is true of the great volcanoes of East Africa. This is the reason for the inclusion of "undifferentiated highlands" on the map—where parts rise to the snowline.

Climate and the African

No aspect of life in tropical Africa exceeds rain in importance. From north to south and from west to east innumerable ceremonies and customs have sprung from the vital necessity of an adequate fall of rain in an area so marked by violent fluctuations from year to year. In the heart of the Low Veld of the Northeastern Transvaal is found the rain cult of the Bantu Lovedu people, which is centered on the Rain Queen, the "transformer of the clouds." [1]

At the other end of Africa as recently as 1943 white government officials attended the solemn ceremony of installation of the *Ret* or rain-making chief of the Shilluk of the Upper Nile Province of the Anglo-Egyptian Sudan. [2]

When the rains come, they may do so with alarming suddenness and ferocity. Kenneth Bradley in his interesting *Diary of a District*

[1] E. J. Krige and J. D. Krige, *The Realm of the Rain-Queen,* New York, 1943.
[2] *African World,* April 22, 1944.

Officer [1] has recorded how in one year at Fort Jameson in Northern Rhodesia the thermometer stood at 103°F. in the shade on November the eleventh. That night 2 inches of rain fell. The next day it was still raining, and the thermometer had dropped to 65°. Within a couple of days burnt-over pastures or brown grass slopes are bright green again, but gulleys may have been formed on overgrazed land or unprotected soil, and a dangerous cycle of soil erosion started. Floods and washouts on roads and railways may happen overnight. It is equally true that the water may drain off before it can really be used.

It remains a curious fact, discussed below, page 89, that the African is not naturally "water-conscious"; he fails to make best use of his resources. Over vast areas with a marked wet and dry season, life during the rains is not difficult. Heat and moisture combine to encourage plant growth, and a varied assortment of vegetables becomes available for human food. This is the time for sowing. The months which follow are the months for harvesting the various grains —corn, millets, groundnuts and rice—but harvesting of all crops is over 2 months before the rains break. Thus the months of March and April north of the equator, September and October to the south, are slack months in the cultivation year, but if the harvest has been poor so that food does not last over this period, or later until other food is available, this is the "hungry season," often one of great distress.

Where there are reliable river floods this "hunger period" is absent. This is clearly seen in the Central Barotse plain of Northern Rhodesia, where the Zambezi floods annually with a maximum in March and April. The people, the Lozi, live on mounds in the plain free from floods (the ownership of which is very important) and cultivate the soil as gardens, at the same time keeping cattle and fishing, so that they enjoy a varied diet.

Climate and the White Man

The high death rate among Europeans serving in the Tropics and perhaps especially the disastrous mortality among British soldiers serving in India and compelled to march and fight in close-fitting cloth uniforms and small caps gave rise to beliefs about the influence of climate on the white man which have persisted, with little foundation, for more than a century. The direct effects of climate have

[1] London and Toronto, Harrap, 1943.

been confused with the serious effects of disease, especially insect-borne and water-borne. Among the myths was—and still is—sunstroke, which was believed to affect particularly the spine (hence the wearing of spine pads) and through the head, which accordingly needed protection by a sun helmet or solar topee, without which no self-respecting Britisher would venture abroad in sunlight or even with the sun lurking behind clouds. For a decade or more medical men had been denying the existence of "sunstroke" in the old accepted sense before the experience of troops in New Guinea, Burma and Africa in the Second World War finally dispelled the myth. Heatstroke or heat apoplexy is real enough and is best countered by all those measures which encourage the body to "breathe"—loose light clothing and abundant water to encourage perspiration. Light rays received through the eyes may be dangerous, hence the wearing of dark glasses.

As exact evidence based on controlled experiments accumulates, the trend of the evidence indicates that there is nothing in the tropical climate to inhibit hard manual labor for whites as well as colored races, though temperature and humidity conditions may be above the optimum for both physical and mental energy. Carrying out tests on myself during some years of residence in the tropics, I found a definite lowering of mental ability at 100°F. in dry air and obviously at much lower temperatures with high humidity. For my own part a controlled temperature of 70° to 75° is most conducive to mental exertion—probably rather lower for physical.

The absence of seasonal rhythm in the equatorial lands has already been cited as a deleterious climatic factor. In addition, high humidity as well as exceptionally high actual temperatures may be quoted as direct effects of climate. That high temperatures have a direct effect is instanced by the relatively harmless but very annoying condition known as "prickly heat," an intense irritation which may or may not show on the surface of the skin.

Tropical climates have of course many indirect effects on the white man. Since the intake of a large part of our food is required for the maintenance of bodily temperature in cold latitudes, it follows that there is less need for energy-giving carbohydrates or "fuel." Yet the white man is reluctant to change his habits, and an accumulation of fatty tissue is often to be noted. The need for a large intake of moisture often leads to excessive intake of alcohol. In short, the feeding and drinking habits among whites in many parts of the tropics are, or have been, such that the survival of the individual becomes a daily miracle.

The long-assumed superiority of the white man has given rise consciously or unconsciously to the concept that manual labor is not for him in a country where there are others to do such work; then to the idea that such work is physically impossible.

If we thus destroy some of the old shibboleths, we do not prove that white settlers can be at home anywhere in the tropics. The harmful effects of certain high temperatures have been admitted, but when the "white man's grave," as West Africa was once called, gained its notoriety it was not primarily the climate which was responsible. Disease is another matter.

Interest in the effects of tropical climates on the white man has shifted from the influence of heat and humidity to more subtle considerations. On the supposedly "healthy" highlands there seems to be some undue stimulation of the nervous system. There is often an increased irritability in the individual, and there is some evidence of decreasing mental stability, especially in the second or third generation of white settlers. Is it the influence of cosmic rays, the increased reception of radiation, the slowness of adjustment to lower atmospheric pressure, or are there other factors? The answers are still lacking.

The African Water Problem

So much of Africa suffers from aridity—permanent, seasonal or occasional—that some writers have gone so far as to say that no rain falling on the surface of the continent ought ever to be allowed to reach the sea. We may perhaps modify this by adding "until it has fulfilled some function of benefit to mankind." Primarily the water is needed to ensure food production, though Africa, because of its plateau character, has more potential water power than any other continent. In the south the Orange River, with the Tana, does not normally reach the sea, drying up before it disgorges into the Atlantic. But the aim that no river should reach the sea is scarcely compatible with the development of power at the falls which mark the main drop from the plateau and are usually near or relatively near the mouth.

In contrast to the peoples, for example, of southeast Asia, where wells, shadoof, water wheels, persian wheels, flumes, "tanks" with irrigation ditches, terracing and many other devices for reaching, storing and using water are almost universal, the Africans of the tropics are not "water-minded." With certain exceptions their crops depend upon the rains when they come, and their domestic supplies are laboriously carried from stream or lake. They rarely dam a stream to maintain a supply either for domestic use or for watering crops. Wells are the exception rather than the rule, and there is rarely an attempt to prevent pollution by animals of other sources of supply such as a pond.

It is with this position in mind that we suggest that the solution of the African water problem should begin with the education of the African and the development of small schemes which he himself can construct and understand. The position will change, but in the early stages a pump is "white man's magic" to be discarded as soon as it fails to work while anything which "belong him government" is something quite apart. The higher up a stream conservation takes place the better, and the first need is instruction in building a dam or weir of any local material—soil, rubble, stone. Of course it is better still if laterite blocks or precast porous concrete is available. The next stage is to teach the advantages of keeping the supply as free as possible from contamination and of saving labor by conducting a gravity supply by pipe or flume to the villages. Since this is largely a saving of woman's work, it is unlikely to rank as first priority among African men.

There is little exact knowledge of the water cycle in tropical Africa. Run-off is probably between 2 and 12 per cent of rainfall; percolation between 2 and 40 per cent, while evaporo-transpiration may be anything between 40 and 96 per cent. Provided it can again be made available, the best place for water storage is underground. Where there are natural water-holding beds, such as gravel or alluvium in which underground water finds its level in the permanent water table and can be reached by shallow wells, the position is excellent. The African can be taught to dig and line wells, and such a primitive device as an endless porous rope of fibers absorbing water and passing through two wooden rollers to squeeze out the supply is within the power of any African to make and maintain. Unfortunately, over so much of Africa with its underlying complex of ancient rocks the water table behaves irregularly, and a well is both difficult to dig and uncertain of its supply. There is much to be said, in hilly or rolling country, for horizontal "wells" into the hillsides from which water would flow by gravity as an artificial spring. It should be noted that artesian conditions are rare in Africa.

Undoubtedly very much might be achieved in Africa by small schemes—dams and wells—made and understood by the people themselves. Big schemes of water control and power development involving capital and experts for construction and maintenance stand in a very different position. The success of the great Gezira scheme (see page 348) is proof of what can be done, but much of Africa is not yet ready for the big project. The Uganda (Nile) project, described in Chapter 10, illustrates the vital need to regard Africa as a series of basins. How rarely the basin, as a unit for water conservation, coincides with a political unit is clearly seen in the map on page 57.

Over the plateau surface of Africa there are many marshy areas. Some are natural hollows; others are due primarily to vegetation acting as a sponge. These marshes present a problem. Some can be drained and converted into agricultural land, but is this the right procedure? It has been argued that their presence has prevented the spread of desert conditions and that it is essential to maintain them as insurance against increasing aridity. This view is perhaps the one now generally held, and the problem is to make the marshes productive by use. Can parts be converted to rice fields? Can regular cutting of papyrus give a valuable source of paper-making material? Can marsh grasses palatable to cattle be established and provide an all-year supply? Can pastures be improved around lakes stocked with fish, giving a much appreciated food supply?

Not unconnected with the marsh land is the puzzling problem of the fluctuations in level of Africa's great lakes. Sometimes this fluctuation is certainly due to accumulation of vegetation (with silt) at the outlets. An interesting case study is afforded by Lake Nyasa and its outlet, the Shiré River. The lake fluctuates in level as much as 20 feet, and the upper part of the Shiré River has such a shallow gradient that water may flow upstream after a heavy rainstorm. Lower down the river flows over a rocky ridge through a gorge with facilities for a power dam site before reaching a flood plain often invaded by water from the Zambezi.

It is of course impossible to separate the water problem from many of Africa's other major problems. Africa has little coal; therefore the chief source of domestic fuel is wood. This means constant cutting of woodland, and a depletion of timber reserves introduces the danger of soil erosion. If water power could be harnessed to provide electricity at a low cost to the peasant consumer, this danger would disappear and more land would be released for other purposes.

BIBLIOGRAPHY

Many basic data will be found collected in W. G. Kendrew's *The Climates of the Continents* (New York, Third Edition, 1937), but this book was written before the modern concept of air masses. For this reason reference should be made to B. Haurwitz and J. M. Austin's *Climatology* (New York, 1944) and to the pioneer work of Brooks and Mirrlees mentioned in the text.

The complex question of the influence of climate on human beings has given rise to a large, if scattered and still incomplete, literature. Reference may be made to the writings of Clarence A. Mills, *Living with the Weather, Medical Climatology*, and the popular summary, *Climate Makes the Man* (London, 1944). A. Grenfell Price's *White Settlers in the Tropics* has limited reference to Africa. A valuable summary of all aspects will be found in C. E. P. Brooks' *Climate in Everyday Life* (New York, Philosophical Library, Inc., 1951). See also Karl J. Pelzer's "Geography and the Tropics" in *Geography in the Twentieth Century* (New York, Philosophical Library, Inc., 1951).

On the water problem reference should be made to E. B. Worthington's *Inland Waters of Africa*, 1933, and to the official reports and other writings of Frank Debenham, especially *Report on the Water Resources of Central Africa* (His Majesty's Stationery Office, Colonial Research Publication No. 2, 1948) and *Journal of the Royal Society of Arts*, C, 1952, 147–158.

CHAPTER

5

Soils [1]

When C. F. Marbut wrote the section on soils for Shantz and Marbut's *Vegetation and Soils of Africa,* much less was known of soils than of vegetation. Vegetation had been described, it may be inadequately and unscientifically, by many travelers and could be studied in photographs, but soils had usually been recorded as "fertile" or "infertile" or described simply as "red" by those same travelers. Although the colored soil map by Marbut on the scale of 1:25,-000,000 is thus impressive and shows sixteen soil groups, it is definitely stated that the differentiation of soils on the map is "based on: (1) studies of about a dozen samples collected in Africa by H. L. Shantz; (2) rather definite data in the literature for certain localities in Tanganyika Territory, Kenya Colony, Belgian Congo and French Guinea; (3) deductions from the known relations of climate, native vegetation and topography to soils as determined by studies made in the United States and Europe and from the relation of climates, vegetation and topography to the soils of those localities in Africa whose soil character has been definitely determined." It is almost true to say that, in 1922–1923, when those words were written, knowledge of the soils of 11,000,000 square miles rested on the examination of a dozen soil samples and a great deal of deduction which, however brilliant, was still based on hypotheses.

The failure of the great East African Groundnut Scheme in 1949–1950, described in Chapter 17, must be ascribed in large measure to a lack of accurate knowledge of soils and their behavior under new methods of cultivation and is an index both of continued ignorance of tropical soils and of the costliness of that continued ignorance.

Yet much progress has been made. There is a large and increas-

[1] For help with this chapter I am greatly indebted to Mr. G. V. Jacks, Director of the Commonwealth Bureau of Soil Science.

ing mass of information on tropical soils in general. We owe a great debt to Dr. R. L. Pendleton not only for his long-continued field and laboratory work on tropical soils in many countries but also for his great labor of love in translating from Dutch into English the monumental work of E. C. J. Mohr, *The Soils of Equatorial Regions.*[1] Although this book refers primarily to the East Indies, the first part is devoted to general considerations in which Mohr defines soils in terms of soil-forming factors and introduces formulae for soils based on parent material, soil, climate and age. In equatorial soils there is little variation in temperature so that once again attention is focused on the fluctuations of soil moisture through the seasons.

An outstanding contribution to the study of African soils was made by Geoffrey Milne,[2] whose tragically early death robbed soil science of a great pioneer. It was Milne who introduced the catena or catenary concept, which he mapped by vertical stripes of varying width to indicate dominance of each constituent type. He wrote: "Throughout districts characterized by an undulating or hummocky topography, certain sequences of changing soil profiles are found repeated. An example, met with over a large part of the dissected peneplain of Uganda . . . , consists of the sequence of soils between the crest of a low hill and the floor of the adjacent swamp, the profile changing from point to point of this traverse in accordance with conditions of drainage and past history of the land surface . . . a sequence of this kind is termed a catena or catenary complex . . . which can be made specific by prefixing a locality name."

It is clear that this principle is of very wide application.

Milestones in the progress of the study of African soils were the International Conference held at Goma in 1948 and the First Commonwealth Conference on Tropical Soils held in the same year. The *Proceedings* of the latter conference include many papers of importance, and in the preceding years a firm foundation of knowledge had been laid by the work of Van der Merwe in South Africa, Trapnell and others in Rhodesia, and Tothill in Uganda and the Sudan. Workers in Africa were greatly stimulated by the extensive journeys undertaken by C. E. Kellogg, whose knowledge of American soils was unrivaled.

[1] Published by J. W. Edwards, Ann Arbor, Mich., 1944.

[2] "A Provisional Soil Map of East Africa (Kenya, Uganda, Tanganyika and Zanzibar) with Explanatory Memoir," *Amani Memoirs* (East African Agricultural Research Station), 1936. See *Geog. Rev.,* XXVI, 1936, 522–523. See also *Transactions of the Third International Congress Soil Science,* 1935, I, 345–347.

Many workers have been preoccupied with the importance of temperature and moisture on soil formation, and earlier work on the importance of mineralogic and microscopic examination of soils has tended to be overlooked. In 1950, however, Cecil F. Charter, di-

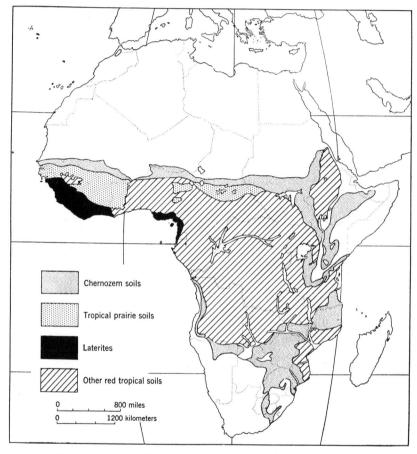

Chernozem soils

Tropical prairie soils

Laterites

Other red tropical soils

0   800 miles

0   1200 kilometers

Figure 1. Simplified Soil Map of Africa. (After Marbut.)

rector of the Gold Coast Survey, demonstrated afresh the supreme importance of the character of the mineral particles examined under the microscope. His work has shown the danger of arguing from one continent to another and has demonstrated the significance of the study of geomorphology—the evolution of land forms. Had the implications of his work been understood earlier many millions of dollars might have been saved in the East African Groundnut Scheme.

More important, many millions will still be spent in vain unless the implications are appreciated by administrators. It is of course universally known that when soils are subjected to mechanical analysis the mineral particles of which they consist can be graded according to size into stones, coarse sand, fine sand, silt and clay. An international classification has been drawn up which defines the size of particles as follows:

Diameter greater than 2 mm.	stones
Diameter between 0.2 and 2 mm.	coarse sand
Diameter between 0.02 and 0.2 mm.	fine sand
Diameter between 0.002 and 0.02 mm.	silt
Diameter less than 0.002 mm.	clay

A "sandy" soil, for example, includes more than 60 per cent of coarse and fine sand but less than 10 per cent of clay. Loamy soils and loams contain a smaller percentage of coarse and fine sand but more of clay, and so on. But what is the origin of these mineral particles? It is of course in general the underlying rocks, whether solid or "drift" deposits. Over the vast areas of Europe and North America the underlying rocks are of sedimentary origin—superficial deposits laid down or redeposited by wind, river water, ice and melt water from ice, sea water or older, solid deposits of sandstone, shale and clay. When examined under the microscope, the tiny mineral fragments, especially of the all-important stable mineral quartz, are found to be more or less rounded—partly rounded if deposited under water, more fully rounded and polished if wind-borne. By comparison we have seen that a very large part of the African continent has been land for many millions of years. The old Miocene peneplanation surface has been subjected to atmospheric weathering for 15 or 30 million years. The mineral particles of African soils are thus very frequently derived directly from the underlying solid rocks; the particles have *not* been transported. The underlying crystalline complex is commonly of varied metamorphic rocks seamed by quartz veins. The quartz veins, and the quartz of the various metamorphic rocks, have been shattered into tiny "sand" grains, but the grains are *sharply angular* and of different sizes. It was the Scottish road engineer, John Loudon McAdam (1756–1836), who realized that angular rock fragments of different sizes could be compacted into a solid durable road surface by simple pressure or rolling. This is the principle of the macadam road. The rock fragments of an African soil thus present the ideal conditions for the formation of a "macadam" surface. It would seem that even the pounding by the raindrops in a tropical downpour may sometimes be sufficient to consolidate the surface. Although the bare foot of the African cultivator may tread with impunity on the soil, a caterpillar tractor has the same effect as a road roller and consolidates the surface into a hard macadam layer. Immediately the majority of mechanical cultivators are ruled out. There are other consequential results of this soil structure. It was found in the East African experiments that disc plows lasted but a very short time. The angular quartz grains

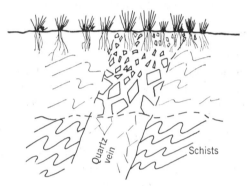

Figure 2. Diagram Showing the Formation of African Sedentary Soils from Subsoil.

(harder than any steel) embedded in a clay matrix seem to have acted just like diamond dust in a circular iron wheel; they rasped the steel discs of a plow in an incredibly short time. If this was the cause of their failure at Kongwa, another weapon of large-scale agricultural science is rendered impotent. There is no real alternative yet, in many parts of Africa, to the African hand cultivator with his hoe, quite apart from the costs associated with mechanized cultivation and other aspects which are considered in Chapter 7.

Any student of elementary chemistry knows that a chemical reaction is normally hastened by the application of heat. That is why the test tube is heated in the Bunsen burner, why a hot solution of acid does its work more quickly than cold. Furthermore, a lump of sugar or salt dissolves more quickly in hot water than in cold. Although it is now recognized that some very interesting chemical reactions take place under cold conditions, it is still true to say that the majority of chemical reactions which can be observed in soils in midlatitudes are hastened in the tropics. With air and surface soil temperatures approximating to 80°F. it would seem that downward leaching—the solution by percolating rainwater of substances in the surface layers and their removal to lower layers—takes place with greater rapidity than in midlatitudes, though this is not agreed by all workers. In the dry season, where a dry season occurs, evaporation is rapid, and with it the deposition of salts in the soil. According to local conditions a "hard pan" primarily of ferruginous oxides may be formed either at the surface or at a varying distance below it. Perhaps of even greater significance is the rapid oxidation of organic compounds when exposed to the atmosphere. In midlatitudes the turning of surface layers of the soil permits air to reach organic matter, encourages the work of aerobic (air-loving) bacteria which converts decaying organic matter into valuable humus and organic food directly available to plants. Plowing in the tropics, on the other hand, may expose organic matter such as fibrous roots so that it combines with the oxygen of the atmosphere so rapidly as to form the gas carbon dioxide which disappears into the air.

It was proved by actual experiments in Ceylon long ago that frequent plowing can literally plow all the goodness out of a tropical soil. It becomes increasingly doubtful whether plowing is the right treatment for the soils of vast areas of tropical Africa. The luxuriant growth of an equatorial rainforest suggests a soil of great fertility, and the fallen leaves suggest a ready source of organic matter. But when the forest is cleared and the atmosphere reaches the soil directly, it is rapidly reduced to complete sterility. The relationship of air temperature to humus content has been demonstrated in Java, where at an elevation of 3000 feet and an average annual temperature of 68°F. the humus content of surface soil was 14 per cent. It dropped to 5 per cent at lower levels and a temperature of 76°F. In tropical lowland soils it is often below 2 per cent. The beneficial action of frost, which, because water expands when it freezes, breaks up clods of clay soil and prepares a natural seed bed in the colder parts of midlatitudes, is absent in the tropics. Instead, the mechanical action of heavy downpours of rain may further consolidate an already heavy soil.

Although the incidence of soil erosion has cast doubts on the virtues and the value of huge plowed areas in middle latitudes, it is still true to say that there the well-managed farm in the fall is likely to exhibit a succession of neatly plowed fields, with the air reaching the soil. It will be a farm kept clean, and the land will be free of weeds. In tropical Africa it is scarcely too much to say that such a farm would be all that is wrong. The exposure of the soil to the atmosphere would result in rapid deterioration in nutrient status; it would be inviting soil erosion. When working in West Africa the worst example of soil erosion I actually witnessed was on a government experimental farm which had been clean-plowed and was then unfortunately subjected to a fall of rain, 2.5 inches in one night. Every furrow was an incipient if not an actual gully.

By our standards the African's farm is very dirty; his land is full of weeds. But the golden rule is to keep the soil covered with vegetation; the problem is to introduce a "cover crop" which will both keep the soil covered and add to its nutrient status. Various leguminous crops (with bacteria in the root nodules which convert atmospheric nitrogen to nitrogenous plant food) have been introduced for this purpose, and the African cultivator has been encouraged to hoe them into the soil. Because this hoeing is done by hand the already heavy labor of cultivation is thereby doubled, and the hoeing-in of greencrops has not proved popular with African cultivators. The custom has long been to clear a tract of land by burning, cultivate by hoeing in the ashes and abandon after a few years. The tract cleared is too small for serious erosion to take place. The tree roots are left and bind the soil, while weeds spring up unhindered to protect the soil. In regions of heavy rainfall the land may be ridged by hoes into a succession of little basins, as shown in Fig. 3.

The practice of clearing land by burning as well as the practice of burning off pastures annually is almost universal in tropical Africa. Is this process injurious to the soil? No one needs to be reminded of the effect of burning clay—it becomes a brick. It is well known too that peat bogs and soils very rich in organic matter may, in middle latitudes, actually catch fire and burn for long periods. Thus burning off the vegetation in tropical Africa may both bake the surface soil to a brick-like form and fire the organic matter in the soil. As a matter of fact this does not happen unless the fire is very fierce so that the secret is to burn off early in the dry season before the vegetation is too dry. In that case the soil benefits from the dressing of ash. Some experiments seem to show that the results of burning off a cover crop are as good as hoeing it in—with an immense saving of labor—but other recent work throws doubt on this conclusion.

Very little is yet known of the part played by organisms and micro-organisms in tropical soils. The microbiology of submerged riceland soils must obviously be very different from that of normally drained soils. Another interesting case of conditions peculiar to the tropics is afforded by those lands where termites (the so-called white ants) are abundant. Their termitaria, reaching many feet in height and believed in some cases to be centuries old, are familiar sights over much of drier tropical Africa. In land suffering from leaching and with soils and subsoils almost free of lime, the material

Figure 3. Basin Cultivation in Southern Nigeria. This is a most effective means of preventing soil erosion. (Copyright L. Dudley Stamp.)

of the termitaria has been found so rich in calcium carbonate as to supply fertilizer for a considerable patch of surrounding land. There are parts of the tropics where these afford the only fertile patches. Yet there does not seem to be any accumulation of phosphates which might have been expected from termite excreta. Termites break down organic matter—such as twigs and leaves falling on the surface—but it is not clear that they help to build up humus and may merely aid rapid oxidation.

The mention of soil erosion introduces a subject of the utmost importance to all Africa. It is sometimes forgotten that erosion is a natural geological process; there is submarine erosion and, as soon as a tract of the earth's surface is raised up above the level of the sea, it is attacked by all the many forces of atmospheric weathering and subaerial erosion. High mountains are shattered by frost; bare rocks are split by the heating of the sun's rays, gulleys are cut in hillsides, the wind blows loose particles as surely as rain separates them from their parent source. The sum total effect is gradually to reduce all land surfaces to peneplains—almost planes or plains—

Figure 4.   A Termitarium or Ant Hill.   (Copyright Geographical Publications Limited.)

and many examples of subaerial peneplanation can be found in the geological past. Since the greater part of Africa is a plateau high above sea level these forces of nature are powerful and active. There are some plateau masses—the flat-topped hills of the Karroo; perhaps the sandy Udi plateau of Nigeria—where rapid erosion of the hillsides is inevitable. Wherever, however, slopes are relatively gentle nature herself slows down the process by providing a mantle of soil, itself protected by a mantle of vegetation in the form of forest, woodland, scrub or grass. Over vast areas, the surface is kept stable long enough for a complete soil profile to develop, for a soil of good depth to form. There is little loss of soil from a forest, little from grassland.

Soil erosion may be looked upon as a disease which is a malignant form of a natural phenomenon. It has rightly been described as a disease of civilization, but one so serious that it threatens the very extinction of mankind. A soil which has taken thousands of years

Figure 5. Geological Erosion in the Udi Plateau of Nigeria. Although hastened by bush clearing, cultivation and grazing, this is natural land erosion—more than just soil erosion—and cannot be wholly prevented. (Copyright L. Dudley Stamp.)

to form may be lost in a single night. The cause is, primarily, the exposure of the naked soil by the removal of its vegetation cover which both protects it and, by the development of root systems, binds it together. The soil may be exposed by clearing the land of its natural vegetation for purposes of plowing and cultivation. While doubts have been expressed as to whether plowing is the right treatment for many soils of tropical Africa, the ever-present danger is that a furrow may become a gulley after a typical downpour of rain. If plowing *is* practiced it must be plowing which follows the contours (contour plowing) so that rainwater will not run *down* a furrow. Though strip cropping is another preventive device, tiny fields separated by uncleared bush so typical of African cultivation are even better. On grazing land soil erosion results naturally and speedily from overstocking. The animals eat the grass and herbs close down to the ground, preventing recovery and regrowth and so leaving the soil between exposed. Furthermore, they cut up the exposed soil with their hooves.

Figure 6. An Attempt to Stop Gullying Shown in the Last Picture. Banks were thrown across the gully, grass and quick-growing trees were planted but the work was not successful. It was all swept away by flood waters after heavy rain.
(Copyright L. Dudley Stamp.)

With increasing pressure on the land by man and animal, soil erosion in Africa has increased in intensity at an alarming rate. As land is lost or rendered unusable by erosion the pressure on what remains becomes greater.

The muddy waters of rivers in spate are ample evidence of soil erosion. But this transport of river mud is a natural phenomenon and not necessarily harmful. If caught and spread over the flat flood plain it may build up fertile land at the expense of hill country of little value from whence it came. That this has been known of the Nile for centuries is seen from Shakespeare's words:

> . . . The higher Nilus swells,
> The more it promises: as it ebbs, the seedsman
> Upon the slime and ooze scatters his grain
> And shortly comes to harvest.

The drainage and economic use of alluvial plains and deltas are thus important aspects of development for Africa. The material removed by soil erosion may sometimes be "trapped" only a short distance away and valuable new land gained. Wind erosion and the so-called march of the deserts present more difficult problems.

It is extremely difficult to judge how far the observed spread of arid conditions in Africa is due to the climatic desiccation described elsewhere and how far it is due simply to misuse of land. The formation of "dongas" or gulleys in South Africa resulted in the appointment of a Commission as early as the 'twenties. Yet when Dr. I. B. Pole Evans, familiar through many years of experience with the problem in South Africa, visited Kenya in 1938 he found some of the native reserves "a shambles—the result of land mismanagement and misuse." He criticizes breaking the grass cover for cropping, the drainage of swamps which he calls "precious assets" for cultivation and the confining of pastoral tribes like the Kikuyu to reserves without control of the number of cattle. About the same time a Commission enquiring into the conservation of natural resources in Southern Rhodesia found the African population had trebled between 1902 and 1938; the number of plows had increased from 3400 to 94,000. As a result 1½ million acres were badly eroded, and some 16 per cent of former arable land had been completely destroyed. Incidentally the erosion was worst on European-owned lands, especially when worked by Africans who, not being owners, had lost interest in conservation of the land.

Remedial measures to check existing erosion are one thing; more important than cure is prevention. It would seem that the twin lines of progress are control of grazing to prevent overstocking and the replacement of native grasses of little nutritive value by new strains capable of supporting a large number of head. Both these objectives have been achieved in New Zealand, but the problem in the tropics is relatively new. Not of least importance is the development of suitable strains of grass, though Guinea Grass (*Panicum maximum*), a native of Africa widespread from Senegal to Natal, has already proved its value in many parts of the world and is certainly the best native forage grass of Africa. Agronomy, which has become of outstanding importance to tropical Africa, was the subject of an international conference held at Yangambi in 1947.

Modern pedologists quite rightly study soils as soils. The description of the soil profile, the determination of the soil series, chemical, mechanical and biotic analyses, the genesis of the soil are all studied without, necessarily, reference to the natural vegetation which the soil supports or its use, actual or potential, by man. The emergence of pedology as a distinct branch of knowledge has resulted in a certain loss, a divorce of the study of soil from cognate studies. Yet, looking back to the early days of soil science, we see that it was Dokuchaev viewing the problem over the wide homogeneous plains of Russia who showed that each major climatic type produced its own peculiar soil or range of soils. His pioneer studies were followed by the well-known work of Glinka. By contrast, in a country of relatively homogeneous climate but great variety of terrain and underlying rocks, it was the British who considered soils in relation to geological formation. A great advance was marked by the work of F. E. Clements and his collaborators, and few scientists today would doubt the validity of his general thesis that the living plant, or assemblage of plants, forms an index of the sum total of environmental conditions, notably climate and soil. It seems clear, therefore, that there ought to be a close relationship between climate, soil and vegetation. There ought, therefore, to be a distribution of great soil belts over Africa similar to that known in North America or Eurasia. Yet Marbut in his pioneer essay of 1922–1923 could say: "No book, paper, paragraph, or sentence dealing with this matter as a whole has been encountered, nor has any reference to the possibility or the probability of the existence of a series of soil belts covering the continent been found." The foundation which he then proceeded to lay and his tentative map have proved their worth. Milne and his co-workers in East Africa found it possible to develop a classification of soils applicable to their field studies based essentially on Marbut's scheme.

A marked advance was the publication of a colored soil map of Africa on the scale of 1:20,000,000, with explanation in Russian, by Z. J. Shokalskaia (or Shokalsky). Mr. V. P. Sokoloff of the School of Geography of The Johns Hopkins University has translated the text and made it available in mimeographed form. The map (with

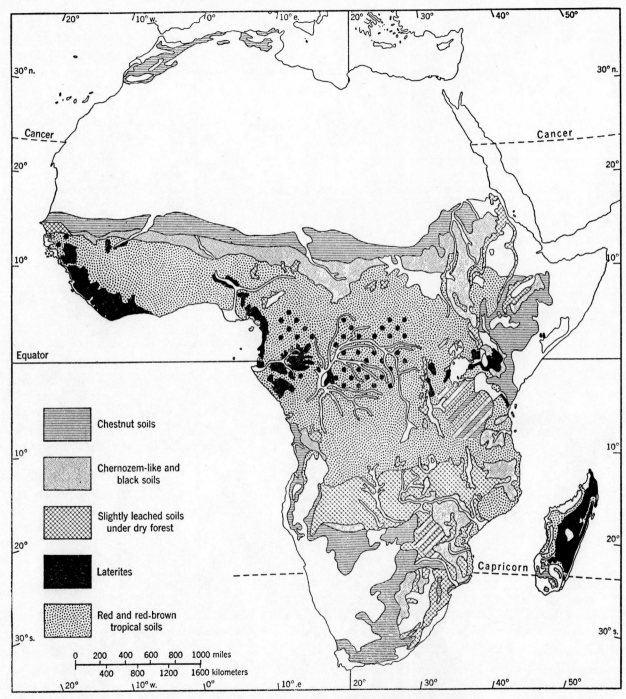

Figure 7. Soil Map of Africa. (Simplified from Z. J. Shokalsky.)

Chestnut soils

Chernozem-like and
black soils

Slightly leached soils
under dry forest

Laterites

Red and red-brown
tropical soils

0   200   400   600   800   1000 miles
    400   800   1200   1600 kilometers

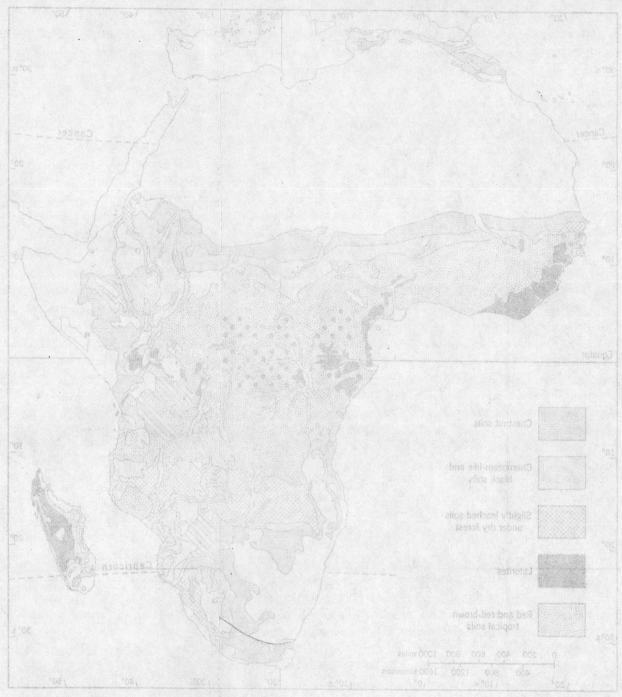

Figure 7. Soil Map of Africa. (Simplified from Z. I. Sbolokboy.)

key in English) distinguishes twenty-two soil types in addition to seven more in mountainous regions. A greatly simplified version of part of the map is included here to show the comparison with Marbut.

A few years later at the Commonwealth Conference of 1948 C. E. Kellogg made "preliminary suggestions for the classification and nomenclature of great soil groups in tropical and equatorial regions" and with F. D. Davol published an important paper on the soil groups of the Belgian Congo. He gets over the difficulties created by the word "laterite" by introducing the general term "latosol."

Since we have described the main climatic types of Africa in a previous chapter we will now attempt to relate the main soil groups to them.

Soils of the Equatorial and Tropical Regions

Marbut showed practically the whole of the equatorial regions of Africa and the moister parts of the tropical regions (except on the high plateaus of East Africa where climate is modified by elevation) occupied by different types of red soils. The heart of the Congo Basin is covered by his "lateritic red loams," the wettest parts of West Africa by "laterites." The huge areas with a good but seasonal rainfall have "red loams" with areas of "ferruginous red loams" and strips of "immature red loams." The dominant soils of equatorial Africa are thus Marbut's "lateritic red loams" and "laterites."

The term "laterite" has given rise to much controversy and confusion. It is derived from the Latin word *later*, a brick, and was first used in 1807 by Francis Buchanan to describe a surface material widespread in the wetter parts of southern India. This material, the result of chemical alteration of many different rocks, may be formed to a depth of many feet, sometimes scores of feet, from the surface. When freshly exposed the whole mass is relatively soft and can be cut with a spade; it is a mottled gray and yellowish rock with red streaks. On exposure to the atmosphere—deliberate exposure is carried out by cutting blocks and stacking them in the open air— the yellowish parts become dark red or brown-red and hard, the grayish parts remain soft and may be washed out by rain, leaving a mass which is not unlike a solidified sponge or a coarse brick. It is hard enough to be used for building and even for road metal. Indeed the blocks form a cheap, convenient and widely used building material in many parts of the tropics. This undoubtedly is the material to which Buchanan originally applied the name laterite, and it is still widely used in the country where he first described it.

Is laterite a rock in the geological sense, or is it a soil? Certainly the use of the term spread, and it became general for the word laterite to be used by travelers as synonymous with the red soils which occur over so much of the tropics. Then came the various attempts, through chemical analysis and microscopical examination, to define laterite precisely. One author at least found that the essential constituent was aluminum hydroxide and that the iron oxides, likewise any quartz grains, were incidental. Other investigations showed that some rocks previously accepted as laterites had no aluminum hydroxide at all, and later came the attempt at a classification based on chemical composition which proved to be highly artificial.

Reference has already been made to the high soil temperatures (approximating to 80°F.) in equatorial lands. Water at or above this temperature is an active solvent and permits of many chemical reactions taking place. It would seem that within the zone of permanent saturation, that is, below the permanent water table, the solid rocks, whatever they may be, are steeped in this warm water, and various minerals such as the felspars of gneisses and schists are converted into a bleached mass of hydrous silicate of alumina, from which iron salts are eliminated. *Above* this is the zone which is alternately saturated and dried according to the season. It is in this zone that laterite is formed. Any quartz grains in the original parent rocks remain unaltered, and a quartz vein from an underlying crystalline mass may be traced upwards into the laterite. But most other minerals undergo a complete change. In the dry season waters with iron and other salts in solution pass up by capillary action, and compounds are left when the water evaporates. In the wet season this zone resembles the lower one, and hydrous silicate of alumina is formed, to be washed or leached downwards. The lateritic layer thus comes to have an accumulation of iron salts— which on exposure to the atmosphere form one or other of the hard red or yellow red hydrated oxides which make up the "brick" structure—and also, generally, aluminum hydroxide. It is not difficult to see that under certain circumstances a hard layer or hard pan may form not far below the surface. It may reasonably be said that laterite is thus a rock formed by chemical action from other rocks rather than a soil.

But clearly a surface soil developed from the underlying laterized rock is very little different except for possible additions of vegetable matter. Thus true laterite soil would be expected where rainfall is abundant (to provide the permanently saturated layer) but where there is a seasonal rhythm to provide the overlying layer alternately wet and dry. These are the natural conditions in the wetter parts of the tropical belt or along the margins of the equatorial belt where there is a relatively dry season. The distribution of laterites on Marbut's map agrees with this hypothesis.

Workers in India and elsewhere have agreed that whereas laterite is formed in situ, the laterite may be weathered and the material transported. "On rolling areas," says Marbut, "where erosion is in progress and is somewhat active thoroughly weathered products are never allowed to accumulate, and the soil belongs in some intermediate stage of development between freshly disintegrated rock and the completely weathered product." There are, accordingly, "red loams" (including immature red loams and ferruginous red loams) and "lateritic red loams" where 25 to 90 per cent of the constituents are those of true laterite.

All these equatorial and tropical red soils agree in being reddish, in being leached to a greater or less extent but always to the extent of having lost their lime. The minerals of the parent rock have been almost completely changed so that the soils consist of quartz fragments (sand, often angular), hydrous aluminum silicates and aluminum hydroxides (clay or clay-like substances) and hydrated iron oxides (giving red or red-brown colors). The organic content is low except where decomposition of vegetation accumulated in swamps and hollows has been slowed down. The downward washing by rain of the finer particles in the soil has often left a sandy surface layer—a hungry sand which easily dries out—over a heavier impervious or "clay pan" layer. Milne and his co-workers in East Africa have distinguished two simple groups, red earths laterized and red earths, non-laterized. Each of these groups comprises a number of subgroups, depending upon the rocks of the subsoil—gneisses of the basement complex, granite, volcanic rocks, shales, sandstones.

The laterized red earths are described as ". . . very freely drained, leached, acid soils of various colors in the range pink, red, red-brown, orange-brown, brown. Uniform open structure and friable 'light' texture independently of clay content. Molecular ratio SiO_2/Al_2O_3, in clay fraction usually less than 2.0; less than 1.0 in soils of advanced laterization. Concretionary horizons are absent except in the non-typical case of a seasonally high water table. This group contains chiefly the soils of the evergeen forests and mountain grasslands."

The non-laterized red earths are described as ". . . well-drained, moderately leached soils of the same range of colors. Free from calcium carbonate, profile neutral or acid. Clod-structured, with heaviness proportional to clay content. Molecular ratio SiO_2/Al_2O_3 in clay fraction usually 2.0 or above. When developed on basic rocks the soil may contain scattered pisolitic concretions, but concretionary horizons are typically absent from the profile, only appearing where

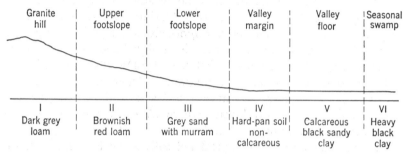

Granite hill	Upper footslope	Lower footslope	Valley margin	Valley floor	Seasonal swamp
I Dark grey loam	II Brownish red loam	III Grey sand with murram	IV Hard-pan soil non-calcareous	V Calcareous black sandy clay	VI Heavy black clay

Figure 8. A Typical Soil Catena in East Africa. (After G. Milne.)

there is seasonally a high water table, when the soil approaches the plateau soils in character."

Shokalsky emphasizes that the end product of lateritic weathering is a rock which may form an "armour plate" (the *carapace lateritique* of French writers), which often forms a protective covering to the tops of hills or surfaces of terraces but cannot serve as a soil-forming material. Thus Kellogg and Davol use the word latosol as "a collective term for those zonal soils formerly called lateritic." They distinguish (1) Red, (2) Earthy Red, (3) Yellow, (4) Reddish-yellow, (5) Reddish-brown and (6) Black-red Latosols.

The *plateau soils* are a group distinguished by Milne in Tanganyika and described as . . . "light-colored soils (gray, yellow, yellow-brown) of sluggish drainage or receiving excess subsoil water seasonally. Usually formed on locally-transported material lying at slight slopes in maturely eroded topography, or where rock tables check percolation. Free from calcium carbonate, but often with concretionary ironstone ('murram') in the subsoil. The vegetation over large areas on this soil is open deciduous woodland." The concretionary ironstone often forms the resistant capping of flat-topped hills or the higher levels of a catena. Shokalsky claims large areas as "slightly leached soils" while Kellogg recognized a podzolic group.

In tropical Africa there are small areas of *mottled clays*, derived from clay beds (for example, in Zanzibar and Pemba) which result from impeded drainage. They thus resemble the lower levels of

Figure 9. Degraded Land near Dakar in West Africa. Exhausted by overcultivation—with millets and peanuts. (Copyright R. J. Harrison-Church.)

laterites discussed above, and there may be a thin red surface layer. More important are the *black* or *gray clays*, which may be calcareous or non-calcareous. These "black cotton soils," sticky when wet and cracking deeply when dry, are dark-colored and ill-drained. Some occur on bottom lands, others are associated with shaley subsoils.

On the drier margins of the tropical lands Marbut maps some *"tropical prairie soils"* in West Africa. Towards the desert these pass into dark-colored soils of chernozem type, then into chestnut-brown soils before fading into the deserts proper. Shokalsky confirms this arrangement.

Soils of the Mediterranean Regions

Although the soils of those parts of north Africa which enjoy a Mediterranean type of climate are far from being fully investigated there is no reason to suspect that they differ fundamentally from the soils developed in other Mediterranean regions of the world. The summer or hot season coincides with the dry season when surface layers are likely to be dried out and chemical action is accordingly greatly reduced. When moisture is present in the soil, air temperatures are low yet not sufficiently low for frost action to be a dominant factor. Consequently soil forms slowly; soils tend to be both thin and immature. Both the coastal ranges of North Africa and the fine ranges of the Cape of Good Hope exhibit the familiar feature of bare rock with pockets of soil in the crevices, and it is on land of this type that the maquis or chaparral type of drought-resisting vegetation flourishes—land of little economic value. Together with other parts of South Africa, the soils of the Mediterranean area have been studied in detail by Van der Merwe. Marbut had mapped most of the Cape areas as "brown soils" with a small strip inland of "chestnut-brown" soils. In North Africa he showed the better-watered parts as "brown soils," the open plains of Morocco and elsewhere as "chestnut-brown." In South Africa the valuable agricultural areas are where the valleys are floored by material washed down from surrounding ridges. Here soil-forming material may be present to a good depth and affords loams or sandy loams where the surface layers are partially leached by downward movement of water but where the rainfall is sufficiently high to prevent any accumulation of carbonates in the soil. Both the relief and climate are sufficiently like those of the Coast range regions of California to produce very similar soils and agricultural conditions. Like the Californian soils, they have moderate to low percentages of lime, potash, phosphoric acid and nitrogen and so require fertilizers and careful management to render them really productive.

Somewhere on the margins of these soil belts one might expect to find a belt or at least patches of black-earth or chernozem where there is a nice balance between downward leaching and upward movement of water and an accumulation of organic matter. Where such soils have been observed the extent is small.

Inland, in both North and South Africa, the Mediterranean soils give place to brown desert soils, shown by Marbut as a strip in

North Africa but covering the whole of the great Kalahari area in the south.

Soils of the Warm Temperate Coastal Strip

Marbut has a special group, his Natal loams, for the soils of the well-watered coastlands of Natal between the Drakensberg and the Indian Ocean. It is a belt of irregular rolling country where soil-forming material is largely due to disintegration of rocks in place and to erosion by numerous small streams and consequent limited transportation of material. The soils are typical humid soils, developed under a higher rainfall than the Cape soils and with a summer maximum. The rainfall, however, varies both in total amount and seasonal distribution though it is, for Africa, relatively constant. In some areas the balance is that needed for the development of chernozem; elsewhere downward leaching predominates, and reddish soils allied to those of the great tropical belt develop. Though varying greatly in texture, these soils have depth and exist in a climatically favored region, so that with addition of appropriate mineral fertilizers they can be and are extremely productive.

Soils of the Plateau Grasslands

The gently undulating surface of the High Veld in the Orange Free State and southern Transvaal, lying west of the great scarp edge, has generally between 20 and 30 inches of rainfall. Under the natural grass cover a mature soil profile has developed; the rainfall is high enough to prevent accumulation of carbonates and other soluble salts in the surface layers but not high enough to leach the soil seriously. These are conditions normal for the development of black earth. It may be that average temperatures are too high and the soils tend to be reddish, but they are fertile and it is on them that the famous "maize triangle" has been developed.

Passing northward on the highlands of the African plateaus Marbut maps huge areas as "chernozem soils" and "light-colored soils of the chernozem group." Some of these, placed in the former group, have a black surface layer with a proportion of calcium carbonate high enough to effervesce with acid, passing down into a bluish gray subsoil with again high carbonate content. The subsoil consists of rocks with little or no carbonate. The dark color of the soil is not permanent; it disappears with the removal of carbonate, and it is doubtful whether these soils are in fact comparable with the black earths of North America or European Russia. Both where they are characteristically dark and where they merge into Milne's "plateau soils" it seems certain that these soils are special to Africa, have their own special behavior and present yet another of the African "unknowns."

BIBLIOGRAPHY

Proceedings of the First Commonwealth Conference on Tropical and Sub-Tropical Soils, 1948, Commonwealth Bureau of Soil Science, Harpenden, England.
Includes papers on South Africa, Madagascar, Uganda, Zanzibar, Congo, Sudan, Nigeria, West Africa and Algeria, as well as general papers.

H. L. Shantz and C. F. Marbut, *Vegetation and Soils of Africa,* American Geographical Society, 1923.

C. R. Van der Merwe, *Soil Groups and Sub-groups of South Africa,* Pretoria, Government Printer, 1941.

G. Milne, "A Soil Reconnaissance Journey . . . December 1935–February 1936," *Jour. Ecol.,* XXXV, 1947, 192–265.

C. G. Trapnell et al., "Vegetation-Soil Map of Northern Rhodesia," North Rhodesia Department of Agriculture, 1947.

J. D. Tothill (Editor), *Agriculture in Uganda,* New York, 1940. *Agriculture in the Sudan,* New York, 1948.

C. E. Kellogg and F. D. Davol, *An Explanatory Study of Soil Groups in the Belgian Congo,* Publication of I.N.E.A.C., 1949 Ser. Sci., 46, 73.

S. Ju. Schokalskaja, *Die Boden Afrikas,* Akademie-Verlag, Berlin, 1953.

Forest, Grassland
and Desert

It is a safe assertion that at least 90 per cent of all Africans derive their sustenance directly from the land and its products. There are still those groups, now few and rare, so close to nature that they fall into the category of "gatherers," gathering wild fruits and roots and maintaining life on what nature provides and they can find. There are others, more numerous, who depend upon the spoils of the chase, coupled with a little vegetable food raised in small clearings. There are still larger groups of cattlemen and herders who rely on the natural grasslands for pasture. Finally those peoples, so often the hereditary foes of the last, who have come to rely on food raised in their small clearings in the bush usually practice a form of land rotation or shifting cultivation and raise a series of crops dictated by the natural factors of climate, soil, and vegetation cover.

It follows logically that to all Africa the existing vegetation is of paramount importance. One is tempted to say the natural vegetation, for so it appears, but there is little doubt that the bulk of the vegetation which seems "natural" has been profoundly modified by man's long-continued activity. It is not uncommon to find evidence of former settlements in the heart of what seem to be primeval rainforests; it is still uncertain how much of the savanna or bush veld of Africa is "natural," how much the result of periodic firing by the human inhabitants and grazing by their animals. This is the same problem as that of the campos of Brazil.

But whether it is truly "natural" or only "semi-natural" the study of the existing vegetation of Africa assumes a very great importance. The trees, shrubs, herbs and grasses are plant indicators affording an index of the total effect of the environment and so pointing the way to potential or agricultural use of the land. The taxonomic botanist and the systematist are interested in collecting and describing species, and some magnificent books have been published on the flora of different parts of Africa. An outstanding example of such is the *Flora Capensis*. This, as its title implies, deals with the flora of the Cape Province of South Africa. It has been argued by some that even such floras covering large areas are "local" in the sense that they do not give a continent-wide picture of the distribution of what may be widespread species described under other names elsewhere.

The careful description of vegetation—primary vegetation survey and descriptive ecology—is newer, and by no means the whole of Africa has been adequately covered. Still newer are attempts to trace the evolution of Africa's plant cover, a study still in its infancy.

A great debt of gratitude is owed H. L. Shantz, at that time of the United States Department of Agriculture, and C. F. Marbut, then of the Bureau of Soils of the same Department, for their pioneer but still standard work, *The Vegetation and Soils of Africa*, published by the American Geographical Society in 1923. The first part, on the vegetation, is by Shantz. It is based on the study of over 500 references, which are listed, followed by an account of a special journey through the entire length of the continent. The provisional map of the continent which had been prepared was revised in the light of the first-hand experience gained. We may regard Shantz's book as summarizing all important work which had been done prior to 1920. Since that time there have been some important studies—notably by I. B. Pole Evans and R. S. Adamson in South Africa; by Trapnell and Clothier in northwestern Rhodesia and perhaps most noteworthy of all by Gillman in East Africa. The last work is singled out because it introduces the dynamic viewpoint, the evolution of African vegetation.

Although Africa did not directly suffer the glaciation which the Great Ice Age brought to North America, Europe and Asia, the climate of the continent must have undergone wide fluctuations. It is one of the great scientific problems for the future to trace the effects of these climatic pulsations on the African vegetation and fauna. The ice ages in Europe seem to have been paralleled in Africa by relatively wet and dry periods—"pluvial" and "interpluvial" periods marked by fluctuating lake levels as well as alternating advance and retreat of ice on such mountains as Mt. Kenya. The dominant African vegetation must have waxed and waned between evergreen rainforest over huge areas and grassland or desert scrub.

The present vegetation shows "relicts" of former vegetation. On the whole the evidence suggests that the present is a period of decreasing desiccation, as in South Africa where rooigras veld has been replaced by desert scrub,[1]—though a great part of the supposed encroachment of the desert is the result of man's activity.[2]

AREA OCCUPIED BY EACH TYPE OF VEGETATION IN AFRICA

(After H. L. Shantz)

	Area in Square Miles	*Percentage*
Forest	*2,056,700*	*18.4*
Equatorial (tropical) rainforest	875,000	7.8
Temperate rainforest	52,300	0.5
Oak-conifer forest	19,500	0.2
Dry forest	885,000	7.9
Thorn forest	77,600	0.7
Temperate brush	128,400	1.1
Oases	9,200	0.1
Mangrove forest	9,700	0.1
Grassland	*4,736,400*	*42.3*
High grass—low tree savanna	1,297,000	11.6
Acacia—tall grass savanna	1,785,000	15.9
Tall grass	99,400	0.9
Acacia—desert grass savanna and desert grass	1,074,000	9.6
Mountain grassland and alpine meadow	363,000	3.2
Dwarf palm—temperate grass	76,000	0.7
Marsh grass	42,000	0.4
Desert	*4,406,900*	*39.3*
Desert shrub—desert grass	1,220,000	10.9
Desert shrub	2,300,000	20.5
Salt desert shrub	4,900	0.0
Desert	882,000	7.9
Total land surface (without lakes)	*11,200,000*	*100.0*

These figures do not include Madagascar, which was not considered by Shantz and not shown on his map.

For the purpose of his general description Shantz divided the vegetation into forest, grassland and desert. Forests cover rather less than a fifth of the whole, grassland rather over two-fifths and

[1] C. E. Tidmarsh, *Farming in South Africa*, XXIII, 1948, pp. 519–530.
[2] See the summary of evidence by L. D. Stamp, *Geog. Rev.*, XXX, 1940.

desert the remaining two-fifths. The bulk of the forest was described as "timberland"; the bulk of the grassland has scattered
trees and is thus savanna. Different types of savanna, covering in
all more than 37 per cent of the whole continent, may be regarded

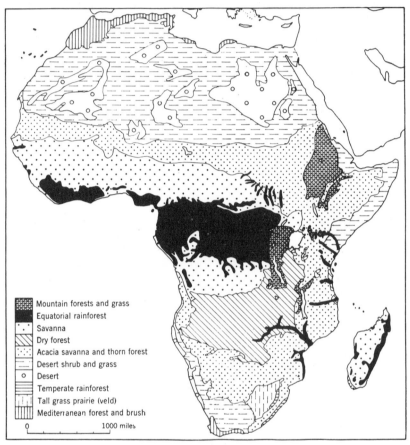

Mountain forests and grass
Equatorial rainforest
Savanna
Dry forest
Acacia savanna and thorn forest
Desert shrub and grass
Desert
Temperate rainforest
Tall grass prairie (veld)
Mediterranean forest and brush
0   1000 miles

Figure 1. The Main Vegetation Belts of Africa. (In the main after Shantz and
Marbut.)

as the really characteristic African vegetation, just as the "tropical"
climate is the characteristic climate. Though later work may have
modified his figures to some extent, it is worth while to quote Shantz's
table of vegetation types.

The large colored map on the scale of 1:10,000,000 published by
Shantz has been simplified for the purpose of showing the main
vegetation zones of the continent in Fig. 1.

Although the simple classification of African vegetation used by Shantz is convenient for descriptive purposes it fails to emphasize the essential unity and continuity of the vegetation of tropical Africa. In fact even the threefold grouping into forest, grassland and desert is artificial. Provided there is sufficient moisture, the climax vegetation in tropical Africa is high evergreen forest. This is naturally found along the equator wherever rainfall is high (60 inches or over), where the dry season or seasons, if present at all, are very short and where temperature range is small. But it also extends into the wettest parts of the bordering tropical regions, notably near the coast of much of West Africa as far as Sierra Leone, where the dry season though marked is not long enough to counteract availability of underground moisture reached by plant root systems or the temperature high enough or the air dry enough in the dry season to induce excessive transpiration. Similarly forest of comparable type may line river banks where abundant moisture is available from the alluvial soils throughout the year and evaporation from water and soil surfaces keeps the air humid.

On the margins of equatorial lands where a dry season becomes marked and the overall rainfall less, leaf shedding as a protection against excessive transpiration during the hot dry season becomes general, growth becomes seasonal and there is less of a struggle upwards to reach light and air. So the equatorial forest passes into what in India would be called "monsoon forest," which is deciduous, lower and more open. With decreasing rainfall and an increasing length of dry season the trees become smaller, more widely spaced and have adopted various protective devices. Some of these devices are designed to lower water loss by transpiration, seen in reduced leaf surface, umbrella-shaped form of the crown and ability to wilt; others to store water by development of fleshy stems and leaves; others to make a permanent underground water supply available by very long roots. Still other devices are designed to avoid destruction by discouraging browsing animals, hence the numerous forms of spines and hooks.

With still lower rainfall such thorn woodland passes through thorn thicket into thorn scrub of widely spaced thorny bushes on the desert margin. There are some species of tree which can exist through a wide range of environmental conditions and may be found from the margins of the rainforest almost to the desert. A very good example is *Acacia arabica* (behaving in much the same way in India also and like its near relative *Acacia catechu* in Indo-China), which forms well-grown trees 50 or 75 feet high in the wetter situations but appears as stunted spiney bushes only a few feet high in its most arid habitats.

There would thus seem to be no place at all for grassland in this scheme. Undoubtedly in the more open woodland and scrub, grass and herbs form an important element in the ground vegetation which springs into life with the coming of the rains, but it is becoming increasingly certain that much, if not most, of Africa's grasslands are primarily the results of man's interference. Fires are difficult to start in the rainforests but elsewhere they start and spread very easily in the dry season. Some may be started by lightning; the majority are the result of deliberate firing of dried grass or under-growth. They have the effect of burning off the dry grass (but not harming the roots), nourishing the surface with ash and so stimulating growth when the rains come. On the other hand, they destroy tree seedlings and even young trees and so favor the extension of grass at the expense of trees. In this they reinforce the action of grazing animals—both wild and domesticated—which eat off the grass and herbs without harm (unless to excess due to overstocking) but destroy tree seedlings.

Thus parallel to the sequence of woodland vegetation from rain-forest to desert scrub is another of grassland with varying proportions of trees which have managed to survive. Another complication results from the very widespread practice of shifting cultivation or bush fallowing. When a cleared patch is cultivated for a few years and then abandoned or left to recover it is colonized in the first instance by a temporary assemblage of plants, replaced in due course by another, but it is often a long period of years before these "seral communities" are finally replaced by the "climatic climax vegetation." Some seres or seral communities become so firmly established that they show signs of permanence; a good example is afforded by thickets of bamboo.

A further complication in tropical Africa results from elevation. Parts of East Africa are sufficiently high but also sufficiently wet for temperate rainforest to replace tropical vegetation, and mountain grasses or alpine meadows occupy considerable tracts.

All that has been said above applies to tropical Africa. In extra-tropical North Africa, north of the great desert barrier, are found those types of vegetation common to countries round the Mediterranean basin. Where rainfall permits, on well-watered hill slopes oak-conifer forest is the climax, but far larger areas are covered by the Mediterranean brush or scrub resembling the chaparral of California. This in turn passes into desert scrub whereas on the high-level basins among the Atlas Mountains there are stretches of what may be called steppe.

Extra-tropical South Africa differs in that it is not cut off completely by a desert barrier from tropical Africa and there is a merging of "Mediterranean" and tropical types of vegetation. The best-watered parts of Natal and the Cape, with the rainfall well distributed through the year, are clothed with a subtropical or temperate rainforest, but the natural vegetation covering those parts of the Cape with a winter rainfall is again a Mediterranean scrub, also merging with decreasing moisture into desert scrub. On the plateau of South Africa, over much of the Orange Free State and southern Transvaal, is the tall-grass–short-grass "prairie" of the High Veld.

Quite clearly Shantz's colored map and still more the simplified version shown in Fig. 1 involve much generalization. In making generalizations, both in the field and in the drawing office, it is difficult to avoid a subjective judgment. It has been pointed out that the impressions which are gained of much African vegetation depend very largely on the time of year at which the traveler sees the country. The grassland with scattered trees after the grass has been burnt off and where the majority of the trees are leafless may appear but little removed from a semi-desert waste. If, however, it is seen after the coming of the early rains, with tall lush grass and herbs, perhaps high enough to hide a man, and trees in full leaf, it appears comparable with an open forest having a very rich undergrowth.

Again, a very important advance was made by Gillman in his recognition of complexes and catenas. As he rightly says, distinct vegetation types, often widely different, occur nearly everywhere in close conjunction or juxtaposition, and the cartographical representation of such complexes is difficult. In his "Vegetation Map of Tanganyika," on the scale of 1:2,000,000, he uses a background color for the dominant vegetation, with dots indicating the relative frequency of associations of minor importance. Further refinement is possible by close or wide spacing of the dots. Much more important, however, is the recognition of a catenary complex. As described in the last chapter, the soil scientist, following particularly the work of G. Milne in East Africa, recognizes that the same sequence of soil types may be repeated over and over again throughout a large area. For example, where a plateau is intersected by broad valleys there will be certain types of soil associated with the valley floor, other types with the valley slopes and other types still with the plateau surfaces or interfleuves. This sequence of soils is matched by a sequence of vegetation. Bearing this repetition in mind, both Milne for soils and Gillman for vegetation have used a system of coloring by vertical stripes (which quickly became known as pajama striping) to indicate those areas dominated by catenary complexes.

Bearing these refinements in mind, we may follow in general the broad classification of African vegetation given by Shantz, noticing, however, names which are commonly given to some of his vegetation types. Gillman, for example, objects to the use of such terms as "savanna," "steppe" and "veld" on the ground, he says, that "legitimate doubt may rise as to whether such importations from the languages of lands harboring their prototypes are correctly used out of their appropriate setting." Similarly, Gillman objects to the use of African vernacular words and claims that it is possible to use simple English descriptive names. Here, however, he immediately encounters a difficulty in that he succeeds in drawing a distinction between forests and woodland, whereas these two words are often used in English interchangeably.

FOREST

Equatorial Rainforest

Shantz uses the term "tropical rainforest," and this well-known type of vegetation has also been known by the descriptive title, "evergreen rainforest." It is the dominant type of forest in those areas having more than 60 or 80 inches of rainfall annually and a consistently high temperature throughout the year. As a rule there is little variation in the mean temperature between one month and another, the mean annual range rarely exceeding 5° or 6°, and averaging about 80°F. Night temperatures rarely drop below 70° or certainly 65°F.; the day temperatures rarely rise above 90° or, still more rarely, above 95°F. This is the constantly hot, humid climate found on either side of the equator. As soon as there is a marked dry season, forest type tends to change.

A typical equatorial forest consists of large trees, approximately 125 feet high, with a relatively dense and interlocking canopy. The equatorial forests of the Amazon are often described as gloomy in the extreme, with little or no undergrowth. This is not typical of Africa, since there is often an understory of small trees, and the undergrowth is usually dense enough to prevent a distant view. Certainly in the more open parts there is a thick growth of herbs on the forest floor. Woody climbers, or lianas, are usually abundant and many of the trees are supported by flanking (plank) buttresses. The thick undergrowth and the woody climbers make these forests extremely difficult to penetrate except along defined paths.

As a rule numerous species of trees are present, and it is rarely that one finds a single dominant or even a number of co-dominants. Although some of the trees yield excellent and much-valued timber, usually hardwood of the mahogany type, and though softwood timbers do occur, the difficulty of extricating examples of the trees desired is so great that there has been no commercial exploitation over very large areas of this type of forest. It may be regarded as one of the great untouched reservoirs of timber in the world.

The equatorial type of forest is not as extensive in Africa as was once supposed. It is broadly restricted to parts only of the Belgian Congo and French Equatorial Africa and relatively small areas lying in the wetter parts of West Africa. It was long supposed that the African equatorial forests could be described as true primeval forests unaffected by man. It has been found, however, that under certain conditions revegetation is very rapid when the original forest is destroyed, and what appears today is in fact only second growth.

Where these forests occur bordering the great river courses, the underlying soil is alluvial and may be described as a rich deep loam of natural fertility. The myth, however, that all equatorial forest soils are naturally of high fertility, has long since been exploded. When cleared there are often sandy or lateritic areas which need dressings of ash and organic matter before they will produce crops, and in the high-rainfall areas there are immediate dangers both of physical soil erosion and of the leaching of plant food by exposure to atmosphere.

These equatorial forests in Africa, because of their relatively open character, have an abundant animal and bird life, especially rich along the water courses where hippopotami and crocodiles are found. The nomadic pygmies of the heart of the Congo forests afford examples of groups of human beings still largely dominated by their physical environment, and just as animals and birds seek light and air by living in the treetops away from swampy conditions or ground likely to flood, so these primitive peoples have in certain cases built their homes high up in the trees. But these are generally temporary dwellings for people who are esentially nomadic. Elsewhere the African inhabitants have destroyed portions of the forest, particularly along the great waterways or where a short, relatively dry season makes burning possible.

Among the principal plants which are of economic value pride of place goes to the Guinea oil palm. It furnishes the oil prized for

Figure 2. Timber Working in the Equatorial Rainforest of Spanish Guinea. This picture illustrates the heavy task of felling a hardwood tree—some with wood hard enough to turn an axe—by African hand labor. (Copyright R. J. Harrison-Church.)

food, as well as for a variety of other uses, including the making of soap. Rubber is obtained from certain of the native trees and lianas, and it is still exploited in some of the remoter areas. To an earlier stage belongs the importance of the forests for the ivory obtained from the enormous elephant herds. At the time when slave trading was widespread it can be said that equatorial Africa yielded two main products to the outside world, ivory and black ivory.

African settlements in the equatorial forests are usually small clearings where a variety of crops can be and are grown, food plants such as yams, sweet potatoes, rice, manioc and sugar cane; fruits such as bananas, mango and guava, as well as tobacco and beans, and of course the oil palm. Over vast areas of the equatorial forests little development has yet taken place under modern conditions, more, it may be said, because of scarcity of labor than because of climatic difficulties.

Temperate Rainforest

Shantz described this as one of the most varied and interesting forests on the continent of Africa. It is that which occurs on the high mountains of Central and East Africa and on mountain ranges with a high rainfall at lower levels towards the south. It is widespread also in the Ethiopian plateau area. Rainfall is high, probably 60 to 100 inches, and there is no long period of drought. Owing to elevation, temperatures are lower than those in the equatorial forests, but again the range both daily and annually is small. Typically the trees are tall with smooth white or light-colored bark and often with buttressed bases. Species are less numerous than in the equatorial forest and are often dominated by the genus *Podocarpus.*

Oak–Conifer Forest

This is scarcely an African forest. It is, in fact, the ordinary Mediterranean forest so well known in countries surrounding the Mediterranean Sea; it is accordingly found in those parts of Morocco, Algeria and Tunis where physical conditions are suitable. Forests are usually relatively open, with a sparse undergrowth of shrubs, grasses and herbs.

Dry Forest

According to Shantz the dry forest varies in density from an open park-like growth of trees to a relatively dense stand. "At no time are the grasses entirely replaced in the substratum. As a rule there are a few shrubs or young trees. The diameter of tree trunks is seldom over a foot and foliage is supported only on the upper part. It is a forest made up largely of flat-topped trees, and one can generally see through it from 100 yards to half-a-mile."

Gillman protests that forest is a misnomer for this type of vegetation, which he prefers to call simply "woodland," that is, land with an open cover of trees, the crowns of which do not form a thickly interlaced canopy.

Figure 3. A Savanna with *Borassus* Palms. One of the many types of African savanna, near Monga on the northern border of the Belgian Congo. (Courtesy Office du Tourisme du Congo Belge.)

The trees are usually leafless for a part of the year, and this resting period is due entirely to drought. It covers a relatively long period of the cool and hot dry seasons. This is the period when forest fires, either deliberately or accidentally started, sweep through the grass cover, and only trees large enough to stand the grass fires are able to maintain themselves. The rainfall is generally between 30 and 40 inches. It is during the rainy season that the main tree growth takes place.

These dry woodlands cover a larger extent than the equatorial rainforests, and certainly form a very characteristic African vegetation. From one region to another different genera of trees are dominant and form a basis for subdivision. In some areas trees are replaced by a thick growth of bamboo, which can be regarded as a tree in its reaction to climatic conditions rather than as a grass.

Thorn Forest

This is the type of vegetation which Gillman prefers to call "bushland and thicket," which has variously been described also as thorn bushland. It is land carrying a more than 50 per cent cover of shrubs and small trees, which may be evergeeen or deciduous, and frequently are spiny though not necessarily so. Herbs and low grass form part of the ground cover. It is on land of this type that the baobab tree (*Adansonia digitata*), with its great thick stems, forms an interesting feature.

Except for the scattered baobabs, the trees do not usually exceed 10 or 20 feet in height, and during the short growing season are a mass of foliage and flowers; but the growth period is short. Often various species of *Acacia* are dominant, including the *Acacia arabica*, which occurs under almost exactly similar conditions in India. In the drier parts *Euphorbia* is often conspicuous. This is obviously the vegetation of the rather drier parts of the tropical climatic region. The thickets are difficult to penetrate, and they hide game more effectively than the dry forests, where they can be so easily seen. The vegetation covers large areas of few people, and it would seem that, except for some areas with good soil, much of such land is unsuitable for agriculture.

The remarkable unity of tropical Africa, exemplified by the widespread repetition of types of soil, vegetation and human activities, is well illustrated by Africa's most fascinating tree, the baobab. With its monstrous trunk, up to 30 feet in diameter, bushy rather low crown, huge white solitary drooping flowers giving place to large fruits (monkey bread) with seeds embedded in a slightly acid mucilaginous pulp, it is a conspicuous tree as distinctive of Dakar as it is of the East African scrub or Victoria Falls. It may be that it was the fresh green leaves which were first seen by the Portuguese who coined the name Cape Verde. The tree seems to owe its widespread distribution in large measure to its power to survive grass fires, and the trunks are often blackened. Its very long roots and water-holding tissue permit it to survive serious drought. The bark yields a strong fiber; the soft white timber though readily attacked by fungi is a useful building material. The pounded leaves are used in food, and they seem also to have considerable medicinal value.

Temperate Brush

This is a type of vegetation which is so well known in lands with a Mediterranean type of climate in most parts of the world. It is the *maquis* of North Africa, closely comparable with the *maquis* of

Figure 4. A Large Baobab Tree near Livingstone, Northern Rhodesia. (Copyright L. Dudley Stamp.)

other lands around the Mediterranean Sea, and it is also the vegetation of the Cape region in South Africa, closely resembling the *chaparral* of California. It is of course characterized by a relatively luxuriant growth of bushes, sometimes with small trees, producing a great wealth of flowers, so that this type of vegetation boasts the richest display of flowering plants to be found anywhere in Africa. The drought which coincides with the hot season precludes many grasses and herbs from flourishing, but there are numerous bulbous plants.

Oases

Although the word "oasis" can properly be applied to all those areas within the desert tracts where underground water is sufficiently near the surface for vegetation to flourish, the oases of North Africa have usually a thicket of trees, of which the most typical is the date palm. But other palms may be found in oases also, and in addition thorny trees and bushes, such as *Acacia* and *Zizyphus*. Wherever oases have been occupied by man it is natural that the date palm

Figure 5.   Clearing Mangrove Swamps in Sierra Leone.   The mangroves provide firewood, the clearance helps to control mosquito breeding and the land can be enclosed and prepared for rice.   (British Official Photograph.)

has been encouraged at the expense of other vegetation, and the oases may become almost forests of date palms.

Mangrove Swamps

Swamp forests are found along many of the coasts of Africa. They consist primarily of trees 25 to 75 feet high, either standing on large stilt roots which lift the main stem of the trees above high tide, or having rhizophores, that is, respiratory roots sticking up out of the tidal mud in which the forests grow.   The trees grow essentially between the tide marks on extensive stretches of mud.   The forests are often richer and the trees larger in those areas where they are only occasionally invaded by salt water at high tide and may merge into freshwater swamp forests.

GRASSLAND

High-Grass–Low-Tree Savanna

In very large measure the distinction between forest and grassland in Africa is artificial. This is certainly true of the high-grass–low-tree savanna, which is composed of coarse rank grasses reaching 5 to 12 feet in height, with small scattered trees throughout. The grasses do not form a turf, each plant being distinct at the base. The dominant grasses are commonly species of *Andropogon* and *Pennisetum*.

Growth is rapid, but in the dry season the grasses dry out and are burnt to the ground. At the beginning of the rainy season a dense fresh green cover quickly forms, and when the grass is fully grown it almost reaches to the level of the scattered trees. Except where there are paths it is extremely difficult to penetrate this grassland, since everywhere the grass grows higher than a man. A belt of such country frequently occurs in the region of relatively heavy rainfall, 35 to 60 inches, bordering the tropical rainforests.

The natural fodder afforded is of little value, and wild game are not as numerous as in the lower drier grasslands, though this is the haunt of such large creatures as the elephant, the buffalo and the rhinoceros. In the drier margins the shea tree occurs.

Acacia–Tall-Grass Savanna

This type covers nearly 16 per cent of the surface of Africa, and considering its wide distribution it is remarkably uniform. The trees are scattered, often thorny and flat-topped, averaging 10 to 50 feet in height, and include many species of *Acacia*. The grass, when fully grown, reaches 3 to 5 feet in height, and when the grass is green and the trees are in full leaf the country resembles in appearance a great orchard or a park.

The natural grasses are not, however, very palatable, so that in parts of South Africa this grassland is known as the *sourveld*. In the dry season the abundant wild game as well as cattle rely largely on grasses which they can find along the water courses. This is the great hunting country of Africa, with a wide variety of antelope, giraffe, zebra and lions. It is the country where corn (maize) and various millets can be grown, peanuts, manioc, beans and peas, but it is country which suffers seriously from vagaries of rainfall.

Figure 6. A Coarse Type of African Grassland, Nigeria. Grassland of this sort is as impenetrable as forest. There is little value in the grass as fodder. (Copyright L. Dudley Stamp.)

Tall Grass

This is the High Veld of South Africa, pure grassland with no trees. The grass when fully grown reaches about 3 feet in height. Although there is a rich flora, the most important plant is the rooi grass. On these grasslands there are winter frosts, and the rainfall of 30 to 40 inches comes mainly in the summer.

Acacia–Desert Grass Savanna and Desert Grass

The grass flora in this type of savanna varies from a relatively even short grass cover to a sparse growth of desert grasses in tussocks. Scattered through the whole are many small thorny trees and bushes. This is natural grazing country, but overgrazing results in the disappearance of grasses, leaving only the trees. Most of the trees and bushes belong to the genus *Acacia,* many of the grasses to the genus *Aristida.*

Soils tend to be shallow owing to the development of a hardpan about a foot or so below the surface. It is this type of country which yields the various gums still so widely collected in Africa.

Figure 7.   The Nile near Malakal, Sudan, Showing Floating Masses of Sudd.
(Courtesy British Overseas Airways Corporation.)

Mountain Grassland and Alpine Meadow

The grasslands which occur at high elevations in Central Africa and the Ethiopian plateau, the mountains of Kenya and elsewhere resemble in certain ways the Alps of midlatitudes, though often coarser in growth and less valuable as pasture. Climate conditions are such that this is land suitable for European-type settlement.

Dwarf Palm—Temperate Grass

This is the vegetation of the valleys and low hills of the Atlas region.

Marsh Grass

In many parts of Central and East Africa there are vast swamps where by far the most important plant is *Cyperus papyrus.* Papyrus swamps cover vast areas in the upper basin of the White Nile.

DESERT

Desert Shrub—Desert Grass

This type is an arid variation of the acacia–desert grass savanna, occurring notably in South Africa where the chief grasses belong to the genus *Aristida* owing to a rainfall of 5 to 15 inches.

In the drier parts of the South African veld it affords excellent grazing land, but of low carrying capacity. It is interesting that the grazing is almost as good during the dry season as the wet, since the dry grass remains palatable throughout the year.

Desert Shrub

The desert shrub is characterized by scattered, evenly spaced plants which are either woody or fleshy. It is like the sage brush desert of the Great Basin in the United States, and is represented in South Africa by the Karroo.

Salt Desert Shrub

This type occurs where evaporating water has left soluble salts in the surface soil, notably sodium chloride and sodium sulphates, or as "black alkali," otherwise sodium carbonate. The last is particularly harmful to vegetation. Most of the plants are fleshy-leafed, and the soil surface is often white with the accumulated salts.

Desert

True desert, a waste of sand, rock or silt, devoid or apparently devoid of vegetation throughout the year, occupies a smaller area in Africa than is commonly believed, in all less than 8 per cent.

Vegetation and Human Life

In the preceding chapter a plea was made for a more intensive study of soils. The need is certainly just as great for a detailed survey of vegetation—plant indicators which do in fact afford a measure of the sum total of environmental factors. It is surely a case for an objective survey, of recording what is actually present, and then of seeking to interpret; but any such survey must show the very close relationship between African ways of life and the vegetation cover. The broad correlation is noted in the next chapter. All detailed studies in tropical Africa have tended to show the inseparable relationship of climate, soil, vegetation and agricultural systems.   At times other factors, notably disease, cut across what otherwise is an almost perfect correlation.   The need for botanical studies relates also to individual species.   How can man hope to establish plants of his own choosing unless it is clear how existing species survive or flourish?   Africa needs, and needs badly, nutri-

Figure 8.   A Large Herd of Elephants Crossing Swamps in the Sudd Region of the Nile.   (Copyright Aerofilms Limited.)

tious fodder grasses to replace indifferent or useless indigenous species.   What precise conditions will they have to face?   Or take the specific problem of Africa's swamps—the *dambos* of the south.   They are held up by accumulations of vegetation rather than rock structure.   Should they be drained and converted to arable land or rice fields, or do they form natural reservoirs of water which would otherwise run off, and do incalculable damage by soil erosion?   Does swamp vegetation give rise to special types of microclimate?   These and so many other considerations point the need for ecological studies before the underdeveloped lands can be safely developed.

African Peoples
and Ways of Life[1]

The Population of the Continent

From the point of view of its human population Africa has three main divisions:

(1) Arab Africa, coinciding roughly with extra-tropical North Africa.

(2) Negro Africa, coinciding broadly with tropical Africa.

(3) White Africa, if one may use that term for extra-tropical south Africa, where whites of European stocks form a dominating minority.

Arab or Moorish Africa, including also Egypt, has been in contact with the successive civilizations of the Mediterranean basin from earliest times. Its history is writ large in ancient monuments as well as in actual records, and it has never been out of touch with the peoples of Europe and western Asia. North Africa absorbed Mohammedanism, and Moslem-Arab traders carried their religion across the great desert wastes to the northern fringes of Negro Africa.

Negro Africa—the *Afrique noire* of the French—is the real Dark Continent, the unknown land, which remained so long isolated from the outside world. Because there are so few outstanding monuments from the past and virtually no written history it seems to have been tacitly assumed that Negro Africa had little history and that its peoples had long been much as they were when first seen by Europeans. In reality much of Negro Africa had for ages been in a state of constant change. There was the continuing antagonism between the war-like hunting tribes and the cattle keepers and cultivators; there were the establishment, expansion and fluctuating fortunes of the Moslem emirates or empires in the broad Sudan belt from the

[1] I am greatly indebted to my colleague Professor I. Schapera, formerly Professor of Anthropology in the University of Cape Town, for reviewing this chapter.

133

Gambia to the Nile; there was the great drift southwards of the Bantu. It is not always realized that the white settlers in the Cape Province of South Africa did not dispossess the Bantu of their lands; the Bantu had not yet arrived. Gradually some of the complex history of Negro Africa is being unraveled, but more important is what has happened in the past century. The partition of Africa resulted in the stabilization—almost the crystallization—of what had long been a very fluid and changing position. It was almost as if a snapshot had been taken of a football game and then every player had been compelled to remain almost as he then appeared in the photograph. Most of the political divisions of Africa are purely artificial in relation to the African peoples.

White Africa of the south embraces essentially the Union of South Africa and Southern Rhodesia—with "islands" of white settlement on the Eastern Highlands farther north. Throughout, unless we regard the southwest of the Cape of Good Hope as a separate unit, the whites are a numerical minority, and for the most part economy of town and country alike is dependent upon African labor.

Demographically, less is known of Africa, especially Negro Africa, than of any other continent. When the United Nations published the *Demographic Yearbook for 1948* only Egypt, Morocco, Tunisia, the Portuguese possessions, Sierra Leone, Nyasaland and white South Africa with its enclaves can be said to have had a proper census, an actual enumeration of heads. Details of age composition were available for Egypt (date 1937) and Portuguese possessions only (1940). Figures for marital status were available for Egypt and Mozambique only, and for no country were figures over a period of years available. In short, the Egyptian census of 1937 and figures for the white population of the Union of South Africa were almost the only reasonably complete records.

Many population estimates exist, and when computations for the continental total show a general agreement it is only because they are all based on the same crude estimates. That estimates, even in the better-known parts of Negro Africa, can be very wide of the mark is shown in the case of Uganda. The population "partly estimated" has been as follows:

1911	2,843,325	
1921	2,921,608	annual increase 0.27 per cent
1931	3,553,534	annual increase 2.00 per cent
1937	est. 3,700,000	
1947	est. 4,063,000	

Then in August 1948 a proper census was taken; the total was 4,993,-965. The estimate had been some 20 per cent below the truth. Similarly the 1947 estimate for Kenya was 4,200,000; the census figure for 1948 was 5,373,078.

Against this background of proved unreliability we may view the estimates of population for the continent as a whole, mentioned in Chapter 1. There the figure of 120 million is quoted for 1900, 170 million for 1950. This suggests an increase of a million a year since 1900 or about 0.8 per cent per annum—probably a little under current world rates.

Population Density

Apart from South Africa and Egypt, the most detailed mapping of population densities is that attempted by the French in West Africa [1] and the Belgians in the Congo,[2] which will be considered in later chapters, though detailed work has also been done in East Africa.[3] Thus the map (Fig. 1) of population density must be regarded as tentative, but it serves to illustrate a number of interesting points. The overall population density of the continent is of the order of 14 to 15 persons per square mile compared with about 42 for the land surface of the world as a whole. Looked at in another way, every inhabitant of the African continent has a share of land of all types of about 44 acres. The corresponding figure for the people of the continental United States is a little under 13 acres. If we eliminate one-third of Africa as being desert or mountain incapable of supporting a permanent settled population, the share of potentially habitable land is still 30 acres per head. By comparison with densely peopled Europe the African continent appears almost uninhabited. The people of Great Britain have a little over one acre of land of all types per head of population (or taking England and Wales alone, about 0.8 acre). In France the figure is about 3.5 acres per head; in Italy with its large mountainous areas only 1.8 acres.

It would be wrong, however, to visualize Africa as a continent of vast open spaces and no people. In the first place there are great contrasts. In the Nile valley, which forms the cultivable heart of

---

[1] *Densité de population en Afrique occidentale et centrale*, Office de la Recherche Scientifique de la France d'Outre-mer, 1945.

[2] P. Gourou, *Atlas général du Congo: densité de la population*, Brussels, 1950.

[3] C. Gillman, "A Population Map of Tanganyika Territory," *Geog. Rev.*, XXVI, 1936, 353–375.

Egypt, population density averages about 1200 persons per square mile, each person, therefore, being supported by the produce of about half an acre of land, and a surplus of some agricultural produce available for export! There is no doubt, too, that given the exist-

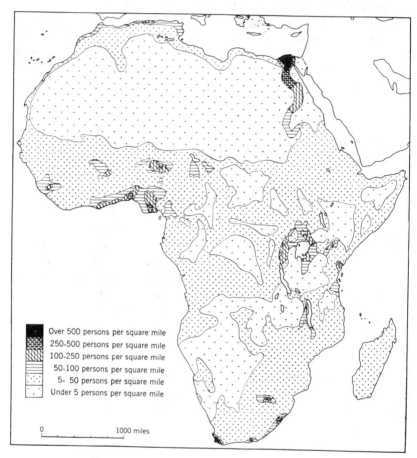

Figure 1. The Density of Population in Africa.

ing forms of cultivation there is overpopulation in parts of Nigeria, where the density exceeds 300 persons per square mile. Elsewhere there are both dry deserts and "forest deserts" virtually devoid of people. Broadly speaking, if one judges by densities in any other part of the world, most of Africa is underpopulated.

What population could the continent support? Calculations of potential population are likely to lead us into dangerous paths whether we are considering Australia, the United States, Canada or Africa. I have dealt with this question at some length elsewhere.[1] It may be demonstrated that in the climatically favored lands of northwest Europe, using present systems of cultivation, one acre of cultivated land will support one person at a northwest European standard of living—measured in calories, 2500 to 3000 per day. Reasons are given in that work for believing that the most "underdeveloped" countries of the world are those lands in mid-latitudes which practice large-scale mechanized farming rather than intensive mixed farming. Far too little is yet known of the possible output of tropical lands. It is certain that a rice economy in favored conditions will support over one person per acre; Egyptian experience suggests two, albeit at a low standard.

We have already seen how tropical Africa is hampered by vagaries of climate, by inadequate control of water, by soils difficult to handle, by numerous and serious plagues of man, beast and plant. Western science has not by any means reached the point when those difficulties can be overcome, and at the moment much of Africa is supporting a maximum population, given the existing form of cultivation and land management and the present incidence of pests and diseases.

The Peoples of Africa

If we exclude the European immigrants who have settled in certain parts of Africa in the past three hundred years, the peoples of Africa fall into five main groups:

1. Certain isolated and relatively unimportant groups, of primitive Negroid character. These "aboriginals" include the Hottentots, who formerly inhabited the southwest, the Bushmen of the Kalahari scrublands, and the Pygmy negrillos of the Congo forests.

2. The "true" Negroes or the Guinea and Sudanese Negroes who live in West Africa and the Savanna belt eastwards to the Sudan.

3. The Bantu or Bantu Negroes who occupy the greater part of the continent south of the equator.

4. The mixed Hamite-Negro peoples of the eastern-central parts of the continent, including the Nilotes of the Sudan.

5. The non-Negroid peoples of northern Africa and the Sahara, including the Hamites and Semites (or Arabs).

[1] *Land for Tomorrow,* Patten Foundation Lectures, University of Indiana, American Geographical Society, 1952.

THE PRIMITIVE NEGROID PEOPLES. The *Bushmen* are nomadic hunters who wander about over hunting grounds using bows and poisoned
arrows. Their only homes are temporary shelters of branches. The
skin is yellowish-brown, the hair of the head is in small separate
tufts, and in stature they scarcely exceed 5 feet. Their interesting
and artistic rock paintings suggest that they were once widespread

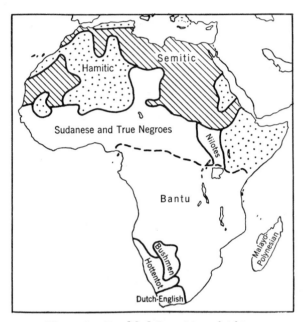

Figure 2.   Simplified Race Map of Africa.

over the East African plateau but were pressed southwards by more
powerful Bantu tribes. When the Dutch reached south Africa they
were already confined to the plateaus of what is now Cape Province
and the scrublands of the northern and eastern Kalahari. They have
never benefited by contact with other cultures, though they seem
slowly but surely to be blending with other peoples.

The *Hottentots* similarly retreated to the southwest under pressure from the north. They are believed by some to result from the
crossing of Bushmen with primitive Hamitic stock and are a little
taller than the Bushmen. They had adopted nomadic pastoralism
with their wealth in cattle and sheep and had semi-permanent settlements of beehive huts within a thorn fence. These were the
"natives" encountered by the Dutch in the Cape, who caused wonder

by the curious development, especially among the women, of fatty tissue on the buttocks (steatopygy). Their tribal organization disorganized by the Dutch invasion and their use as servants by the settlers, they have largely disappeared as a separate race, but there is a strong Hottentot strain in the Cape colored people (see page 450).

The *Pygmy Negrillos*, in stature only about 4 feet, 6 inches, were formerly widespread but now live in small communities, especially in the equatorial forest regions, obtaining their food from fruits, nuts, roots and from animals killed by poisoned arrows. They are noted for their marked Negroid features of very broad nose and prognathous jaws, and though in friendly contact with surrounding Negroes have remained distinct. In some of the wetter regions they construct shelters in the trees.

THE GUINEA AND SUDANESE NEGROES. Whatever may be the focus of differentiation of the human race, it would seem that Africa was populated by successive waves of people from the northeast. What is regarded as the "purest" Negro type, the West African Negro, has gradually been pushed into the coastal belt of West Africa and there, in strongholds amid the rainforest, has remained unmixed with alien blood. Northward and eastward, in the more open savanna country, there is evidence of decreasing purity or rather of increasing admixture with Hamitic blood, and the peoples profess Mohammedanism, although that religion sits but lightly upon them.

The true Negroes are tall or of average height (males 5 feet, 8 inches), with somewhat long narrow heads (moderately dolichocephalic: index 75), intensely dark skin color—really black in most cases—woolly hair, broad nostrils, thick lips and prognathous jaws. They are essentially small cultivators, *not* pastoralists, using different types of hoe and living on yams, beans, millets and bananas. They were formerly grouped into kingdoms, some of great extent and widespread influence. Good examples are afforded by the old kingdom of the Wolof (roughly now French Senegal), the former great kingdom of Mandenga stretching from Sierra Leone eastwards and antedating the Moslem era, the Ashanti kingdom centered on Kumasi, and the progressive Yoruba kingdom with its large towns of Ibadan and Abeokuta. Other groups include the Kru of Liberia—well known because they have long provided crews for merchant vessels along the coast—and the Fanti of the Gold Coast.

Passing northward, the Songhai, who destroyed the Mandengan Empire about A.D. 1500 and established their capital at Timbuktu, show Hamitic mixture, were converts to Islam and retained a strong military tradition. On the other hand, the Mossi farther south resisted Islam.

Farther east there are "islands" or small groups of primitive character, such as the so-called pagans of northeastern Nigeria. More conspicuous are the large Islamic kingdoms or emirates linked together by language (Hausa) with a Hamitic-Negro ruling class (the Fulani) and a more markedly Negro populace. Under the British system of indirect rule, the emirs control their respective domains. Good examples are the Emirates of Kano, Katsina, Zaria and Sokoto; culturally and economically they are advanced peoples famed for their skill in the preparation and working of leather and textiles.

Still farther east the Negroes are represented by the tribes of the Anglo-Egyptian Sudan, but everywhere the Hamitic influence is considerable.

THE BANTU. The Negroes who inhabit the greater part of central and southern Africa, though in excess of 50 million in total, exhibit a number of common physical characteristics. They also speak variations of a common language. In fact Bantu (properly Aba-ntu, or human beings) refers primarily to language. The peoples are split culturally into the contrasted groups of war-like hunter-pastoralists and the settled agriculturalists. The former acknowledged the paramount authority of a chief who lived in a village or kraal built for defense and protection of the all-important cattle. Being aggressive, they seized the best lands, though despising agriculture, which might have been highly productive. A good example of these peoples is the Zulu. The agriculturalists were thus relegated to the poorer lands, and apart from suffering the vagaries of the climate their unfenced lands were open to depredations from the cattle peoples. In social organization they were more democratic. The council of elders designated an "heir apparent" among the eligible sons of a chief by his several wives, and acts were not by the chief so much as by the elders. The operation of this system among the pastoral-agriculturalists of Basutoland and Bechuanaland under conditions prevailing in 1950–1951 is described elsewhere (pages 156 and 491).

A broad grouping of the Bantu into Eastern, Southern and Central groups has been generally adopted. Among the Eastern Bantu the Baganda or people of Buganda, now part of the Protectorate of Uganda, form one of the most progressive peoples of Africa. Before coming under British influence they had already evolved a political organization resembling a constitutional monarchy. They have latterly devoted themselves to the commercial cultivation of cotton, and are rapidly adopting European standards of education, housing and dress. On the Kenya plateau the Kikuyu are excellent cultivators, though like other Bantu they recognize cattle as symbols of wealth. The Akamba are likewise agriculturalists, though they too keep cattle,

Figure 3. Baholo Performing a Hunters' Dance. These people are Bantu from the Angola-Congo border. The dancer's mask represents an antelope's head. Notice the characteristic drums and grass-thatched round hut. (Courtesy Office du Tourisme du Congo Belge.)

sheep and goats. Both are traditionally at enmity with the pastoral nomadic Masai (Hamite-Negro). Along the East African coasts are Bantu peoples speaking Swahili, a language which has become a *lingua franca* of East Africa so that it is difficult to distinguish the "Swahili" peoples from others who have adopted their tongue.

The Southern Bantu include the groups which, over the past three centuries, have been most influenced by the European penetration from South Africa northward. In their territories the Bechuana, Basuto and Swazi have preserved their tribal organizations. They live mostly in villages, with a larger village or town as a capital and residence of a paramount chief, and are pastoralist-agriculturalists. Over the Union of South Africa and the Rhodesias tribal organization has been greatly disturbed; the people have become integrated

Figure 4. A Typical Bari Village Matron from the Southern Sudan. Notice the shaved head, tattoo marks, bead necklaces and charm, chin and ear ornaments, and the good fat European pipe. A Negro type, with probably small Hamitic mixture. (Courtesy Sudan Government.)

to a greater or less extent into the European economy as workers on the farms, in the mines or in the towns. "Zululand" is now an integral part of the province of Natal; Matabeleland and Mashonaland are parts of Southern Rhodesia, and with this territorial assimilation has gone much of the tribal identity.

The Central Bantu include the peoples of the Congo and French Equatorial Africa, organized at the time of European exploration into loosely defined Negro empires. The various groups, such as the Fang, are mostly argiculturalists, practicing shifting cultivation and making clearings in the forest, but are still semi-nomadic rather than settled, moving their whole sphere of operations after a few years.

THE MIXED HAMITE-NEGRO PEOPLES. Although the Bantu are believed to have a varying admixture of Hamite blood, there are

Figure 5. A Mangbettu Man from Niangara, Northern Belgian Congo. Among these people deformation of the skull by tight binding is still practiced. They were formerly inveterate cannibals. The aquiline nose and beard betray a Hamitic mixture with Negro stock. (Courtesy Office du Tourisme du Congo Belge.)

peoples, mainly north of the equator in Central and East Africa, who are quite definitely of mixed blood. They include many of the people of the upper Nile Basin, hence the general term Nilotes. The Dinka, a typical group, live in the Sudd region. They are tall cattle-rearing people having, by marked contrast to the Bantu, milk as a staple article of diet. The Masai, who are war-like in character and have penetrated southward into the East African plateau, form another well-known group. Broadly, the southern penetration of the Hamites and their intermarriage with the Negroes produced virile peoples. They introduced many arts, such as the working of iron, previously unknown to the Negroes, and probably the arts of cattle keeping and sheep rearing.

Figure 6.   Morning Tea in a Moroccan Village.   The men are typical Berbers. The charcoal fire, bellows, brass tray, teapot and glasses are practically the same throughout northern Africa.   The tea is often flavored with mint and is made very sweet.   (Copyright Geographical Publications Limited.)

THE NON-NEGROID PEOPLES.   If North Africa were not isolated from the rest of the continent by the great Sahara, its people would still mark it off clearly and distinctively.   The Hamites and Semites are absolutely distinct from the Negro though, as we have already seen, there have been numerous intermixtures.

The Hamites are typically tall or fairly tall, light brown in color, with wavy or fuzzy dark brown to black hair, thin straight noses, marked non-receding chins and thin rather than full lips.

The pre-Dynastic Egyptians were Hamites, and the modern Egyptians are still primarily of Hamitic stock, though in the north mixed with Arab; and in the south the Nubians show a Negro admixture. Farther south the Ethiopians are also basically Hamitic, though Semitic influence is there strong in culture and language. Though at a different cultural level, the Galla and Somali of the eastern horn of Africa are also Hamites.

The typical Saharan nomads of the central desert tracts, the Tuareg and Ahaggar, are likewise Hamites. There seems to be a general tendency for the ruling class to be relatively pure whereas there is a Negro admixture in the lower classes, below whom are Sudanese Negro slaves. Farther south the Fulani of northern Nigeria are definitely a Negro mixture.

The third or western group of Hamites are those who inhabit the Atlas lands, the Berbers who have given their name to the Barbary States. The position is complicated throughout North Africa by the infiltration of Arabs who are typical Semites. In northwest Africa the so-called Arabs or Moors are rather Hamites who have absorbed the Moslem faith and perhaps some of the Semitic blood of the Arab invaders of the Middle Ages, especially of the eleventh century. Sometimes a distinction is drawn between the Berbers as sedentary agriculturalists organized into small village communities and the tent-dwelling Arab nomad acknowledging the autocratic leadership of a sheikh, often regarded as deriving his authority from Allah.

It would seem that true Semitic Arab blood, if weak in the Barbary States, increases eastwards and that the nomadic "camel men" of the Libyan desert and the semi-nomadic cattle men farther south are mainly Semites.

There is no doubt that the distinction between Semites and Hamites owes much to their traditional origin from Shem and Ham, who, with Japheth, were the sons of Noah and so saved from the deluge. The record is in the tenth chapter of Genesis. The typical Semites are the Jews; the sons of Ham were dwellers in tents.

Language in Africa

In common with other parts of the world, in Africa the spread and consequent present distribution of languages tend to obscure race relationships. The map of languages given here (Fig. 7) is simplified from one prepared by Joseph H. Greenberg and published in the *Southwestern Journal of Anthropology*, 1949–1950. He distinguishes sixteen families of languages, but some of these are spoken by very small and restricted groups only. Broadly, the whole of

Negro-Bantu Africa is shown as speaking languages of one family, the "Niger-Congo," and almost the whole of Bantu Africa, the "central branch" of this group. Greenberg's map shows a large enclave

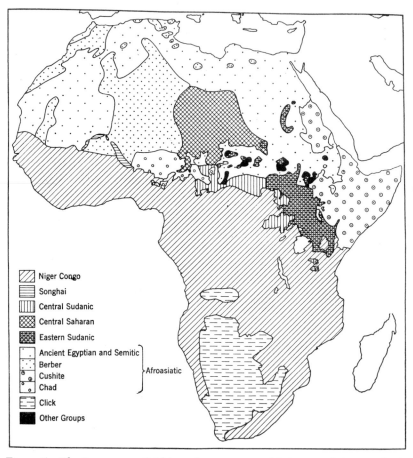

Figure 7. The Languages of Africa. In some ways this is a revolutionary classification of African languages and departs in several respects from the older orthodox views. (Simplified from Greenberg.)

in southern Africa as the click family, so-called because there are click sounds incorporated in the languages. The Bushmen and Hottentots speak such languages, and there are clicks in the Bantu tongue of the Matebele. In reading Greenberg's map, we must remember that the more numerous Mashona and Bechuana of the Kalahari speak Bantu languages.

Over the whole of North Africa are the Afroasiatic (Hamite-Semitic) languages. The other smaller families of languages are those of the Hamite-Negro borderlands—mixed blood, specialized linguistic developments.

African Ways of Life

In general it is the environment, especially the climate and resulting vegetation, which determines the varying modes of life in Africa, and to a considerable extent degree of civilization. Racial influences are obscure, geographical factors clear. In broad terms the dense forests correspond with the distribution of the more primitive peoples, the savannas to settled agriculturalists, the more open grasslands to pastoral and hunting, often war-like, tribes. Peoples very distinct in their modes of life may nevertheless be closely allied in their physical anthropology and language, whereas social organization tends to be rather a function of geographical environment.

Along the Mediterranean borders we find an agriculture established from very early times, with cattle, the plow, cereals and Mediterranean fruits—especially barley, wheat, olives, figs and the grape. Southward towards the desert margins nomadic pastoralism based on sheep replaces cultivation; in the deserts cultivation is limited to oases, and human life depends on date palms and camels.

South of the deserts in the semi-arid open lands of the Sudan are again pastoralists depending for their livelihood on cattle and sheep. Southward, with increasing rainfall and a modest rainy season, there is again some cultivation, precarious, and dependent mainly on sorghum and millet. Cultivation is by the hoe; use of the plow remains unknown.

The area of intermediate rainfall of the savanna between the steppes of the desert margins which are too dry and the forests of the equatorial margins which are too wet is favorable to cultivation. Large villages are the rule; there have been in the past empires of considerable size. Dependence for food is on millet and corn (maize), latterly on groundnuts on the uplands and rice along the rivers. Tobacco is grown, sometimes cotton; kola nuts are gathered. Often cattle are bred, sometimes sheep and horses, and among the cultivators or mixed farming communities are tribes almost exclusively pastoral.

Unfortunately, where the rainfall becomes more reliable and where mixed farming should reach its maximum intensity, we encounter the "fly belts" where the tsetse fly virtually eliminates domestic animals.

Here the basis of life becomes the yam, manioc, banana and palm oil, with cocoa as a "cash crop" now developed to a great extent in the Gold Coast and elsewhere.

As the closer forest is reached, villages are smaller, population sparser and patches of cultivation (shifting cultivation) more scattered.

Figure 8. The Guinea Oil Palm. When wild, the palm grows very tall, with the consequent necessity of climbing the tree to obtain the fruit. (Courtesy Lever Brothers Limited.)

On the plateaus of East Africa, and formerly in South Africa, the balance is somewhat different. The settled cultivators tend to be less numerous than and subordinate to the aggressive, often warlike, pastoral tribes. It is here that wealth has come to be measured in head of cattle, independently of quality; indeed the cattle have little more practical value than the gold bars we civilized peoples bury in our vaults. Madagascar differs somewhat from the continental mainland in that cattle breeding is there associated with rice cultivation.

Africa is peculiarly poor in native food plants. Of those widely cultivated, one certain type of millet (Guinea corn) and perhaps some strains of rice are native. Despite its wide use, corn (maize) was introduced from America, and so were tobacco, groundnuts, yams and manioc. Actually it was the Portuguese, to feed their slaves before and during shipment, who introduced into West Africa

Figure 9. The Guinea Oil Palm in a Nigerian Plantation. When cultivated, the palms are kept low so that the fruit, to which the Agricultural Officer is pointing, can be reached easily. (Copyright L. Dudley Stamp.)

the many new food plants which later became such a blessing to the people—manioc, sweet potatoes, yams, corn, groundnuts, coconuts and bananas coming straight from America, oranges from Portugal.

The barley and wheat of the north were introduced from Europe at an early date, so was the date palm from Arabia. Coffee seems to be native to southern Ethiopia as the kola nut is to West Africa, but most other fruits have been introduced. Cloves were introduced by the Arabs into Zanzibar because they could there use slaves for picking the buds.

The ass may be native to East Africa, the camel to Egypt, but cattle and horses have been introduced as well as European strains of sheep. West Africa gave us the guinea fowl.

Shifting Cultivation

The system of agriculture commonly though somewhat misleadingly known as "shifting cultivation" is practiced through a very large part of tropical Africa. As a system it is better described as "land rotation" or "bush fallowing." In those areas inhabited by sedentary farming peoples, each village or settlement has proper to it a tract of surrounding land. The tract is probably only loosely defined except where settlements are close and population dense. In a given year the villagers working together as a community will clear a part of this village land, cutting and burning the woodland or scrub and then planting the crops appropriate to the climate and soil of the area. In due course the crops are harvested communally and the land used for a second and perhaps a third year. It is then abandoned, and a fresh tract of the village land is cleared. The abandoned land quickly becomes covered with a second-growth woodland or scrub. In due course the clearings reach a full cycle, and if a given tract has been allowed to "lie" fallow for about fifteen years it may be regarded as fully rested. Bush clearing is largely man's work. There is also surrounding the village itself, often as a series of enclosed gardens or "compounds" attached to individual huts, the "women's land," cultivated regularly to afford a supply of vegetables for the pot. Often the kokoyams, peppers, beans, melons, bananas, etc., are scarcely grown at all in the open farmland. The women's land is enriched by house sweepings, ashes, refuse and manure afforded by chickens, goats and human beings.

The system has often been condemned as wasteful of natural forest, of land and of labor. But it has many good points. The natural forest is probably second growth of little value anyway. The land cleared in small patches protected by surrounding woodland escapes the evils of soil erosion, and its nutrient status temporarily enhanced by the ashes of the burnt bush is maintained by the fallowing, the soil not being exposed to the atmosphere long enough for serious oxidation. Expenditure of labor is minimized by burning, and no attempt is made to remove large stumps. The cultivation is by hand —by hoeing—so the stumps do not constitute the obstacles there would be if the plow were used. We may accordingly agree with Lord Hailey when he says that shifting cultivation is "less a device of barbarism than a concession to the character of a soil which needs long periods for recovery and regeneration."

Dr. E. B. Worthington, as a scientist, goes farther and claims that "shifting cultivation is admirably adapted to the needs of primitive peoples, provided there is sufficient land available." This last proviso leads us to enquire how much land is needed under this system. I see no reason to revise the calculations which I made some years ago in Southern Nigeria.[1] I worked on the basis that the average family was 3.6 persons and that each family required the produce from two acres of cultivation annually. If the land is allowed to rest 7 years after one year of cultivation each family would actually require 16 acres of village land. This gives a population density of 144 per square mile as the maximum which can be supported. Where the population density exceeds this figure, the fallow period must be cut down, and the land is likely to deteriorate seriously. In Northern Nigeria, with a lower and more precarious rainfall, I calculated that an average family of 3.3 would require 3 acres or 24 acres in all—a density of 88 per square mile, above which the land would be overpopulated. There are indeed some parts of West Africa so crowded that a year of cultivation is followed by only two years of bush fallowing. On the other hand, where villages are widely scattered, only a part of the "village tract" is even used, or alternately there are stretches of "no man's land" between village tracts.

If we accept these calculations it is interesting to return to the population density map and note those parts of tropical Africa which appear to be overpopulated. Figure 10, reproduced from a map in my article, shows the position in Nigeria.

Agricultural Mechanization

Does the solution to the pressure of population on land lie in mechanization? In 1948 the British Government sent a mission of three experts to enquire into the problems involved in the mechanization of native agriculture in tropical Africa. Their lengthy report [2] contains much material of great interest, and they point out that natural, economic and social forces have combined to cause a low productivity of land and labor with little or no accumulation of

[1] L. D. Stamp, "Land Utilization and Soil Erosion in Nigeria," *Geog. Rev.* XXVIII, 1938, 32–45.

[2] Colonial Office, Colonial Advisory Council of Agriculture, *Animal Health and Forestry*, Publication 1, London, His Majesty's Stationery Office, 1950 (by J. W. Y. Higgs, R. K. Kerkham and J. R. Raeburn).

capital, but that pressure of population on natural resources is so great in many areas that mechanization of agriculture would only be worth while if there are new and substantial demands for labor in non-farm work. Furthermore, the substitution of tractors and other equipment demanding fuel and expert handling "for ordinary native farm labor would be the substitution of costly for cheap factors of

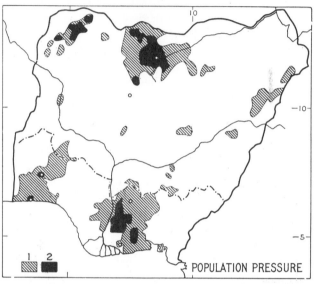

Figure 10. Map Showing Relative Pressure of the Population on the Land in Nigeria. (1) Density over 100 to the square mile in the Northern Provinces or over 144 in the Southern Provinces. (2) Density over 200 in the north, 300 in the south. (From L. D. Stamp, *Geog. Rev.* 1938. Courtesy of the *Geographical Review*, American Geographical Society.)

production." They argue that cheaper means of raising productivity than mechanical cultivation should be used wherever possible—especially the saving of labor by provision of proper water supply (to obviate the great expenditure of energy in carrying water from the river, pond, spring or well to the home) and small water-driven grain mills (to save the endless labor of grinding by hand). It is argued that mechanical aids in the clearing of forest, breaking fallows, leveling for rice and perhaps in farm transport might be advantageous but that "further use of tractors in weeding, harvesting and threshing would usually cost too much as compared with any net increase in production it might bring." It is further argued that costs of tractor cultivation tend to be inflexible from year to year whereas crop yields and prices are highly variable. Provided high overheads can be avoided, there is much to be said for "share" rather than cash charges for mechanical services. The authors also believed that mechanization will accentuate rather than relieve the social consequences of a transition from subsistence to commercial economies.

It is clear that effective use of mechanical implements would involve many changes in farm layout, land tenure and systems of cultivation, perhaps only answered by the collective farm or some form of communal ownership and operation. Despite the arduous labor associated with cultivation by the hoe, as I have already said, there is some doubt whether even the plow should be used widely in tropical Africa. In Southern Rhodesia plows increased in number from 3400 in 1902 to 94,000 in 1938, and in that period 16 per cent of all the arable lands had become badly eroded. In one territory of Uganda plows increased in number from 282 in 1923 to 15,388 in 1937, and the fields had been increased in size but there was no improvement in crop yields.[1] If it does not promote erosion, the clearing of the soil by plowing compared with hoeing means that when the land is left fallow natural vegetation re-establishes itself much more slowly, and the period of fallowing needed to restore fertility is much longer.

The Political Development of Tropical Africa

In the mid-nineteenth century, when the heart of Africa was being explored for the first time by white men, the people were organized broadly into what may be called tribes. Essentially the members of a tribe enjoyed a common language and a common economic motivation; they might be hunters, herdsmen, cultivators. Those of the first two groups were nomadic or semi-nomadic, roaming within a recognized but loosely defined range. A tribe would have its own social and cultural organization, its own rituals, ceremonies and laws, above all its own methods of electing its leaders or chiefs. Tribes were often grouped and recognized the authority of a paramount chief or king. Less frequently "empires" existed where a ruling race demanded recognition by subject peoples of different language, race and customs.

Aims and objects of African tribes were often in conflict, and standing feuds were common. It was this factor which encouraged the slave trade—slavery had long been traditional among Africans

[1] Frank Stockdale, *Report on Visit to East Africa, January–March 1937*, His Majesty's Stationery Office (Colonial Office), 1937.

themselves; the traders needed only to help one warring party against another. Where settlements were established, notably by the Dutch in South Africa, some African peoples (such as the Kaffirs and Zulus) defended their lands against the invading settlers, but others, the

Figure 11. The Islamized Hausa of Northern Nigeria. The son of the Emir of Kano, then acting as a District Officer, and members of his staff, standing outside his home in a village near Kano. (Copyright L. Dudley Stamp.)

Hottentots, for instance, took the easier course of accepting service with the white man, with resulting breakdown of tribal organization.

With the partition of Africa there was often a conflict of interests among the Europeans concerned. Missionary pioneers like Livingstone were fired with the great urge to bring the benefits of Christianity—coupled with Western medicine to heal some of their suffering—to the "heathen"; it was they who stirred their governments at home to take steps against the evils of the slave trade. Many were the early administrators who devoted their whole working lives to improving the lot of the hapless African by stamping out this evil.

There were others who sought to develop legitimate trade and a fair *quid pro quo* for the products of the country. Other traders preferred sheer exploitation—a handful of beads for the much-desired ivory—and whose methods of securing carriers and servants differed but in degree from slavery.

As the European administrations became stronger these abuses were steadily mitigated, but two developments followed. One was based on the assumption that the European concepts of justice, law and order as well as standards of values were unquestionably right and proper and should replace whatever existed before—if anything existed at all, which it was no one's business in particular to bother about. The other resulted from the large-scale development of resources, especially of minerals, and the encouragement of African production of cash crops. Mineral exploitation and other European developments made large demands on "labor," resulting inevitably in a disruption of tribal life, while the demand for crops such as cacao, palm oil and peanuts meant a new emphasis and reorganization of economic life. Yet on the social side there was no tangible substitute for the old tribal organization, threatened with complete extinction.

Then there appeared on the scene the anthropologists and Lord Lugard. The social anthropologists set out to study objectively and scientifically the tribes of Africa, their modes of life, their laws and customs. Without this basic knowledge it would have been impossible to develop the system of indirect rule which has become so closely associated with the name of Lugard. This remarkable man, Frederick John Dealtry Lugard, born in 1858, entered the British Army and, at the age of thirty, came into prominence in command of an expedition of Nyasaland settlers against Arab slave traders. Administrator of Uganda on behalf of the East Africa Company, he later effectively prevented the British Government from abandoning Uganda in 1892. Later sent to West Africa, Lugard rallied chiefs to support the British Royal Niger Company against French and German rivalry and raised the West African Frontier Force (1897). Appointed Commissioner of Northern Nigeria, he unified that territory before he left in 1906. Returning to Nigeria as Governor of both Northern and Southern Nigeria in 1912, he secured their amalgamation as Nigeria on January 1, 1914, and ruled with great wisdom till 1919. It was in 1922 that he published *The Dual Mandate*, in which he deals with the duties of European powers in tropical Africa. His great principle, which he put into practice in Nigeria and which has since been followed elsewhere in Africa, is to encourage and strengthen the traditional authority of the chiefs, to secure the progress of their people through them. This system of indirect rule is in sharp contrast to other systems of government, for example, the French, which encourages African chiefs to become good administrators deriving their authority from the Central Administration rather than from their own people.

Perhaps neither approach is the right one for these times. Although Lugard's principles may be said to have been applied with success over more than half a century in the three British protectorates in southern Africa (Basutoland, Swaziland and Bechuanaland) as well as in many parts of Africa, is not the old tribal concept as well as organization doomed to disappear? As more and more Africans receive their education in Britain or France or America they return more truly "Westernized" than those Africans who have just drifted into towns to seek employment. They have concepts of democracy, of state and of nation quite foreign to their compatriots; they no longer fit into the old life any more than do their European clothes. A very interesting example of the clash of ideas was afforded by Seretse Khama, chief-designate of the Bamangwato tribe in Bechuanaland. While studying law in Britain at Oxford University he married a white girl and returned in 1950 with her to Serowe, the tribal capital. Although the rank and file of the people accepted her as their "white queen," the elders were divided. The British authorities realized that to permit the couple to remain meant at least a deep cleavage among the Bechuanas, at worst riots and bloodshed. Temporary banishment was decreed, and the final solution was left for the future. This action was not based on racial discrimination, though sections of both blacks and whites disapproved strongly of the mixed marriage. Other sections disapproved of the "banishment" of one who had done no more than absorb modern Western standards and was admitted by all to be of the highest intellectual caliber.

Another example may be of interest. When my wife and I were working in Northern Nigeria in 1938 we were received in audience together with the Resident, the British Commander-in-Chief and his wife, by the Emir of Kano. He received us seated on his throne, his cabinet on his right, the three white men on state chairs to his left facing the cabinet. As a compromise of Moslem and Christian views of the status of women, the two white women were permitted a small chair each a short distance away. The audience, the subsequent friendly chat, the tour of the palace with its purely African rooms and its Western type of dining room (with large refrigerator) and the entertainment to afternoon tea left an indelible impression of a great man and a dignified ruler. He spoke no English, but his son, a fine stalwart man over six feet tall, educated in Britain, spoke

Figure 12.   The Paramount Chief of the Ashanti Holds a Grand Durbar, 1951. The Golden Stool, symbol of the nation, is displayed.   (British Official Photograph.)

English perfectly and entertained in Western style. He was ·acting as a District Commissioner, as training. But which is destined to last, the Emirate and Palace rule, or the Civil Servant?

In 1950 growing national consciousness—not, it should be noted, a strengthening of tribal organization—in the Gold Coast had led to various disturbances and to the imprisonment of certain "agitators." But the British Colonial Office, realizing the pace of political progress, granted a new constitution with an Assembly of seventy-five Africans and nine Europeans. An electoral roll of some 500,000 electors (broadly, all males and females over twenty-one) had to be prepared. The urban electors voted directly for their representatives; the rural electors in 2000 subdistricts chose their member of the electoral college to elect 33 members. Voting started on February 5, 1951, and it was recorded that between a quarter and a third of the rural electors came to vote. A candidate had to be proposed

Figure 13. A Successful Candidate Chosen to Represent His Party on the Electoral College, Gold Coast Elections, 1951. (British Official Photograph.)

and seconded, and often the local voters had had a preliminary "palaver" and the candidate was unopposed. At other times a man was put forward with the words: "The chief and the elders have spoken. Is not that enough?" It was not enough, and so once again tribal organization bowed before Western democracy; the gorgeously robed chiefs deferred to the Western uniform of the Returning Officers.

The great variation in political organization will be considered in the regional sections.

It is perhaps not too much to say that any form of "development" on Western lines seems destined to destroy the old tribal organization. The construction of railways, roads and other public works means recruitment of large labor gangs, and so do large-scale agricultural developments (see page 423). The Rand gold mines need 100,000 African workers; other mining enterprises have similar large labor demands. This would happen even if the whole control of development were in African hands.

The weakness of the British concept of indirect rule is that it ties the modern development to a tribal system which many—European and African alike—regard as outworn and in any case doomed to extinction. As Professor W. M. Macmillan has observed: "Anthropological studies give more evidence than one had feared of the cruelty and sometimes the essential injustice of tribal institutions. . . . I would deny that there is evidence that any African people wants to be left as it is." He suggests rather that the African's desire to acquire "not only our mechanical and material efficiency but that spiritual freedom, unknown to tribal society, which comes of respect for the dignity of personality and for the rights of the individual, and is nourished by free play of critical opinion." [1]

In Northern Nigeria, with its firmly established emirates, indirect rule had an excellent foundation on which to work. The position is very different elsewhere. The African in general has a profound respect for age; tribal leaders are likely to be advanced in years and correspondingly fixed in outlook. Not appreciating that authority came from age, the British officials naturally encouraged younger energetic Africans to take leading roles in tribal affairs. In so doing they unwittingly destroyed the very authority they sought to strengthen. If not dead, indirect rule is dying. The struggle becomes a three-cornered contest between Westernization and maintenance of union with Western nations, independence and isolation, or dominance by communism.

Most that has been written above is broadly applicable to the whole of tropical Africa, though examples have been chosen mainly from the British territories. In Chapter 13 some space has been devoted to contrasting British and French policies, and in Chapter 16 it is noted that Belgian policy in the Congo is in some respects intermediate between the two. The French are essentially realists. Their plan has been broadly to extend to Africa the system of administration tried and proved in France and to train Africans to take their places as administrators who derive their authority by

[1] W. M. Macmillan, *Africa Emergent* (1938, revised 1949), Penguin Books, London.

appointment from above, not by election or nomination by chiefs. The French Empire has been replaced by a Union, "colonies" have given place to Overseas France (France d'Outre-mer), and the African has been offered the prospect of becoming a Citizen of Greater France. The French are believers in individualism and private enterprise. Frenchmen have been encouraged to settle in Africa, even tropical West Africa, to make their way as traders or professional men just as Africans have been shown how the way is open to them to succeed along the same lines. The French have never bothered much about color bars. Intermarriage and concubinage are regarded as matters for individual decision.

The ·French system implies supreme faith in their own organization and culture, and it is not certain whether both or either will be acceptable in the long run to Africans. The Belgians recognize the identity of separate African groups more fully by a great use of African languages. It is difficult to generalize regarding the Portuguese area because Portuguese Guinea, Angola and Portuguese East Africa, the three chief territories, offer such marked contrasts. The relative stagnation in the first and large parts of the third may reflect natural conditions as much as Portuguese apathy. In Angola and Portuguese East Africa much of the development which has taken place—railways, roads and ports—has been by foreign capital. If the African population is to be regarded as having been left very much to itself, the one conspicuous result has been the marked outward migration.

Christian Missions

In recent years there has been a distinct tendency to overlook, perhaps to forget, the dominant part played by Christian missions in the material as well as the cultural development of Africa. The early navigator-explorers were followed shortly by missionary priests, but thenceforth the growth of the slave trade obviously rendered untenable any permanent stationment of missionaries drawn from the same peoples as the slavers. Nevertheless, as inland Africa came to be known, all the great Christian churches were early in the African field and vociferous in their condemnation of the evils they found. Livingstone's base was the mission in Bechuanaland. His reports and the reports of other missionaries roused public opinion in America and Europe against slavery to such a stage that governments, however unwilling, had to take action, sometimes to the extent of expending millions of dollars with little prospect of return, as in the case of the East Africa railway from Mombasa.

Christian teaching has always included the education of the young and the care of the sick. Almost everywhere in Africa the mission-

Figure 14. Higher Education in British Africa. Achimota College, Accra. In addition to many such schools, British tropical Africa now has four University Colleges organized since the Second World War under special guidance of the University of London. These are at Accra (Gold Coast), Ibadan (Nigeria), Makerere (Uganda) and Khartoum. The last became independent in 1955.

aries, supported entirely by voluntary contributions from home and often tolerated rather than helped, occasionally even obstructed by administraters on the spot, have been the pioneers in establishing schools and hospitals. Usually when the missions had successfully built up the framework of education and of medical services governments stepped in and took over both management and credit.

Missions have always realized that to reach the people their workers must know the local language. In the study of African languages missionaries have been pioneers. Since they came to convert the "heathen" and to teach them what they believed to be right and true, missionaries as a whole may lack the interest, which is basic to the anthropologists, in the study of all that is now denoted by indigenous cultures. Certain tenets of dogma and ritual may have been stressed in ways inappropriate to African circumstances; Western ideas of behavior may have been pressed with little realization of the effect. For example, it is often said that by their insistence on the Western attitude toward nudity, that it is of itself an evil, missionaries are responsible for the spread of an undesirable attitude towards sex. Certainly in education, curricula and methods of teaching have often been transplanted bodily from the home country. In the British areas I have often heard African children being taught the irrelevant details of English history and geography. The boy or girl educated in the mission school learns, it is said by some critics, to despise his fellows and to seek only to copy his teachers, with the disastrous result that he becomes an outcast from his own people rather than a leader. Despite all this, the Africa of tomorrow will be even more an essential part of a world which has been largely framed for good or ill according to Western ideas. If our Western world is to survive it must be founded and operated on Christian principles—not least on the Ten Commandments, which the teaching of Jesus Christ assumes as basic. In familiarizing the Africans with the background of our culture the missions have done a great and pioneer work.

Some statistics of leading Christian denominations are published annually, but certain matters are not revealed by figures. One is the growth of indigenous African churches, notably in West Africa, where aspects of old pagan beliefs and customs may have been absorbed in forms of Christianity, thus differing from the American or European churches which first brought the faith to the people. Somewhat different is the Dutch Reformed Church of the Afrikaans-speaking South African, sometimes described as the strongest national church in the world. Of ancient origin is the Coptic Church of Ethiopia, to be considered later (see Chapters 10 and 15).

BIBLIOGRAPHY

C. G. Seligman, *Races of Africa*, Second Edition, London, 1939.
R. L. Buell, *The Native Problem in Africa*, New York, 1928.
Lord Hailey, *An African Survey*, Second Edition, Oxford, 1945.
L. P. Mair, *Native Policies in Africa*, London, 1936.

Lord Lugard, *The Dual Mandate in British Tropical Africa*, Third Edition, London, 1926.

W. D. Hambly, *Ethnology of Africa*, Chicago, 1930.

W. M. Macmillan, *Africa Emergent*, Second Edition (Penguin), 1949.

M. Fortes and E. E. Evans-Pritchard (Editors), *African Political Systems*, London, 1940.

I. Schapera, *Migrant Labour and Tribal Life*, London, 1947.

CHAPTER

8

The Plagues of Africa
Pests and Diseases[1]

The evil reputation which Africa, especially tropical Africa, so long held as an unhealthy continent was linked essentially with climate. It was the "unhealthy climate" which caused West Africa to be known as the "White Man's Grave," and different parts of the continent are still referred to as unhealthy or contrasted with such areas as the healthy Kenya highlands. That climate has a direct effect upon the healthy normal functioning of human beings is of course undeniable but not to the extent, or anything like the extent, formerly believed. The dangers of life in most parts of tropical Africa are not due directly to climate but to the many diseases which flourish under those climatic or other physical conditions prevalent in the continent. Diseases to which man and animals are subject are numerous and severe, often fatal, and although their causes are now generally known their elimination is another matter. It has been said with good reason that the tsetse fly, carrier of the germs of sleeping sickness in human beings and nagana in domestic animals, is still the real ruler of Africa. In the tsetse fly belts both animal husbandry and mixed farming are impossible so that agricultural progress is virtually eliminated. Though the locust does no direct harm to man, a countryside devastated by locusts is a countryside of starvation. Pests and diseases thus constitute a very important factor in African development, past, present and future.

Mosquitoes

We are accustomed to summer plagues of mosquitoes in many parts of the world, and many a fishing or hunting vacation in the far north has been ruined by the unwelcome attention of mosquitoes.

[1] I am indebted to Professor P. A. Buxton for the final revision of this chapter.

Annoying and even painful, mosquito bites are not in themselves serious, but when the mosquitoes are carriers of serious disease it is another matter. Malaria, the most widespread of all diseases in tropical Africa, and yellow fever, one of the most dreaded, are both carried by mosquitoes. Directly or indirectly, malaria is the chief

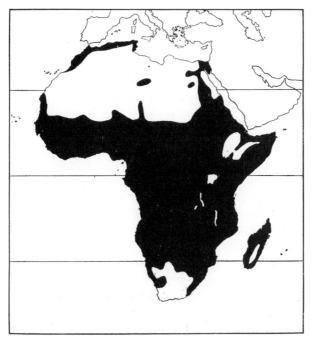

Figure 1. Malarial Mosquitoes in Africa. Species of mosquito carrying malaria exist in all parts of Africa shown in solid black on this map. (Adapted from the world map published by the American Geographical Society, 1951.)

threat to health and life in most parts of tropical Africa. It can be fatal, but its indirect effects in undermining health and so rendering its victims more susceptible to other infections are even more important. It is a debilitating disease and so the greatest contributor to inefficiency in the whole range of human activities. Malaria is caused by a minute animal parasite transferred by mosquitoes of the genus *Anopheles* from man to man. The female parasite is fertilized in the stomach of the mosquito. The resulting offspring pass into the saliva of the mosquito so that when it bites a man they are transferred to his blood, and fever develops after a period of a few days. There are four types of malarial parasite of the genus *Plas-*

modium which cause fevers of somewhat different types. The commonest is subtertian. Several species of *Anopheles* are known to be carriers, but it is *Anopheles gambiae,* widely distributed in Africa, which is the chief villain. It was formerly restricted to Africa but was accidentally introduced into Brazil. Incidentally this is one of the great dangers of the speed of modern air travel—the accidental transportation of noxious pests—and explains the elaborate precautions now insisted upon by the health authorities of many countries. Blackwater fever, a consequence of malarial infection, has been a most serious disease.

The control or elimination of malaria depends upon the destruction of the mosquito by preventing it from breeding. Unfortunately *Anopheles gambiae* breeds very easily and does not bother greatly about the character of the water where it deposits its eggs; small rain pools, stagnant water left in riverbeds in the dry season, even marshes with up to 66 per cent of sea water will all serve. Not unexpectedly the incidence of malaria is greatest at the end of the rains and while there is still stagnant water not dried up. A thin film of oil over the stagnant waters prevents the larvae from breathing and so eliminates the mosquito. Although the spraying of pools and other water surfaces around a town may be possible and there are areas which have been rendered malaria-free, such control would seem to be virtually impossible for a whole continent. It is not improbable that over large areas of tropical Africa all children who survive to adolescence have been infected with malaria and have developed an immunity. Although apparently healthy, they have probably lost both stamina and efficiency. In such populations adults may develop an acute attack of fever which runs its course and after a few days terminates naturally just as in temperate latitudes a cold disappears after it has run its course. To the stranger, especially the European, coming into these malarial areas the disease strikes with devastating effect. Quinine has long been used as a prophylactic lessening the severity rather than preventing the disease, but more effective is a small daily dose of atebrin (or mepacrine). A course of atebrin to a sufferer seems to produce immunity. The American Geographical Society has devoted Plate 3 of its great *Atlas of Diseases* (*Geographical Review*, XLI, 1951, pages 638–639) to the chief species of malaria vectors. It shows the distribution in Africa of the chief species of *Anopheles* widely distributed in the world and also of other species important in Africa.

Yellow fever is a terrible infectious disease caused by an ultra-microscopic virus transmitted from man to man by the mosquito *Aëdes aegypti*. An attack of yellow fever confers immunity, that is, if a victim recovers from his first attack he is safe for life. It seems certain that immunity is earned by many Africans in early life by mild attacks, but if the disease strikes severely it is fatal in 90 per cent of cases. The unfortunate victim starts vomiting and goes on and on vomiting until the strain causes death by heart failure. There

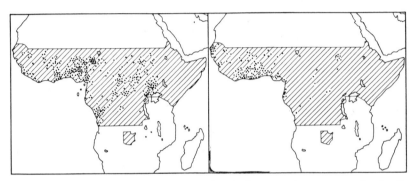

Figure 2. Yellow Fever in Africa. The hatched area is that recognized officially by health authorities for international purposes as liable to yellow fever. (Delineated by the Expert Commission on Quarantine.) The map on the left shows by dots where positive results have been obtained in immunity tests. The map on the right shows by dots yellow fever cases recorded 1924–1941. (After Findlay.)

is nothing that the attendant can do but watch the patient die this horrible death. Every now and then there are epidemics, and, although the numbers involved are in ordinary years small, there is this constant fear of a serious outbreak. Fortunately there is a safe and effective inoculation against yellow fever, and for all travelers to and from tropical Africa it is an essential requirement. The mosquito *Aëdes aegypti* is very widely distributed, far more widely than the disease, and it breeds freely in anything which will hold water, especially it would seem in villages and towns. The provision of piped water supplies and efficient drainage would make towns safe provided other water surfaces were controlled. In parts of West Africa efforts have been made to make illegal the growing of certain palms which hold stagnant water, but unfortunately even the banana holds water between its great leaves and the stem. The same mosquito in Africa is responsible for transmitting dengue, or "break bone," fever. Though rarely fatal, this fever throws the victims out of action for two or three weeks. New arrivals are particularly liable; they have high temperatures and a skin eruption while the pain in joints and muscles is acute. They feel as if every bone in their bodies were literally breaking.

There are other diseases transmitted by mosquitoes. The condition known as elephantiasis, the enormous swelling of the legs and sometimes of other parts of the body, is caused by a minute worm transmitted by mosquitoes.

Tsetse Flies

The name tsetse fly is given to the twenty odd species of African blood-sucking flies of the genus *Glossina*. They are rather larger

Figure 3. A Tsetse Fly (*Glossina*). Notice the position of the wings when at rest and the characteristic proboscis projecting horizontally forwards. (Courtesy of Professor P. A. Buxton.)

than houseflies and can be recognized by their prominent proboscis projecting horizontally in front of the head and by their habit of resting with the wings lying one upon the other. They are found in "fly-belts" especially on the margins of bush or forest near rivers or lakes and are particularly active and troublesome during the hotter parts of the day. Certain species carry the single-celled organisms known as trypanosomes, which are the cause of fatal diseases both in man and animals. When the tsetse fly sucks blood from an infected subject it draws up some of these organisms, which undergo a developmental phase within the fly and are then passed into the blood of the man or animal on which the fly may next feed. The fly *Glossina palpalis* transmits *Trypanosoma gambiense,* causing sleeping sickness in man, and the fly *Glossina morsitans* transmits *T. rhodesiense,* causing the Rhodesian form of sleeping sickness in man, and also several other trypanosomes causing nagana disease among domestic animals. It is possible that monkeys can act as "carriers" of sleeping sickness, and many wild antelopes, though unaffected themselves, are carriers of the diseases of cattle. Sleeping sickness spread from West Africa, where the population has acquired a certain immunity, to Uganda and East Africa generally and caused severe mortality in the early years of the century. Not only are the insects difficult to control—clearing of vegetation round villages and elimination of scrub are important—but the pupae lie buried in shady ground difficult to attack by insecticides. The toll taken of cattle has led to a demand for the wholesale destruction of African wild animals, believed to be carriers. The accompanying map, for the material of which I am greatly indebted to Professor P. A. Buxton and Mr. H. S. Leeson, shows the distribution of tsetse flies (*Glossina*) in general and within that the areas (shown in black on Fig. 4) where sleeping sickness in man occurs. The huge area is obvious.

In the early years of this century, sleeping sickness produced an immense epidemic in Uganda, where it appears to have killed two-thirds of the local population within a very few years, perhaps the greatest epidemic that has ever been recorded. Elsewhere in Africa it was a killing disease especially when associated with insufficient food and consequent poor physique. The French in West Africa found that the annual mortality of patients treated by the best skill then available varied from 5 to 15 per cent. Owing to advances in the production of drugs, the disease has now ceased to be a menace, and no longer makes a large contribution to deaths in tropical Africa, though a certain number of people still die of it, coming for treatment too late, or living beyond the range of medical services. Several drugs, not chemically related, have contributed to this remarkable victory. A point in their favor is that the patient does not have to be admitted to hospital, because he can be treated in his village by an itinerant team. The most recent drugs are not used in treatment of the sick, but for the protection (prophylaxis) of those who are exposed to the risk of sleeping sickness. With these drugs, all individuals, as far as possible, are given an injection which pro-

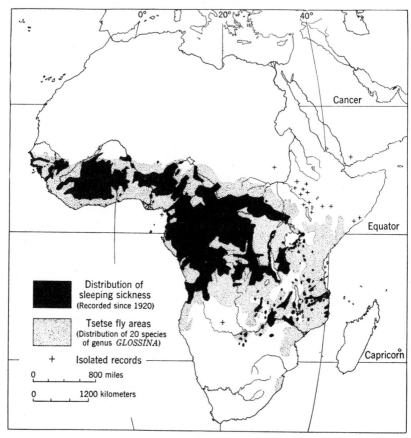

Figure 4.   Sleeping Sickness and Tsetse Fly Areas.   (Compiled from information supplied by P. A. Buxton and H. S. Leeson.)

tects them completely for a large number of months, so that the chain of infection between man and fly is effectively broken.

Cattle, horses and dogs bitten by *Glossina morsitans* carrying the "fly-disease" or nagana usually die.   At first no effect is seen, but a few days after the animal has been bitten the eyes and nose begin to run, a swelling appears under the jaw and the muscles become flaccid.   The animal begins to stagger and may go mad before it dies. It is found on dissection that the cellular tissues under the skin have become injected with air. The result of this fatal effect is twofold. There are severe losses on the margins of the fly belts in cattle country, as in East Africa. In the second place it is virtually impossible to introduce these domestic animals into the fly belts, and consequently mixed farming is not a practicable method of improving the management of the land and increase of crop yields.

Hookworms

It is probable that hookworm disease or ankylostomiasis occurs among a very high proportion of Africans, but, because very severe cases are few and it is rarely fatal, it has been much neglected. The tiny worms when adult live in the human intestines attached to the gut wall, from which they suck blood. Thus the victim suffers a continuous loss of blood. Extreme cases result in marked anaemia, and there are many who believe that hookworm disease in milder but pernicious cases is responsible for much of the mental and bodily lethargy of many Africans. The eggs of the worms leave the human body in the faeces, the larvae develop on the ground and then enter through the skin of feet and ankles of persons walking unshod on contaminated soil. Europeans wearing shoes are rarely infected, and clearly proper sanitation would eliminate contaminated soil.

Water-Borne Disease Organisms

Throughout tropical lands diseases of the intestines and stomach, ranging from mildly upset digestions to killing diseases, are much more common than in temperate lands. Climate is only indirectly responsible by favoring the rapid decomposition of foodstuffs and lowering man's resistance. Infection may be conveyed by dust, by the hands coming in contact with infected material (hence the imperative need of washing before meals), by house flies but above all by contaminated water, especially that which has been infected by human excreta. Danger may come from water even if one does not drink it; it may simply be used for washing cooking utensils or on vegetables to be eaten uncooked. For this reason salads so popular in temperate lands are particularly dangerous in the tropics. Fruit with a firm skin (for example, bananas or oranges) is safe, but bruised or damaged fruit should never be eaten. Milk is also very liable to contamination and should always be boiled.

The two forms of dysentery, the one caused by an amoeba living in water and the other by a bacillus, are very common. Various forms of diarrhoea are even more frequent.

The unpleasant disease known as bilharziasis, or schistosomiasis, one form of which is characterized by discharge of blood and mucus from the rectum, and the other affects the bladder, is common throughout Africa. It is caused by drinking water contaminated by the fluke parasite *Schistosoma* or *Bilharzia*. The intermediate host is a water snail, such as *Planorbis* or *Isidora* (much enjoyed by ducks), and the obvious control is by elimination of these hosts. Fortunately if water contaminated by *Bilharzia* is kept for two days it becomes innocuous for domestic purposes. The disease can be cured with relative ease, but is a killing malady because of the disorganization of the internal organs. The snails flourish in bathing pools near villages and are able to live in water fouled by urine or excrement. Once again the control of the disease is dependent upon general improvement of sanitary conditions.

Fortunately diseases of the typhoid-paratyphoid group seem to be rare in Africa, and so is cholera.

The Guinea threadworm (*Dranunculus medinensis*), though only a millimeter in diameter, lives under the human skin and may reach a yard or more in length. It causes ulceration and much incapacitation. The embryo lives in a minute freshwater crustacean, and once again infected drinking water is the source of infection.

Lice, Ticks and Fleas

Unpleasant as the unwelcome attention of these parasites of man and animals may be, it is the diseases they carry which are far more important. Relapsing fever is caused by a blood parasite (*Spirochaeta spp.*) carried by a louse or a tick. Although diagnosis is easy by a microscopic examination of the blood, the fever has symptoms closely resembling those of malaria and may not be suspected in time to prevent a severe epidemic. If diagnosed in time it is readily curable, and the disease can be controlled by delousing the population; but epidemics of unparalleled intensity have occurred in the past. In 1921–1922 an outbreak in French Sudan and Niger killed at least 10,000 persons; in 1926 one district in Darfur (Anglo-Egyptian Sudan) lost 10,000 out of a total population of 20,000.

Another louse-borne disease is typhus, but this—by way of contrast—is a scourge of colder lands and rare in tropical Africa. It has affected Morocco and Algeria with some severity, as it did in 1942.

It is well known that murine plague is transmitted from rats to man by rat fleas. The domestic house rat, *Rattus rattus*, is the chief host and fortunately is restricted in Africa to main ports, though a mouse, *Mastomys natalensis,* is known to be a host in certain areas. In the First World War plague due to rats was a serious menace in

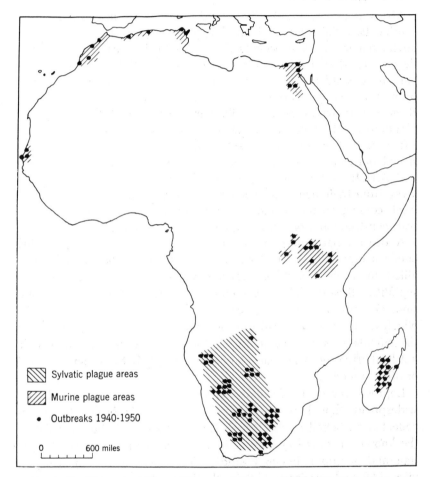

Figure 5. Plague in Africa. (Map specially compiled by D. H. S. Davis.)

Dakar, and in 1920 15,000 human cases were reported from French West Africa.   Because of an energetic campaign waged against the rats cases of plague and resultant deaths dropped steadily so that in 1938 only four cases were reported in French West Africa and for the first time no deaths.   Normally about 60 per cent of cases are fatal.   The other epidemiological form of plague, sylvatic plague, is confined to southern Africa. In that case the permanent hosts are certain wild rodents, mainly of the genera *Tatera* and *Desmodillus.*

Other Human Diseases

Africa does not escape the world-wide killing diseases of other continents. Tuberculosis is probably the most frequent cause of death; pneumonia is especially dangerous to ill-nourished and scantily clad children liable to sudden changes of climate (as when the harmattan suddenly begins to blow); smallpox is likely to spread by movements of laborers and to assume serious proportions; gonorrhoea is very widespread; syphilis has become the commonest cause of admission to hospital in many districts of Africa. Polio affects Africa as it does other continents, especially it would seem in transient labor camps, and so do influenza and trachoma. It would seem that Africans are particularly susceptible to epidemic diseases when away from their homes or when vitality is lowered by heavy manual work coming on top of indifferent feeding. Thus mortality on railway construction work has frequently been very heavy.

A disease particularly prevalent in tropical Africa and affecting children especially is yaws, caused by *Spirochaeta pertenuis,* closely allied to *S. pallida,* which causes syphilis; it is not, however, a syphilitic disease. The germ enters the body through cuts, abrasions or sores. It causes skin eruptions and ulcers all over the body, which themselves may lead to other infections. We may here blame the climate to some extent, for in the tropics cuts and wounds do not heal as easily as in cooler lands and are likely to become the seat of other infections.

Leprosy, caused by *Bacillus leprae,* is another contagious disease widespread, though irregularly so, in Africa. According to figures collected on behalf of the British Empire Leprosy Relief Association the known incidence of leprosy in East Africa in 1950 was 17.8 per thousand of population in Uganda; 10.2 in Kenya; 18.1 in Tanganyika; 14.0 in Nyasaland; 12.6 in Northern Rhodesia and as high as 55.1 in the Belgian Congo. There were estimated to be 580,000 sufferers in the Belgian Congo alone and 265,000 in the other countries mentioned.

The mention of smallpox gives an opportunity of recording the very active steps taken by the French to combat disease in West Africa. In 1937 alone 2½ million persons were vaccinated, about a sixth of the total estimated population.

Locusts

So far we have been considering briefly the plagues which affect man directly; Africa has many others which attack his food supply —his crops and his animals. Many are pests and diseases of wide, if not world-wide, occurrence such as rinderpest and foot-and-mouth

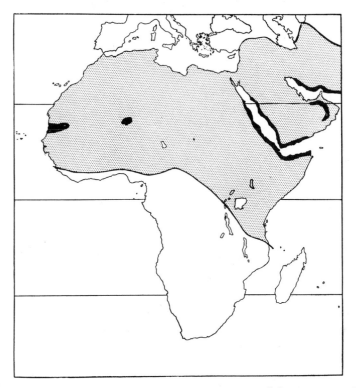

Figure 6.   Desert Locust.   Maximum invasion area stippled.   Known and suspected outbreak areas in black.   (After B. P. Uvarov.)

disease among cattle; some are ancient and well known, others seem to be new—like the swollen shoot disease of cocoa. We have already indicated that the tsetse fly makes impossible at present improvement of agriculture over huge areas of Africa. Similarly the wide prevalence of poultry disease has made poultry farming impossible over large areas. We cannot deal with the geographical distribution and possible causes of all these many pests and diseases, but for several reasons particular interest attaches to the study of the locust. Locusts are among the oldest enemies of mankind. The locusts brought by the east wind were the seventh of the plagues which Moses caused to be brought to Egypt in his effort to secure the release of his people from bondage. Throughout the Old Testament the destructiveness of the locust is proverbial. In Egypt, "Very grievous were they: for they covered the face of the whole earth,

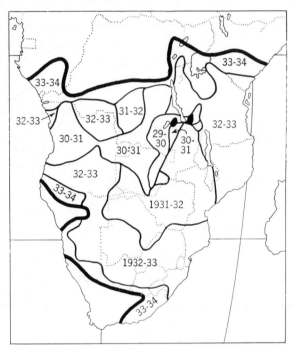

Figure 7. Red Locust: Annual Spread 1927–1934. Black areas show the swarms of 1927–1929 (After Uvarov.)

so that the land was darkened; and they did eat every herb of the land, and all the fruit of the trees: and there remained not any green thing in the trees, or in the herbs of the field, through all the land of Egypt." [1] Yet it was not until about 1930 when a great locust plague seemed to be threatening Africa and western Asia that several governments, including the British, French, Egyptian and South African, realized the need for investigating not only the best means of killing locusts but also the reasons for their periodic swarmings. Later, in 1945, a permanent Anti-Locust Research Center was established. [2]

[1] *Exodus*, X, v. 14–15.
[2] B. P. Uvarov, "Some Recent Advances in Locust Research," *The Advancement*

Tropical Africa is subject to plagues of three different locusts: desert locust (*Schistocerca gregaria*), African migratory locust (*Locusta migratoria*) and red locust (*Nomadacris septemfasciata*). Each has its own "invasion area," though they partly overlap. It has been found that the normal cycle of locust life in each breeding area is

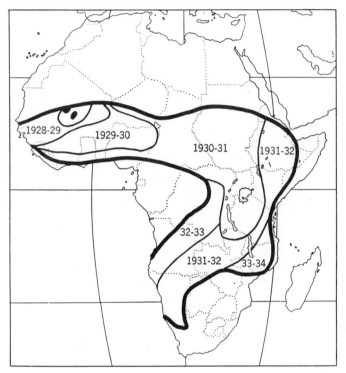

Figure 8. African Migratory Locust: Annual Spread 1926–1934. Black areas show the swarms of 1926–1927. (After Uvarov.)

closely correlated with the climatic cycle, especially rainfall, whereas migrations of swarms between breeding periods are largely connected with wind systems. Where climatological data are adequate, it is now possible to forecast locust breeding and movement of swarms and so to warn areas of the impending danger. Where thermal convection currents develop over heated ground they provide a lift to locust swarms just as they do to birds or aircraft, and the swarms

of Science, VIII, No. 29, 1951, pp. 17–22. This is a convenient summary of the official account, B. P. Uvarov, *Locust Research and Control, 1929–1950,* London, His Majesty's Stationery Office, 1951.

may fly at several thousand feet from the ground, maintaining a speed of about 11 miles an hour. Such swarms may travel hundreds of miles. Quite different is the mass marching of millions of young locusts or "hoppers." They march actively when warmed by the sun and maintain direction by the sun's rays (though probably actuated by hunger, they may actually march for this reason into the

Figure 9. A Plague of Locusts in Nigeria. (Copyright Geographical Publications Limited.)

desert), resting by night when temperature falls. Their activity is definitely stimulated by warmth. Each species of locust occurs in two phases—solitary, when the consequences are not series, and gregarious, when the danger of swarming appears. It would seem that there exist certain permanent breeding grounds from which swarming periodically takes place. For example, small swarms of the African migratory locust were observed on the flood plains of the River Niger near Timbuktu in 1926–1927 over an area of some 50 by 120 miles. In 1928 the swarms invaded Senegal and Sierra Leone; by 1929–1930 the whole of West Africa had been invaded; by 1930 the plague had reached Khartoum and by 1932 swarms which had of course bred on the way reached Rhodesia and Angola. From the small initial center some 4 to 5 million square miles had been affected, and the plague lasted 14 years. Similarly small swarms of red locust observed in Northern Rhodesia in 1927–1929 had become 6300 recorded swarms over 3,000,000 square miles by 1935. Although modern insecticides render the protection of a given area of crops comparatively easy, it needs a well-planned campaign to control a plague. In 1943–1947 co-ordinated campaigns, highly successful, cost roughly $5,000,000 a year. It may be that by intensive study of the ecology of initial breeding areas human beings may one day master this powerful and baffling enemy.

The Control of Pests and Diseases

With the constant spread of medical science and the teaching of hygiene and the general raising of the standard of living, human mortality throughout Africa is being lowered. Survival rate is increased, and unless there is a corresponding drop in the birth rate, the population of Africa is bound to increase enormously. Despite the increasing measure of control over animal diseases and pests attacking agricultural crops it is doubtful whether the output of food is keeping pace. There is increasing pressure on land resources which threatens the traditional methods of African agriculture. Over all Africa the readjustment of the people and the land becomes the primary problem. Nor does the problem end with the control of pests and diseases. In a preceding chapter we have seen the need for water control; we have seen the need for new methods of managing tropical soils and the failure of modern machinery designed for North American or European conditions.

There remains a whole range of diseases among plants, animals and man himself due to some deficiency, often difficult to detect, in the land or the soil itself. Major deficiencies in the soil, such as low content of lime, phosphates and nitrogen, can be detected by chemical analysis and to the trained eye may be apparent from the growth and form of plants themselves. It is much more difficult to detect absence or excess of "trace-elements," the full significance of which is not yet fully known.

A deficiency disease of world-wide occurrence is goiter—not so much a disease in itself as a symptom of ill health due to an unbalanced diet deficient in iodine. The unsightly swelling of the neck is due to malfunctioning of the thyroid gland, and the influence extends widely into reproduction, growth rate, intellectual development and deaf-mutism. The people of Africa, living close to the soil, are on the whole remarkably free from this disease except in the

Figure 10. The Fight against Malaria. Only recently was it found that the little-known *Anopheles melas* bred in these Black Mangrove Swamps of Sierra Leone. (British Official Photograph.)

Figure 11. A Helicopter Spraying Cotton Crops in the Sudan. The spraying is for control of jassid insects. (Courtesy of Pest Control Limited.)

Nile Valley and Delta, patches in the Abyssinian plateau, on high country near the source of the Niger, Northern Nigeria, round the Ebola River in northern Congo and in the Katanga. In each case the incidence would appear to be due to the constant use of river water deficient in iodine. In a small but interesting area of the Langkloof Mountains near Knysna in South Africa local waters and soil are normal in respect to iodine content but very rich in available lime, though low in phosphorus. This lime-phosphorus unbalance seems to lead to increased demand for iodine and may explain the popular association of goiter with limestone areas elsewhere in the world.[1]

There were parts of Kenya where the mysterious disease "nakuruitis" swept away the settlers' cattle and sheep until it was traced to deficiencies of trace elements in the soil. With a dressing of cobalt the same land now carries excellent livestock.

If this chapter conveys one lesson it is the need for continued study and research and the realization that Africa still holds many problems common to the whole world besides a number, often most baffling, of problems peculiarly its own.

BIBLIOGRAPHY

Much of the material on which this chapter is based has been supplied from unpublished sources and I am especially indebted to Professor P. A. Buxton and Professor G. Macdonald of the School of Hygiene and Tropical Medicine (University of London), Dr. C. J. Hackett of the Wellcome Museum of Medical Science, Mr. H. S. M. Hoare of the Leprosy Relief Association, and Dr. H. S. Gear and Dr. D. H. S. Davis of the Institute of Medical Research, Johannesburg.

Under the direction of Dr. J. M. May the Department of Medical Geography of the American Geographical Society has in preparation an *Atlas of Diseases*, the first comprehensive attempt to deal with the geography of the world's diseases. In 1951 the British Government for the first time collected for publication in one annual volume entitled *Colonial Research 1950–1951* (His Majesty's Stationery Office) reports which had been previously issued separately, dealing with insecticides, fungicides, herbicides, locust control, tsetse flies, animal health and many other subjects.

[1] World Goitre Survey, *Iodine Facts*, London, April 1946.

CHAPTER
9

Transportation in Africa

Those who are inclined to underestimate the importance of natural factors in the economic development of Africa would do well to study the means of transportation, past and present. In common

Figure 1. A Typical Path through Farmland, in the Gold Coast near Sekondi. These paths are ideal for bicycles. (Copyright L. Dudley Stamp.)

with other Mediterranean lands, the ass was in common use as a beast of burden in North Africa from very early times. There is no need to do more than mention in passing the obvious association of the camel, the "ship of the desert," with the desert regions, nor is there need to stress the well-known but nevertheless striking adaptations of the animal for desert life—the broad spreading foot, the arrangement of the stomachs, the safety reservoir of food in the hump, the tongue and mouth able to laugh at thorns, the nostrils closing at will against sand and dust. That the camel is fully conscious of its successful adaptation to environment, so vastly better than that of clumsy-footed man, is clear from its supremely haughty bearing and supercilious expression.

Figure 2. An Ox Wagon of the Old Type on the High Veld. It has the full span of 16 oxen. Such ox wagons played a large part in the development of South Africa but are now becoming scarce. (Courtesy South African Railways.)

South of the desert, in African Africa, where the tsetse fly reigns, there are no domestic animals which can be used as beasts of burden. The areas where they could have been used are so limited that broadly the attempt was not made. We may almost say in consequence that the wheel remained if not unknown at least unused until the advent of Europeans. In tropical Africa human porterage (where water courses were not available for dug-out canoes) was practically universal. So the routes from village to village, to the tribal meeting place, to the juju shrines in the forests were worn by human feet, traveling single file. There were no wheels, no wheeled vehicles, no cart tracks with the two deep wheel ruts so universal in India or Indo-China. In the forests or closer type of savanna country the tracks made by human feet were narrow. Suddenly the African realized in the early years of the present century that Western civilization had produced the ideal form of transport which he could really use, the bicycle. Millions of bicycles, of British and continental makes, for a time also of Japanese, disappeared into the African bush.

In the open savanna and the grass veld or steppe, vehicles with more than two wheels could also be used. In the south, where no tsetse fly hindered their use, the Dutch introduced at an early stage the lumbering ox wagon—the covered wagon of the Great Trek. With its standard "span" of sixteen oxen it is still to be seen in parts of South Africa and the Rhodesias. Professor R. U. Sayce has claimed that the development of South Africa as a whole is intimately connected with the ox and has stressed the many thousands of ox wagons which were in use, notably in the period 1880–1890.[1] With the coming of the present century the bicycle proved its usefulness in South Africa as elsewhere in the continent, but after the First World War it became clear that the modern automobile could go, at least in the dry season, over much of unforested Africa with but little in the way of formal roads. It would be too much to say that the drier parts of Africa have now a network of roads, but, except in the rains, most parts can be reached by automobile.

The qualification "except in the rains" may exclude a period of 6 or even 8 months in parts of tropical Africa. Human porterage is usable, although with difficulty, throughout the year. The same is true of the bicycle, but for all-the-year movement of passengers and goods overland either railroads or all-weather roads are essential.

Railroads

In North Africa, Egypt and South Africa, railroad construction began early. In South Africa the building of the line from Cape Town began in 1859. It was completed to Wellington in 1863, but it did not reach the Kimberley diamond mines until 1885 or Johannesburg on the Rand until 1892 and Bulawayo until 1897. It may indeed be said that the "railway era" for tropical Africa began shortly after the partition of the continent and that strategic factors were stronger than economic ones in determining which lines were built. There was no co-ordination; gauges were chosen at the whim of the companies or of the governments who backed them. Most railways in tropical Africa were begun after 1890, and railway construction went

[1] R. U. Sayce, "The Transport Ox and Ox-Wagon in Natal," in *Studies in Regional Consciousness and Environment*, New York, 1930.

Figure 3. Unloading Ships at Accra, Gold Coast. In the absence of a modern harbor goods have to be offloaded into surf boats, seen in the background, and then carried by African porters to the shore. (Courtesy British Overseas Airways Corporation.)

Figure 4. Unloading at Accra. The automobile in open crate has just been lowered on two surf boats. (Copyright L. Dudley Stamp.)

on spasmodically and rather slowly until the First World War. As the territories of the European powers became demarcated and widely accepted, so economic considerations (especially the exploration of valuable mineral deposits) replaced strategic as the main factors determining routes. It should of course be noted that Africa has many short lengths of line, especially in the Belgian Congo, constructed to join navigable stretches of waterway either by circumventing rapids and falls or by linking one waterway with another.

Figure 5. African Craft at Freetown, Sierra Leone. Many of the Africans of the West Coast are great seamen. (Copyright L. Dudley Stamp.)

It was really not until after the First World War that the motor truck for goods, the motor bus for African passengers and the private automobile assumed first-class importance and the construction of all-weather roads became more significant than that of railways. This change of emphasis is well illustrated by the famous Victoria Falls Bridge over the Zambezi. It was designed and built as a railway bridge and completed in 1904–1905. When I first visited the area in 1926 it was still a railway bridge, but the adventurous, with or without permission, would drive a model-T Ford (invaluable because of its high clearance) over the bumpy wooden surface. Later it was definitely converted to a rail and road bridge.

Some examples of early "strategic" railways may be quoted as interesting. The line from Lourenço Marques in Portuguese East Africa to Pretoria in the Transvaal, built by the Netherlands Railway

Company, was completed in 1895. The Transvaal was an independent Republic, but the line from Pretoria to Durban in the British Colony of Natal was opened the next year. In 1891 the Imperial German Government took over the administration of German East Africa from the German East Africa Company, and the Tanga railway was begun in the same year, though it did not reach far inland for many years. In 1892 the old Imperial British East Africa

Figure 6. A Troop of Young Elephants in Convoy in the Belgian Congo. African elephants are less easily trained than Indian but can be used. (Courtesy Office du Tourisme du Congo Belge.)

Company surveyed a railway route from Mombasa to Lake Victoria; construction was undertaken by and at the expense of the British Government in 1896. In this case Britain's decision, made by Prime Minister Lord Salisbury, was based on a determination to suppress the slave trade.

Farther north the French in 1894 secured a concession to build the railway from their port of Jibuti to Addis Ababa, the capital of Ethiopia—still the only railway link between Ethiopia and the outside world. It is perhaps indicative of the changing relative significance of road and rail that the Italians during their occupation of Ethiopia (1936–1941) built many motor roads but no railways and that at the end of the Second World War the Addis Ababa railway was not sufficiently important for through running to be resumed.

Most of the railways in tropical Africa were begun after the Berlin Conference of 1884–1885. St. Louis was linked with Dakar in 1885; the line to link the Senegal River at Kayes with the Niger, though actually begun in 1882, did not reach Koulikoro on the Niger until 1906, and it was 1923 before there was through running from Dakar to the Niger.

It was Stanley who is credited with saying that "without railways the Congo is not worth a penny." He knew well the great navigable stretches of the mighty river and its tributaries and realized how those navigable stretches must be linked up by railroads circumventing the rapids and falls. Because the force of his argument was appreciated the line from Matadi to Leopoldville was opened in 1898, uniting the estuary with Stanley Pool and thus conquering the obstacle of the Livingstone Rapids. The short stretch of line from Stanleyville to Ponthierville around the Stanley Falls in the heart of the basin was opened in 1909.

Many years ago the late G. G. Chisholm in his *Handbook of Commercial Geography*, first published in 1889, showed how expensive and inefficient is human porterage. A man carrying 100 pounds on his head might travel 15 or even 20 miles a day; two men driving a railway engine could haul, for example, 1,000,000 pounds 1000 miles in a day. Is it little wonder that goods valuable enough to stand the costs of human porterage were few in number—gold, diamonds and ivory, to mention the traditional African ones—and the commercial opening up of Africa awaited the railroad? This is still largely true for such heavy commodities as minerals, though the truck and automobile have added greater flexibility and extended the range reached from a railroad. Sarraut [1] records that during the First World War the French required to transport 4200 tons of cereals in the Ivory Coast. It took 125,000 porters 2,500,000 working days, with an incalculable loss in cultivation as a result!

The Cape to Cairo Railway

Most of the continents have had their great railway romances. The destinies of California and of British Columbia were both in the balance before the forging of the railway links which bound them to the East, and the concept of the railroad as a unifying as well as a civilizing influence was uppermost in the minds of the great Empire builders before the automobile and air age. The idea of a through

[1] *La mise en valeur des colonies françaises.*

railroad from Cape Town to Cairo is associated especially with the name of Cecil John Rhodes—scholar, financier, statesman, dreamer, philanthropist. Born in England in 1853, he was never a strong lad, and at 16 he went to Natal to join his brother on a plantation to lead an open-air life. Within a few months the brothers joined in the diamond rush to New Rush, afterwards named Kimberley, and soon Rhodes was averaging $500 a week. In 1873 he returned to England to try to get his degree at Oxford University. His scholastic attainments failed to gain him admission to the college of his choice, but the more discerning Provost of Oriel College admitted him. After a few months the climate affected his heart again and he had to leave, taking his Greek classics to the diamond fields. After 8 years, he did succeed in putting in enough terms of residence to qualify for his Oxford degree. By the time he had reached the age of 21, however, the bold young financier was already deeply involved in South African gold and diamonds and had begun reorganizing small companies into combines. Eventually, in 1888, he joined his great rival Barny Barnato after years of rivalry. There is no doubt Rhodes wanted to make a vast fortune to enable him to turn his dreams into reality.

Quite simply and with all modesty, he believed the English-speaking peoples had followed the highest ideals of justice, liberty and peace and that God had called upon Britain and America to rule the world for its own good. He regarded the split between the United States and Britain as the greatest tragedy of history, one day to be remedied, and in the great task of bringing the whole world under one beneficent government he allotted himself Africa.

By long tradition the territories of the old British Empire, now the Commonwealth, had been colored red on political maps, and it has been said that it was Rhodes' ambition to "paint the whole of Africa red." He saw Africa on the road to progress and prosperity under the British flag. First he desired the union of South Africa and so, in 1881, entered the Cape parliament. He was largely responsible for extending control over Bechuanaland in 1884–5. He became prime minister of the Cape in 1890. At the same time he was chairman and virtual dictator of the chartered British South Africa Company (founded 1888), which, after the manner of the famous old chartered companies such as Hudson's Bay and East India, acquired, developed and ruled the vast heart of Africa now known as Rhodesia. This lasting memorial to his work is matched in his other sphere of interest by the Rhodes Scholarships he endowed to permit students from the United States and the British Commonwealth to study at Oxford University. He saw many of his hopes dashed by the Boer War in 1899–1902. He died on March 26, 1902, two months before the war came to an end.

Death came at the age of 48 from a particularly distressing form of heart disease in the great house Groot Schuur that he had built for himself on the slopes of Table Mountain, where he wandered from

Figure 7. The Grave of Cecil Rhodes, Matopo Hills, Southern Rhodesia. This also illustrates the "onion weathering" of granite under the sun's action. (Copyright L. Dudley Stamp.)

room to room trying in vain to get enough air to breathe. His home he bequeathed to South Africa to be the official home of future prime ministers, though he was not to know that his dream of a Union of South Africa would so shortly be achieved, largely through the efforts of Jan Christian Smuts then fighting on the Boer side. He was buried, according to his wishes, amid the granite boulders of the lonely Matopo Hills near Bulawayo in his own Rhodesia.

Today Rhodes is sometimes regarded as an outdated "Empire builder," but if he had put his life's aim and ambition into a single paragraph he might well have antedated Point IV by more than half a century.

The two maps (Figs. 8 and 9) reproduced here show the British sphere in southern Africa in the year 1881 when Rhodes entered parliament and at the close of 1902, the year in which he died.

What of the Cape to Cairo railway? By 1885 it had reached Kimberley; five years later the territory in which Kimberley is situated (Griqualand West) had become part of Cape Colony. It was in 1885 that a British protectorate was established over Bechuanaland and during 1896–1897 the railway was constructed right through Bechuanaland to reach Rhodesia. Rhodes had obtained a mineral concession from the chief Lobengula covering the whole of Zambesia

Figure 8.   Africa in 1881.   British   Figure 9.   Africa in 1902.
            territory in black.

(Northern and Southern Rhodesia) in 1888 which was thus proclaimed a British sphere of influence the same year. Lobengula's kraal was on the site of the modern Bulawayo. He was a great man and foresaw that the future of Africa lay in collaboration with the Western world. He sent two of his sons to be educated in England, something quite unique in 1892. At a small but famous private school in the heart of England's county of Kent they became fellow students of my eldest brother. Lobengula paid a state visit to England and saw his sons in school, he absorbed many ideas and ideals of the Western world and imported into his own country large numbers of top hats as appropriate symbols of authority. But his people, the Matabele, were restless. They rebelled, but their rebellion collapsed with an outbreak of smallpox, Lobengula himself dying in 1894. In 1896 the Matabele again murdered a number of settlers and were driven into the Matopo Hills. There Rhodes and three companions went unarmed and negotiated peace.

The next year (1897) the railway had reached Bulawayo only a score of miles from the heart of the Matopos. Again construction was pushed on. In 1905 the Victoria Falls Bridge was opened, and

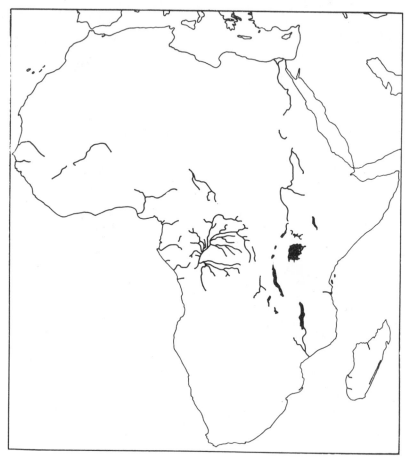

Figure 10. The Navigable Waterways of Africa. This map shows in dramatic fashion how the navigable stretches of waterway are isolated by falls and rapids and that no river affords penetration deep into the continent.

Northern Rhodesia was linked directly with Cape Town. Construction continued across the territory to the mining area of Katanga on the border of the Belgian Congo and so to Bukama on the navigable Congo system, where the through route may be said to end. Bukama was reached in 1918. By this time the automobile had come to supply the really flexible link, and steamer services filled in other gaps. Before the end of 1902, the year in which Rhodes died,[1] only the existence of German East Africa interrupted the red on the map from the Cape of Good Hope to the border of Egypt, then a nominal vassal of the Turkish Empire. With the grant by the old League of Nations Mandate over former German East Africa after the First World War that territory became, if not red, at least pink. Before the outbreak

Figure 11. A Typical African River Steamer. This steamer is serving on the River Gambia between French territory and the port of Bathurst—a six-day journey—but is typical of many African river services. (British Official Photograph.)

of the Second World War tourist agents were issuing through tickets, using rail, road and water links from the Cape to Cairo.

Roads in Africa

Speaking in general terms, the importance of the surfaced all-weather road did not come to be appreciated until the growth in use of the automobile, and particularly the truck and motor bus, after the First World War. Prior to that time reliance was placed essentially on the railroad for the "opening up" of territories. There is an interesting example of the road pioneer who was before his time in the story of the "Stevenson Road" planned by Mr. James Stevenson,

[1] Sarah Gertrude Mills, *Rhodes*, London, 1933.

a Glasgow business man and one of the founders of the African Lakes Corporation in 1878. It was designed to link Lake Nyasa (at Karonga) with the southern end of Lake Tanganyika near Abercorn

Figure 12. The Sierre Leone Railway near Freetown. Most African railways are 3 feet, 6 inches or meter (3 feet, 3⅜ inches) gauge, but this one is only 2 feet, 6 inches. The difficulties of railroad engineering in the wetter regions are well illustrated. In the rainy season the water here may be almost up to the rails. (British Official Photograph.)

and so to make river-road communication possible from the mouth of the Zambezi to the north of Lake Tanganyika. William McGowan, a young engineer who went to survey and assist in the construction of the road, has left an interesting diary kept from his arrival at

Quilimane in 1884.[1] The road was never finished. The railway from Beira via Blantyre to Lake Nyasa superseded the proposed use of the Zambezi whereas Lake Tanganyika was reached at Kigoma direct by rail (begun in 1905) from Dar-es-Salaam in 1914.

Transportation in Africa in 1950

If it is true that the economic development of Africa does depend on the existence of modern forms of transportation, what was the position in 1950?

With a network of regular air lines, especially British, French and Belgian, all the main centers had been thrown into ready communication with Europe as far as passengers and mail were concerned. It is now relatively simple to hold Pan-African conferences, the delegates traveling by air. European administrators, technicians and scientific or other advisers can reach most African centers in a couple of days from Europe. There is an economy of time for the administrator going on leave. A West African "tour" of duty of 18 months formerly involved 3 weeks' sea travel each way; now it is 2 days. There are thriving African centers almost inaccessible by other means which air travel has made possible. A very good example is Costermansville in the healthy Lake Kivu area of the eastern Belgian Congo.

Freight of a specialized kind is handled by air, but for the development of ordinary commerce reliance must be on railroads and navigable waterways, with roads acting as "feeders." Figure 13 shows by the thick black lines all parts of Africa within 20 miles of a railway or navigable waterway. It tells its own story; much of Africa, even the well-watered and potentially productive areas, is still inaccessible.

Among areas of modern development which would not have been possible without modern forms of transportation we should note especially the gold fields of the South African Rand, the copper belt of the Katanga and Northern Rhodesia, the tin fields of the Nigerian Jos plateau, the groundnut-cotton areas of both French and British West Africa, the cotton areas of Uganda, the Gezira irrigation area of the Sudan and many others.

Although the importance of roads as feeders to the railroads has been mentioned in the preceding paragraphs, Africa like other continents has now its trunk roads and long-distance highways. The special case of the trans-Saharan routes is considered in Chapter

[1] *Scot. Geog. Mag.,* LIX, 1943, 31–36.

12. In South Africa it is increasingly the habit of many to journey exclusively by road, just as it is in North America, and to make little use of the railroads. Even in equatorial Africa, as described in

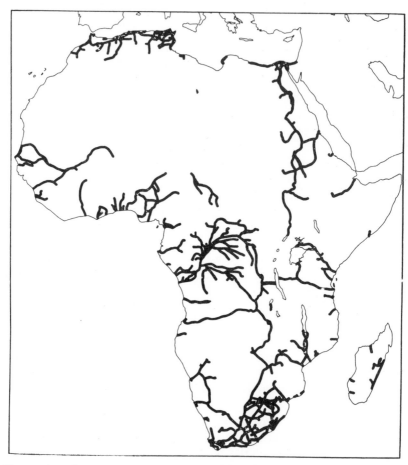

Figure 13. Africa, Showing in Solid Black All Parts within 20 Miles of a Railroad or Navigable Waterway.

Chapter 16, the French are building roads rather than railroads, whereas everywhere where Italian influence has been marked roads, not railroads, have resulted.

With the development of roads has come the increasing neglect of waterways, but the Nile, the Great Lakes and the Congo—with the Niger in part—remain as great highways of trade.

The Countries and
Regions of Africa

CHAPTER

10

Egypt and the Nile

Nearly every country in the world has its own individuality, but of Egypt it may be said that here is a country in many ways unique. Because it is unique it is not in any sense typical of Africa. In its earlier historical associations Egypt is linked rather with its neighbors on the continent of Asia. For the last 2000 years at least Egypt has looked to the Mediterranean Sea, and indeed since its ancient association with Rome is to be regarded as European more than either African or Asiatic. It is then as a country very distinct from the remainder of the continent of Africa that we consider the Republic of Egypt.

The Republic of Egypt (Misr)

Although the total area of the Republic of Egypt is recorded as being 386,198 square miles, the settled and cultivated area comprising the Nile Valley, the Nile Delta and the inhabited desert oases covers only about 13,500 square miles—less than a third the area of Pennsylvania. In its physical setting the whole of Egypt is in fact part of the enormous desert belt stretching from the Atlantic shores across the whole of the North African continent and, interrupted only by the Red Sea, into Arabia and Iran. It is in fact one long oasis, 700 miles from north to south, but only some 10 to 15 miles wide, except where it is enlarged towards its seaward end into the Delta. If Egypt of the Nile is thus to be described as an oasis, it is again a unique oasis where two factors, the annual flooding of the Nile and the alluvial soils which have been deposited by that river, combine to render the oasis not only unmatched in natural fertility but having a fertility annually renewed.

Whether Herodotus, when he wrote of Egypt some 3000 years ago, was alreadying quoting some previous authority, or whether his *bon mot* was indeed original, it is to Herodotus that we commonly give credit for a statement which has perhaps been repeated more times than any other in geographical literature—that "Egypt is the gift of the Nile." However banal the statement may be, it remains eternally true. Thanks to the Nile, what would otherwise be a complete desert is a fertile and prosperous country with a history of human settlement unrivaled anywhere in the world.

Apart from a small and irregular amount along the Mediterranean fringe of the Delta, Egypt receives practically no rain during the whole of the year.

The country as a whole falls quite simply into a number of physical divisions. The Nile itself runs between parallel lines of cliffs, in some places only 220 yards wide, but normally a few miles apart. From the edge of the bounding cliff on the east, the so-called Arabian Desert rises towards the shores of the Red Sea, culminating in a mountain range with peaks reaching between 4000 and 7000 feet. The drop to the Red Sea is sudden, and northwards where the Red Sea narrows into the Gulf of Suez the rugged relief is continued in the peninsula of Sinai. By contrast, to the west of the Nile Valley, the Libyan hills subside gently into the broad flat plain of the great Libyan Desert. In places the surface of this plain sinks in shallow, broad depressions in which are to be found series of scattered oases. The Libyan Desert as a whole becomes lower in its general elevation from south towards the north, and it is in the north that over a large area its surface lies below sea level, before rising slightly into the Libyan Plateau, which itself overlooks the Mediterranean Sea in the low scarp so well known to those who served in the North African Campaigns in the Second World War. One depression in this Western Desert, lying near the Nile itself, is the famous oasis of El Faiyum, lying below sea level and in such a position that flood waters from the Nile can be directed into it. It is thus extensively cultivated and able to support a large population. Below Cairo the Nile divides into its distributaries which pass through the Delta on their way to the Mediterranean. The shape of the Nile Delta is the inverted capital Greek letter Δ (delta), and it may even be claimed that the word "delta" is one of the oldest geographical terms in existence.

Climatically, it may be said that the Egyptian year falls into two parts—a cool winter from about November to April and a hot summer from May to October, which is often ushered in by that scorching wind from the south known as the khamsin. As understood in

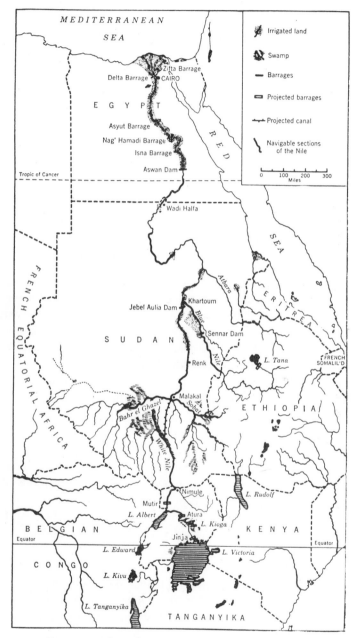

Figure 1. The Nile Basin Showing Projected Works.

midlatitudes there are no spring and no fall. The absence of the cyclonic disturbances which are so usual in midlatitudes results in a monotony of climatic conditions; sudden variations in temperature are rare. Since vegetation depends upon irrigation water, man has control to a very considerable extent over times of harvest. There is the end of the cool season when the midlatitude crops come to fruition, in April and May, followed by a second harvest when tropical crops are ready for gathering, in July and August. Despite the fact that Egypt is 700 miles from north to south, stretching over some 8 or 9 degrees of latitude, there is little difference between the main crops which can be grown throughout the country. We shall consider later in this chapter the regime of the River Nile in detail with its spectacular seasonal flood, coming between July and December—a natural phenomenon long unexplained, but recognized for 5000 years as the basis upon which cultivation and settlement depend.

Historical Outline

Such in brief is the physical background of the country whose history recorded in substantial monuments from the past is longer and less interrupted than that of any other land. Although some writers distinguish Upper, Middle and Lower Egypt, the time-honored division is Upper Egypt—broadly speaking the Nile Valley above Cairo —and Lower Egypt, the Delta below Cairo.

It was Menes, the founder of the First Dynasty, who united Upper and Lower Egypt, and from that time to the present day, between six and seven thousand years, Egypt has remained a unit and under a single government, except for very brief periods. Although this unity may be explained by saying that Egypt is an oasis naturally isolated by sea and desert, it remains a remarkable fact. It is true that where irrigation has to be planned and executed in terms of the country as a whole, unified control is essential. It may also be said that once the foreign invader has braved the sea and the desert and reached the fertile oasis his task of conquest is easy, and no natural barrier remains to prevent his hold over the whole.

The oasis-island which is thus Egypt has had another and most interesting effect upon its people. Though there are some slight differences between the people of the Delta with somewhat lighter skins than the people of Upper Egypt there is an essential unity throughout Egyptians in both their physical and mental characteristics. If one can judge from the representations of their ancestors in the days of the Pharaohs they have remained physically the same for thousands of years.

Through all the thousands of years of their history the Egyptian

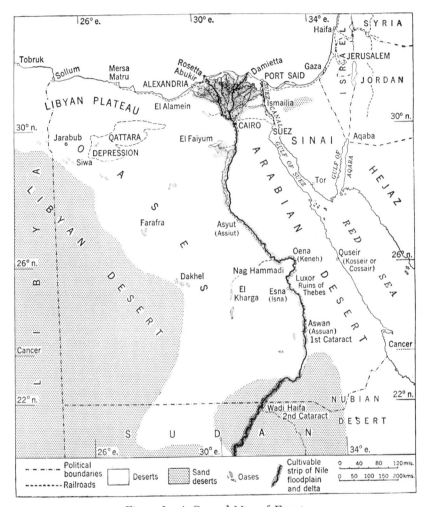

Figure 2. A General Map of Egypt.

people have enjoyed, or perhaps one may say have suffered from, an essentially autocratic and highly centralized government. In Dynastic Egypt the Pharaohs were absolute rulers with a few carefully selected and autocratically appointed ministers. Their rule was absolute throughout the country. There was no tradition of local autonomy, no hereditary feudal aristocracy so general in other lands. It may be said that Egypt has known bureaucracy from its earliest days. The rank and file of the Egyptian people, the peasants, or fellaheen, of today have thus always been subject to a strict, sometimes harsh and oppressive, government. The effect of this has been clearly assessed by Professor Charles Issawi in his interesting book, *Egypt: An Economic and Social Analysis.* He suggests that ". . . the result has been greatly to weaken individualistic feeling and completely to uproot the spirit of municipal enterprise. Several millennia of centralized autocracy have accustomed the Egyptians to look to the government for the initiation of any business whatsoever. At the same time the rapacity of the governors has led to a proven distrust of the government, the effects of which are still unfortunately too visible. In addition to political oppression Egypt has always suffered from intense economic exploitation." He goes on to instance the enormous amount of human labor which must have gone into the erection of the Pyramids and how at intervals even the long-suffering Egyptians attempted to unite in popular revolts.

The autocratic centralized government of Egypt has always, it may be said, been superimposed, and throughout practically the whole of its history the Egyptian people has been under foreign domination. In Dynastic Egypt there was the invasion and the control of the country by the Hyksos or Shepherd Kings from the heart of Arabia. Even if the Pharaohs of ancient Egypt are to be regarded as assimilating themselves with the people of the country which they ruled, and in that sense may be regarded as Egyptians, they often chose foreign advisers to carry out their designs. The favorite Old Testament story of Joseph is a most interesting example. Because it was reported that Joseph, languishing in prison, was an able interpreter of dreams, the Pharaoh of the day had him brought forth, and because his interpretations of Pharaoh's dreams appeared authentic and carried conviction he was immediately made second only to Pharaoh himself in control of the whole country.

Complete outside control of Egypt definitely came into existence with the Persian conquest in 525 B.C. The Persians in due course were ousted in 332 B.C. by the Macedonians under Alexander the Great, and in 30 B.C. the Romans took the place of the Macedonians. The varied interpretations which have been given to the story of Cleopatra, from Shakespeare to George Bernard Shaw, may serve to illustrate the relationship between Roman governors and Egyptian leaders. As the Roman Empire faded and Byzantium took its place,

Egypt was left open to conquest by the Arabs, and to its lasting incorporation in the Moslem world. The Arabs acquired the country in A.D. 642 and controlled Egypt for two centuries, always from outside the country, from Medina, from Damascus and from Baghdad. In A.D. 868 the first Turkish dynasty was established. Almost exactly a century later the Moslem Fatimite king—this time from the west—

Figure 3. The Nile Valley in Upper Egypt at Thebes, Luxor. The air view shows very clearly the rocky wall of the Nile valley and the desert which lies beyond. It is clearly impossible to extend the irrigated land shown in the foreground. (Copyright Aerofilms Limited.)

overran the country, but it was a Kurdish successor to the Fatimites who saved Egypt from the Crusaders. Although the country was conquered again by the Turks in 1516, Egyptian rulers preserved their identity and acknowledged in a somewhat perfunctory way the nominal authority of the Sultan of Turkey.

When Napoleon I turned his attention to Egypt and the French Expedition of 1798 reached the country, Egypt was a poor, isolated and neglected backwater of the Ottoman Empire. Its once prosperous trade centered on the ancient port of Alexandria had been ruined by the diversion of world trade routes from the Mediterranean to the Atlantic after the discovery and development of the Americas. Although the conquest of Egypt by Napoleon Bonaparte was itself ephemeral, it was the beginning of a new era in Egyptian development. It marked the return of Egypt into the sphere of European commerce and laid the foundation for the future role of Egypt in the life of the world around the Mediterranean Sea.

Napoleon was less interested in the internal development of Egypt and the restoration of the age-old agriculture of the country than he was in the possibilities of developing Egypt on a colonial model, its destiny being to supply such tropical products as cotton and cane sugar which could not be produced in the homelands of France herself, but which were of enormous importance in the Napoleonic French World Empire. The seeds were sown and when, a few years later, the national dynasty under Mohammed Ali became established, Egypt herself went ahead, and more and more the economic prosperity of the country became linked with the expansion of cotton cultivation, the development of the Delta, and commerce with Europe. Although Egypt remained nominally a part of the Ottoman Empire, the influences of the Sultan at Constantinople became less and less. Mohammed Ali himself, following the autocratic procedure of his innumerable predecessors, attempted to create an industrialized, closed and state-controlled economy, and to expand Egypt so as to include part of the remains of the Ottoman Empire.

But in the meantime European powers had come to have other interests in Egypt, and Mohammed Ali's plan was defeated by those European powers in 1841. This is another key date in Egyptian history.

It was a design of Napoleon Bonaparte who first, if he did not originate, brought to the fore a concept for a canal through the Isthmus of Suez to link the Mediterranean Sea with the Red Sea and thus to provide a seaway from Europe to India and the Far East. As British interests in India expanded and were consolidated it was naturally they who would appear to have had the main interest in such a project. Actually British personnel of the great East India Company passing to and from Britain and India were taken by ship to Egypt, to the old port of Alexandria. They traveled by river boat up the Nile to a point above Cairo, where they transferred to desert caravans for the land passage across to the shores of the Red Sea, there to embark on the second sea stage of the journey to their Indian destinations. The ships of the old Peninsular and Oriental Steam Navigation Company (P. and O.) provided the means, and when any such route, however tedious and inconvenient, has become established vested interests are unwilling to see such a radical change as would result from the construction of a canal and a through route. We deal below with the story of the Suez Canal, but, although the British even more than the French had become concerned with the destiny of the project, so essential to the development of easy communication from the Home Country to India and the Far East, the British Government officially opposed the scheme!

In 1870 came the defeat of France by the Prussians, only one year after the opening of the Suez Canal. Britain's interest in Egypt immediately became a positive one, the desire—indeed the need—to secure effective control if not over Egypt herself at least over Egypt as part of the vital sea route to the east. The opportunity came when the Egyptian ruler asked for Britain's help in quelling a revolt and restoring order.

From 1882 to 1914, although remaining nominally a vassal of the Turkish Empire, Egypt became in effect a British Protectorate. British troops were stationed in the country to maintain order and in particular to guard the Suez Canal. With the outbreak of the First World War in 1914 Turkey allied herself with Germany and thus became ranged on the side of Britain's enemies. Consequently Egypt was declared on December 18, 1914, a British Protectorate. This was a wartime expedient, and the Protectorate came to an end on February 28, 1922, when the Sultan of Egypt became hereditary ruler and was proclaimed king on the fifteenth of March. Since that date Egypt has been an independent kingdom, and steadily the evidences of independence have become more and more marked. Extra-territorial privileges enjoyed by European powers were abolished in 1937. Later, after the conclusion of the Second World War, when Egypt so nearly became a victim of German invasion, British troops were withdrawn from Egypt. They left the quarters which they had so long occupied in Cairo, a small number remaining for guard duties along the Suez Canal.

Thus with the proclamation of the late King Fuad I as king in 1922 the dynasty established by Mohammed Ali became the recognized ruling house of Egypt, and the declaration of 1922 established the succession of kings in the direct male line by primogeniture, after the European model. A constitution was introduced in 1923, and, although suspended from 1935 onwards, it was reintroduced in 1945. In 1952 a military group, focusing widespread discontent, forced the abdication of Fuad's successor, and though for a year his infant son was nominally accepted as King, in 1953 a Republic was proclaimed with a military leader as President. A treaty of 1936 defined relationships with Britain and recognized Britain's right to station troops to guard the Suez Canal. This treaty Egypt declared to be at an end in 1951.

The Population Problem of Egypt

Few populations are as homogeneous throughout as the people of Egypt. The fundamental element is constituted by the fellaheen, or peasants, which form some 82 per cent of the total. From earliest times they have kept their Hamitic type almost pure. Moderately tall, slightly built, with long limbs and broad shoulders, and a pronounced nose, they are very strongly contrasted with their Negro neighbors to the south. Although there has undoubtedly been some mixture with the Arabs of the north and the Negroes of the south, this seems to have exercised but little influence on physical type, and still less on manners and customs. The habitation of the fellaheen is still built as it was in the time of the Pharaohs of dried mud over a framework, a house often without any opening save the door, and the sole furniture of which is a chest for clothes, a low table and a few cushions and mats. There is an advantage in the absence of other openings, for the smoke which accumulates within acts as a deterrent to the eternal plague of mosquitoes.

The fellaheen were converted to Mohammedanism, and consequently Egypt is a keystone in the great Moslem world. Next in importance is that element of the population represented by the Coptic Christians, descendants of those ancient Egyptians who adopted Christianity in the fourth century, and whose head is the Coptic Patriarch of Alexandria. They are grouped especially in Middle Egypt, around Assiut (Asyut), which is sometimes called the Coptic Capital, and in the Faiyum. Unlike the fellaheen, who are almost exclusively farmers and who remain essentially dwellers in the country, the Copts have tended to drift into towns and become artisans, traders, merchants and money lenders. Until recent times they often lived in walled and guarded enclosures, as in Cairo.

These are the two essential elements in the indigenous population. There are besides half a million mixed Bedouin Arabs in the deserts of Lower Egypt, and pure Bedouins in the Nubian Desert.

The population of Egyptian towns is much more mixed. There may be found by the side of indigenous Egyptians, Arabs, Nubians, Turks, Greeks, Syrians, Armenians and Jews, and especially that mixture of races so typical of the ports and bazaars of the eastern Mediterranean, commonly called Levantine. To this total it is necessary to add 100,000 French, English, Belgians, Italians and other Euro-peans.

In common with other countries of the Mediterranean the popula-tion of Egypt has shown a remarkable rise in the last century and a half. The French mission of Napoleon Bonaparte estimated the num-ber in the whole country rather under 2½ million people. In 1821

Figure 4. Inside a Modern Egyptian Cotton Mill at Mehala el Kobra. One of the industrial developments of Egypt. (Copyright Deane Dickason from Ewing Galloway.)

Mohammed Ali found a little over this figure—2,536,000. Under the wise agricultural policy for which he was largely responsible, the population grew rapidly. Incidentally Egypt is the only African country for which adequate and accurate population statistics exist over a considerable period. In 1846 the population had reached nearly 4½ million, in 1882 nearly 7 million; by 1927 this had doubled to 14¼ million. In 1937 the census gave a total of no less than 15,932,694; and ten years later, when the census was taken on March 26–27, 1947, the staggering figure of 19,087,304 was recorded, equiva-lent to a population density of 1398 on what is described as the settled land surface of 13,496 square miles. Although Egypt exhibits the world-wide tendency towards urbanization, there are still only two large towns—Cairo, which exceeds 2 million according to the census of 1947, and Alexandria, which had not quite reached the million in 1947. The modern port of Port Said at the entrance to the Suez Canal approached 200,000, the older port at its southern end, Suez, only a little over 100,000. Figures for other urban centers will be found in the Appendix.

The rapid population increase combined with the already extremely high density on the cultivable land gives Egypt a population problem which seems well-nigh insoluble. Along the margins of the valley and delta, by lifting the water higher, the area of the irrigated land may be extended a small amount, and there are some areas where the old basin irrigation may be replaced by the more efficient perennial irrigation, but any increase in food output which might result' would not match the needs. Moreover, in contrast to other parts of Africa, crop yields are already very high, and from the point of view of yield per acre Egyptian farming is already so efficient that there is little hope of an adequate solution in this direction. The Egyptians look to increasing industrialization as their main hope. Much money has been spent on the development of various textile factories—cotton, wool, rayon and silk—and manufactures include also glassware, soap, fertilizers, leather, metal working, pottery, sugar, cigarettes and alcoholic beverages. How far these developments will go towards supporting a surplus population running into millions is another matter.

The Regions of Egypt

For a consideration of the country as a whole, we may regard Egypt as divided into: the Western Deserts (Libyan Desert); the Eastern Deserts (Arabian and Nubian Deserts); the Nile Valley, or Upper Egypt; the Nile Delta, or Lower Egypt; the Faiyum. The two great desert tracts represent 97 per cent of the surface of the country but have less than 2 per cent of the population.

THE WESTERN DESERTS (LIBYAN DESERT). The plateaus which make up the greater part of the surface of the country consist in the extreme south of the ancient metamorphic rocks and granites of the great African Massif. These are covered as we proceed northward by gently inclined sheets of sediment, giving rise, as a result of weathering, to great flat-topped, table-like hills or mesas. The sedimentary rocks dip gently northward but at a slightly higher angle than the surface of the country, so that geologically the beds become younger and younger as one goes towards the Mediterranean. North of the southern outcrops of ancient rocks are found the wide stretches of Nubian sandstone, then northward wide expanses of limestone. This explains the essential structure of the Libyan Desert to the west of the Nile Valley. In the south the surface is covered with superficial deposits of sand. It is one of the least habitable parts of the whole Sahara, avoided by nomads and caravans alike, no oasis relieving its arid surface, no settlement of significance existing.

The northern portion of the Libyan Desert formed by the lower plateau surfaces of limestone is relatively more habitable. A long line of oases, shown in Fig. 2, occupies the depressions over a distance of 600 miles. There are numerous salt lakes, but in places wells reach fresh water. Where this is the case the oases can support populations which run into thousands. The oasis of Dakhel, for example, has at least 15,000 people and a permanent capital town with as many as four mosques. Between the actual oases several nomadic tribes contrive to find sufficient pasture for their camels and provide means of transport for the oasis inhabitants. It is one of the great features of life in the Mohammedan world that the pilgrimage to Mecca demands movement, and even these remote oases supply their quota of pilgrims for the sacred journey. Catering for pilgrims is one of the great occupations throughout the Mohammedan world. Thus these oases of the northern Libyan Desert are linked by a regular and frequented route, leading particularly to the capital.

THE EASTERN DESERTS (ARABIAN AND NUBIAN DESERTS). To the east of the Nile, to which is naturally attached the Sinai Peninsula, the desert tract between the Nile and the sea is relatively narrow, but its surface is much more varied, and the country has in places considerable natural resources. The mountain belt, largely of volcanic origin, which borders the shore of the Red Sea, is continued along both sides of the trough or rift valley of the narrow Gulf of Suez, and so into the southern part of the Sinai Peninsula. As any voyager by steamer down the Gulf of Suez is able to recognize, the arid shore is far from hospitable. Actual access to the shore is rendered dangerous by coral reefs so that there is no port between Suez, the southern end of the Suez Canal, and the little harbor of Quseir or Cossair. Here and there in little basins amid the rugged sandstone or basalt mountains are little agricultural villages; and along the south there is an inhabited trench, the depression of Keneh, lying between the volcanic belt and the true Arabian Desert.

In the Peninsula of Sinai the desert plateau fades northeastwards into the Palestinian or Israeli desert, inhabited by a few nomadic pastoralists. In the southwestern parts of the peninsula, along the shores of the Gulf of Suez and the Red Sea, there are little cultivated basins among the rocky mountains and numerous fishing villages. The Peninsula of Sinai is indeed a land of transition. The east looks to and fades into Asiatic lands, the west looks towards and is dependent upon Egypt proper.

The eastern deserts of Egypt and the Peninsula of Sinai are not without economic significance. There are precious stones, notably the famous turquoise, some deposits of phosphate rock and nitrate and the small but significant oil fields which have long been worked along the western shores of the Gulf of Suez. To this must be added the big oil field discovered in 1949 south of Sud in the peninsula. There are salt deposits too, and it is from the mountains of the Arabian Desert that Egypt obtained and still obtains those magnificent building stones—porphyry, granite and sandstone—used in Egypt's famous monuments dating from the time of the Pharaohs.

THE NILE VALLEY OR UPPER EGYPT. This valley is the Khem (signifying "dark") of the Egyptians, a name which points the contrast with the white shimmering desert stretches on either side. The Nile enters Egypt just north of Wadi Halfa and the Second Cataract.

Looking from Egypt southward, we may regard this as the gateway from the land of Egypt and the country of the Egyptians to the land of what the French would call *Afrique noire*, the Africa of the Negroes. The gate-like character of this southern entry into Egypt is emphasized by the fact that it is the southern terminal of riverine navigation, possible throughout Egypt from the Delta, by-passing the First Cataract at Aswan by a canal. The fact that there is no river navigation through the northern part of the Anglo-Egyptian Sudan has given a special importance to Wadi Halfa, the first city of the Sudan, from which the railway runs to Khartoum, or to the Red Sea port of Port Sudan.

Upper Egypt consists of a succession of irrigated basins marked off from one another by those points where the two cliff-like walls of the river valley approach close to one another. Those who distinguish a Middle Egypt regard Upper Egypt as stretching as far northwards as the Thebes Basin. This basin, the ancient site of Thebes, was perhaps the richest of all the basins of the Nile Valley in ancient times, and it was around it that the Middle Empire developed. The incredible richness in ruins of temples and palaces of this part of the Nile Valley, at Thebes, at Karnak and at Luxor in particular, is lasting evidence of ancient glories. At the present day the ancient richness has been in large measure restored through perennial irrigation derived from the great storage dam at Aswan. This area, for example, has become the principal region of cultivation of the sugar cane and the site of the principal sugar factories, which have given new prosperity to modern Egypt.

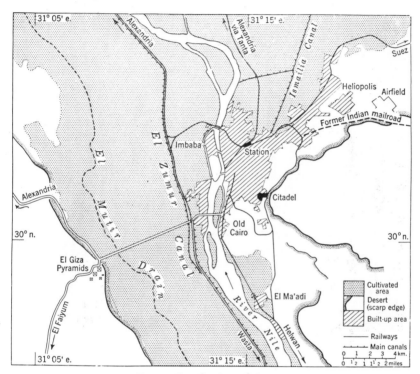

Figure 5. The Site of Cairo.

On the whole the valley widens northwards and is lined by a succession of towns and large villages, among which one may regard Asyut as the chief of this very rich region of Middle Egypt.

The Nile Valley stretches as far as Cairo. Curiously enough, Cairo has been the capital of Egypt only since 1863. Prior to that time it had a marked economic importance but was not to be compared in historical significance with the great cities of Upper Egypt. The fact that Cairo has become the heart of Egypt is due to the economic development of the Delta in the past century and a half. From the point of view of modern Egypt, Cairo is perhaps the most rationally situated capital in the world. Its ancient predecessor, Memphis, was on the western or left bank of the Nile, nestling under the low limestone cliff on which were built the great pyramids and the Sphinx. In contrast Cairo originated on the right or eastern bank of the river, on a projection of the desert plateau. There the Arab conquerer of Egypt, 'Amr, built a mosque on the site of the former

Figure 6. The Nile near Cairo. On the left are date palms along the bank. The picturesque Nile sailing boats (*dahabiyas*) carry a large proportion of the goods transported by the Nile waterway. (Copyright Ewing Galloway.)

Roman citadel. To the Arab town was added later the Turkish town, followed in due course by the Levantine town built by Mohammed Ali and his son. The modern cosmopolitan city of Cairo flowed from the foot of the hills, across the alluvial plain, to the Nile itself, and its suburbs have crossed over the river to the western side. But as every visitor to Cairo knows, along the road from Cairo to the pyramids one can still see the cultivation of the Nile alluvium in full swing.

THE NILE DELTA OR LOWER EGYPT. The area of the Delta is double that of the Nile Valley or Upper Egypt. If, therefore, the whole could be placed under cultivation it would play a prominent role in Egyptian economy. Whereas Upper Egypt, the Nile Valley, has a history of cultivation going back for thousands of years, the conquest of the Delta is the result of the comparatively modern activity of man, armed with the knowledge and the tools of science. For long the delta of the Nile was simply an immense triangle of sand, traversed by the seven branches of the river, two of them reasonably navigable, interrupted by long lagoons, or land periodically flooded or impregnated by salt. Ancient Egypt scarcely used any of the delta lands. The Delta in fact remained a desert barrier between Upper Egypt and those centers of commercial activity, the ports of Alexandria, Abukir, Rosetta and Damietta. The branches of the river were the commercial routes which linked the Mediterranean ports with Egypt proper. Today modern perennial irrigation has made the Delta the principal economic region of Egypt, where cotton reigns supreme. The population has become widely distributed and dense, but it is the land and not the sea which matters. Much of the delta coast itself is still deserted and cut off by a line of lagoons from the cultivated lands. So much of the Nile silt is trapped in the irrigation basins that the Delta is growing seawards very slowly.

For 2000 years Alexandria, founded by Alexander the Great, was a naval base against the Persians as well as an outlet for Egyptian commerce, and it remained for the succeeding 2000 years the largest city in Egypt. Like most ports associated with the world's great deltas it lies not on the Delta but to one side—in this case the western side—where it is free or relatively free from silting up, which would have resulted in the past from deposits of Nile alluvium. Thanks to the Island of Faros, the port enjoys shelter from Mediterranean storms and suffered an eclipse in fortune only when the Atlantic sea routes replaced the Mediterranean. Although it might be thought that the opening of the Suez Canal would have taken trade and traffic exclusively to Port Said, Alexandria has more than shared in the great redevelopment of Mediterranean commerce.

THE FAIYUM. Properly speaking, the Faiyum is a depression in the Libyan Desert comparable with those previously mentioned in which are found the oases. The only difference—but it is an essential one—rests in the fact that it lies below sea level, and by a connecting channel with the Nile Valley receives the vitalizing waters from the main river. Although this connecting channel is doubtless natural, it has been carefully remade and controlled by the hand of man. It is a large basin, over 500 square miles. Already in 1882 it had more than 200,000 inhabitants, and by 1927 the total had reached over half a million. The capital, Medinet el Faiyum, is a town of considerable size and is surrounded by numerous villages in which the inhabitants live by the exportation of fruits, baskets made from local oziers and pottery made from local clay. In addition to the ordinary crops cultivated throughout Egypt, the oasis of the Faiyum specializes in fruits such as oranges, lemons, grenadines, figs, apricots, nectarines, grapes, olives and the traditional grape. As a result of this fruit cultivation, the area has a delightfully wooded appearance, quite different from that of the open Nile Valley.

Irrigation and Agriculture

In its course through Egypt the Nile runs smoothly and evenly, usually nearer the eastern side of its valley. The river level falls slightly from January to May and June, when it reaches its lowest level. In July the water rises rapidly and continues to do so through August and September, reaching its highest point in Lower Egypt in the month of October, when it is normally $7\frac{1}{2}$ meters or about 25 feet above its low level of May–June. The level of the river then falls rapidly through November and December, more gradually through the succeeding months.

As in so many eastern countries water can be lifted from the river and equally from wells by the shadoof, which consists of a bucket, or bag of skin, suspended from the end of a long pole balanced by a counterweight. By the shadoof water is commonly and easily raised 7 to 10 feet or more, and a succession of lifts may raise water considerably higher. Another method of lifting water a short distance is the Archimedean screw, and the more elaborate types of lift operated by cattle or donkeys are also used. The traditional form of irrigation in Egypt, however, is basin irrigation. The waters of the river at the time of flood are led off into carefully constructed inundation or flood canals, from which the water passes into a basin where the flat field or fields are enclosed by low earth banks. These basins vary in size and may be anything up to 100,000 acres. The Nile waters at time of flood are rich in a reddish-gray silt, which is naturally deposited and left behind in the basins. Unbeknown to the ancient Egyptians, the slime or ooze to which Shakespeare refers is derived from far-away Ethiopia. It represents the results of natural geological as well as soil erosion from distant areas, and as much of the silt is derived from areas of basic volcanic rocks it is naturally rich in mineral salts.

The peasant sows his seed broadcast in the damp mud which is left when the waters are led off from one basin into the next. There follows for the cultivator a period of comparative rest until the harvest is ready. The corn which has been sown at the beginning of November is ripe by early February. Other plants sown a little later, or with a longer vegetative period, may not be ready until April cr May. This is the natural winter harvest, the so-called *chetoi*.

It happens naturally that the borders of the valley are too high to be covered by the river floods which inundate the basins. Water must be lifted to these higher fields by a shadoof, or a succession of shadoofs, or by other means. The water which is thus distributed is free from sediment, and it becomes necessary to fertilize the fields with such material brought to the spot as dung and organic debris from the villages. There is more work for the peasant, and he sows his seeds later; and the harvest, in this case known as the *nili*, is later.

The traditional crops of Upper Egypt, sufficient for feeding—and clothing—of a dense population, are cereals (wheat, barley, maize), cotton, vegetables (beans, peas, lentils, onions) and especially lucerne or bersim for cattle. Grapes and olives are perennial plants, likewise made possible by irrigation.

It will be seen that such a system of basin irrigation is dependent upon the height of the flood, which fortunately in the case of the Nile is remarkably constant, and also on a system of co-operation between landowners, which will permit the development of a system of basins. · It was Mohammed Ali in the early part of the nineteenth century, following doubtless upon the lead given by the members of the French Commission, who saw the possibilities of a system of permanent irrigation by canals. The French were not interested so much in extending the existing production of traditional Egyptian crops as they were interested in securing from Egypt those products of warm climates which Europe needed, notably cane sugar and cotton. The concept of Mohammed Ali was that every peasant should have enough land to support himself and his family, which he calculated to be between a hectare and a hectare and a half, or $2\frac{1}{2}$ to 4 acres. Two factors made the materialization of such a partition of the land impossible. In the first place the Islamic law ordains that property shall be divided equally between all the heirs, and hence the subdivision of land. On the other hand, large-scale perennial irrigation is only possible under some unified system either of land ownership or land control. The question is so important that careful statistics are kept of land ownership.

Extent of Holdings in Feddans	Total Area		Landowners	
	Feddans	Percentage	Number	Percentage
Less than 1	818,524	13.7	1,980,098	72.8
1 to 5	1,237,359	20.8	584,987	21.5
5 to 10	529,642	8.9	79,483	2.9
10 to 20	576,994	9.7	42,699	1.6
20 to 30	296,319	4.9	12,309	0.5
30 to 50	351,496	5.9	9,149	0.3
Over 50	2,127,883	36.1	11,960	0.4
Total	5,938,217	100.0	2,720,685	100.0

One feddan = 1.038 acre. Data for December 31, 1948. Out of the total 4562 landowners were "foreigners" holding 335,014 feddans or 5 per cent of the whole.

From this table we see that nearly 95 per cent of Egyptian land-owners are small holders with less than 5 acres of land, but they hold between them less than 35 per cent of the cultivated land surface. By contrast there are fewer than 2000 landowners who hold over 50 acres, but these larger proprietors own over one-third of the whole land surface. Late in 1952 long-promised reforms were put in hand.

The modern system of canal irrigation may be regarded as having begun with the construction of small dams at the head of the Delta from 1861 onwards, to be replaced in 1890 by the great dam of Boulaq and later by the Mohammed Ali barrages. The barrage of Zifta was added to this system in 1901, and the year 1902 marked the completion in Upper Egypt of the great Asyut dam, followed in 1909 by the dam at Esna (Isna) and still later, in 1930, by the dam at Nag Hammadi 150 miles above Asyut.

Although these various dams both increased the area of cultivable land during flood water and assured more abundant harvests, what was needed to provide water during the long dry period when the level was low was a reservoir along the southern border of Egypt. It was for this purpose that the great dam at Aswan was constructed. Completed in 1903 at an original cost of $15,000,000, it was successively enlarged in 1907, 1912 and 1933. Whereas the old basin irrigation utilized the flood season so that both water and silt were spread over the land, the water is allowed in the Aswan reservoir in the latter part of November when the water is almost free from silt. The water is used in the summer and makes a second harvest of tropical products possible.

Thus the old peasant irrigation is now responsible for less than one-fifth of the land actually irrigated, permanent canal irrigation for the remaining four-fifths. Permanent irrigation has made possible an extension both of the crops possible and the harvest season. In particular, even in the Delta where the soil is slightly salt, there are large rice fields. In the neighborhood of the towns market gardening is extensively practiced, often by Greeks and Italians rather than by Egyptians, for the production of vegetables—artichokes, tomatoes, onions, etc. The great system of permanent irrigation has of course rendered necessary strict control by a large Government Department, the Water Supply Department. The principal food crops now cultivated in Egypt are corn (maize) and wheat, followed by rice, barley, beans, lentils and millet, with extensive areas under sugar cane and numerous vegetables.

An interesting study of irrigation and land use in Upper Egypt has been made by Douglas D. Crary (*Geographical Review*, XXXVII, October 1949). He gives a map to show the extreme fragmentation of the land in a particular basin (that of Zeiniya-Bahari watered from the Isna barrage), and notes that the age-old methods of sowing seed broadcast by hand and then turning them into the soft mud by dragging with a piece of wood are still followed. This is especially the case with the first crops sown in the mud left by the receding waters, which are the forage crops, particularly white clover (bersim) and flat peas (gilban) and fenugreek (hilba). Land from which the water has been drained off after 10 or 15 days is firm enough to support animals, so that it is plowed before the sowing of the food crops, wheat, barley, cow peas and lentils with small quantities of safflower (for orange dye from the flowers and oil from the seeds). It should be noticed that crop rotation between cereals and leguminous crops is practiced.

Since animals are taken to the source of feed rather than the feed carried to the animals, the land also benefits from natural manuring. This may even result in a form of transhumance, and the use of temporary housing units, known as ezbah.

As a result of this intensive hand cultivation acre yields in Egypt are very high, and the country affords an excellent example of efficient peasant agriculture.

Egypt's Economy and Commerce

In Upper Egypt practically the whole production from the irrigated lands is needed for the feeding of the people. Improved supplies of irrigation water, better agricultural techniques and a knowledge of fertilizers have resulted in increased output, but this has been more than balanced by increase in population. It is the development of the delta lands over the last 100 years which has made possible the production for export of those agricultural commodities on which Egypt depends for foreign currency. Even the greatly increased output of cane sugar has been consumed within the country itself. So too has the increased output of corn and to an increasing extent that of rice. More than 80 per cent of the total exports are normally represented by cotton, produced in the Delta and exported through the great port of Alexandria. From an acreage of just under a million in 1945 it climbed to a post-war peak of 2,000,000 in 1950 or a third of all the cultivated land of Egypt.

Two main types of cotton are grown, the long staple and the medium staple. For a long time the famous long-staple cotton with a silky luster (1½ inches staple) known as *sakellarides,* usually contracted to *sakel,* was recognized as being second in quality only to the famous Sea Island cotton of the West Indies. From 1935 onwards a new and heavier yielding variety perfected at the experimental station at Giza, opposite Cairo, and consequently known as *Giza 7,* surpassed *sakel* both in acreage and yield. Other long-staple cottons have been produced and the possibilities are by no means exhausted. The shorter-staple cotton, *cashmuni,* though of good quality, is not up to the standard of *sakel.* It is grown to some extent in Upper Egypt. A remarkable feature of cotton production in Egypt is the very high yield per acre. The average between 400 and 500 pounds of ginned cotton per acre is still about double that of the average American figure, despite recent improvements, and more than five times that of the yield common in India.

Though spinning and weaving mills have been developed in Lower Egypt, notably in the Delta at Mehala el Kobra, the bulk of the crop is exported as cotton particularly to the United Kingdom, India and the cotton-consuming industrial countries of continental Europe such as France and Italy.

It was the American Civil War which, by cutting off supplies to Europe, especially to Britain, was mainly responsible for the rapid development of the Egyptian cotton cultivation and export.

The varied range of imports into Egypt reflect the demands of a country with a high and growing standard of living for the manufactured products of Europe and America.

Communications

Naturally the Nile, in addition to its function in supplying irrigation water, has from time immemorial been the main highway of the country. Shallow draft steamers ply regularly as far as Aswan (the First Cataract), where connection is made with various services offered by the Sudanese Government southwards. Many thousands of sailing vessels ply on the Nile and the waterways of the Delta. The Egyptian State Railways focusing on Cairo comprise some 3000 miles of standard gauge line, contrasting with the usual 3 ft. 6-inch gauge of Africa south of the equator. Lines run south through the whole length of the country to Shellal just above Aswan, the terminus of the Sudanese steamers; they run north to Alexandria, to Ismailia, near where they connect by a swing bridge across the Suez Canal with through lines via Israel, Lebanon and Turkey to the Bosphorus, and thus link Egypt directly by rail with the European network. The main Egyptian line continues along the west bank of the Suez Canal to Port Said. There is also a direct line from Suez to Cairo. In addition to standard gauge lines there is a considerable mileage of narrow gauge lines serving the agricultural regions of the Delta.

The focal position of Cairo has been enormously emphasized since the development of international air transport. On high ground east of the city is the fashionable and wealthy suburb of Heliopolis, and near by the main airfield, which is one of the main air junctions of the world, with regular services to the chief capitals of Europe several times daily, services through East Africa to the south, services east to Iraq, Iran, India, the Far East and Australia at frequent intervals. It would be surprising if Egypt had failed to respond to the development of modern motor transport. Magnificent motor roads connect Cairo with Alexandria, with Port Said and with Suez, so that each of these points may be reached in the minimum of time from the capital.

The Suez Canal

So long as the world's commerce was focused on the countries around the Mediterranean Sea between Europe on the north, Asia on the east and Africa on the south the existence of the Isthmus of Suez was mainly of importance as providing part of the land route between Egypt and its Asiatic neighbors, or from farther afield between the extremes of the Arab domains of the Middle Ages and the Turkish Empire which succeeded it. With the extension of Euro-

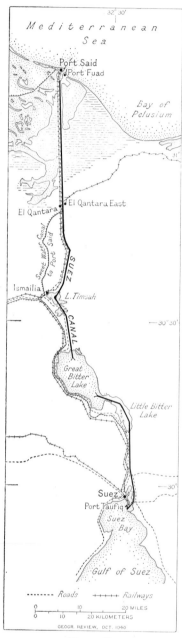

Figure 7.
The Suez Canal.

pean interest in India and the Far East, the Isthmus became a barrier, interrupting the natural line of sea communication from the Atlantic seaboard and the Mediterranean to the Red Sea and the Indian Ocean. A glance at the map shows that the Gulf of Suez and equally the Gulf of Aqaba (Akabar) on the other side of the Sinai Peninsula are continuations of the system of rift valleys so marked throughout East Africa. From the head of the Gulf of Suez to the Mediterranean sea coast is less than 70 miles in a straight line. The land between is flat—at most only a few feet above sea level and in part occupied by shallow salt lakes, the so-called Bitter Lakes. It is not always realized that the Suez Canal as we know it today was not the first waterway to unite the Mediterranean with the Red Sea. The earlier idea of course was to link the heart of Egypt with the Red Sea at a time when the largest ships then in use were shallow-built, using the lower branches of the Nile. Consequently a canal was constructed—a fresh-water canal, known as the Canal of the Pharaohs—leaving the Nile in the neighborhood of Heliopolis, following a course due east to the neighborhood of the modern Ismailia, whence it passed southwards to the Gulf of Suez near the present site of the town of Suez. In the days of

(From H. L. Hoskins, Geog. Rev. 1940. Courtesy of the Geographical Review, American Geographical Society.)

the later Roman Empire, it fell into disuse, but was resuscitated in the days of the Arab domination, since the Arabs always had the great idea of trading between the Mediterranean and the East. The Ottoman Turks, seeking always to preserve the isolation of the Moslem world and to interrupt any means of communication between Christians and Moslems, abandoned the canal. With the discovery of the Cape route to India the former canal seems to have been completely forgotten.

When France at the beginning of the sixteenth century took the initiative for eastern development and exploration, and when Richelieu founded the *Compagnie générale du commerce,* the idea of a canal came under consideration. The idea remained, however, one of a route from Alexandria, using the Nile, and thence from the neighborhood of Cairo to the Red Sea. It was the struggle between the French and the British in the time of Napoleon Bonaparte which gave birth to the idea of a direct canal from the Mediterranean to the Red Sea in order to enable the French to wage war against England in Indian waters. Mohammed Ali, as in so many other things, took up the idea left him by Napoleon Bonaparte, and it is recorded that he referred to making "a Strait of Bosphorus in the Desert of Suez."

After the idea had been discussed for some 50 years it was the Frenchman, Ferdinand de Lesseps, who brought the plan to realization, securing the approval of Napoleon III and the support both of the Turkish Sultan and of the Egyptian ruler, Mohammed Saïd, successor to Mohammed Ali. Britain under Prime Minister Palmerston opposed the whole scheme. But the *Compagnie Internationale Maritime de Suez* was formed, with a capital of 200 million francs.

The Canal was constructed rapidly from 1860–1869, and on November 18, 1869, a flotilla of 68 ships carrying the Empress Eugénie of France, the Emperor Francis Joseph of Austria, the Khedive of Egypt and many other dignitaries passed through the Canal and inaugurated it, after it had received both a Christian and a Moslem blessing. It is interesting that the British themselves played no part, other than one of opposition, in a project afterwards of greater importance to them than to any other country. The original shareholders in the Suez Canal Company included the Khedive of Egypt. Knowing that the Khedive was particularly hard up for funds and anxious to dispose of his holding, the British Premier, Disraeli—afterwards Lord Beaconsfield—in 1875 made an instantaneous and personal decision to acquire the Turkish holding on behalf of the

British Government. He borrowed $20,000,000 in the name of the Cabinet and presented the British Parliament with what was virtually a *fait accompli.* Had it not been for this bold stroke of an individual, the opportunity would doubtless have been lost by which the British Government holds 295,026 shares out of a total issued of 652,932, and has three representatives on the governing board of 32. The concession granted to the Suez Canal Company was for 99 years from the date of inauguration; hence it expires on November 17, 1968.

The Canal runs straight through Egyptian territory. It is 103 miles long, including 4 miles of approach channels for the harbors, which have been added since its original construction. In the early days there was no traffic by night, and vessels had to tie up until daylight and could pass only in certain places. As improved by 1950, the Canal had a depth of 34 feet and had cost about 90 million dollars (30 million pounds) to construct. By the Convention of Constantinople of 1888 it is open to the vessels of all nations and is free from blockade. By agreements made in 1949 Egyptian representation on the Board of Governors was increased from 2 to 7, and the Company agreed with the Egyptian Government to make numerous improvements.

At the northern end of the Canal, on the western side, stands Port Said. It is built on a low sandy island between a vast lagoon and the Mediterranean Sea. Facing Port Said on the eastern entrance to the Canal is Port Fuad, but the population and the development remain concentrated in Port Said. The majority of vessels passing through the Canal halt at Port Said for Canal formalities, for oiling or coaling, or perhaps for revictualing, and Port Said has grown into one of those curious international refuges of mankind, associated only with the great seaways of the world. Luxury hotels, bazaars and shops, operated by members of almost every nation, are likely to be just as active in the middle of the night as during any of the daylight hours. From Port Said is the railway to Cairo, which at first parallels the Canal as far as Ismailia. It was during the Second World War that a steel swing bridge was built at Kantara across the Canal and made through running possible from Uskudar (or Haida Pashar) opposite Istanbul to Tobruk in Libya.

South of Ismailia the Canal passes through the great Bitter Lakes, through a deepened channel marked out by buoys and where there is no longer any need for the speed restriction imposed in the Canal.

At the southern end of the Canal is the Port of Suez, again linked by road and rail with Cairo.

In the period between the two world wars nearly 5000 steamers a year, with a net tonnage of some 30 millions, passed through the Canal in a year. More than half of them were British, followed in order by Italian, German, Dutch, French, Norwegian and Japanese. In the years which followed the Second World War tonnage passing through the Canal had doubled, taking merchant shipping alone. Although British ships easily outnumbered all others, and the tonnage represented one-third of the whole, vessels under the United States flag took second place, with a tonnage approaching one-half that of the British. In addition government vessels, warships and transports also passed through the Canal in great numbers. It is obviously unnecessary to stress any further the enormous strategic as well as commercial importance of the Suez Canal.

The Canal has the great advantage that there are no locks; it is open to the sea at both ends.

The River Nile

So far we have considered only the course of the River Nile as it passes through Egypt. From time immemorial, as the life of Egypt depended upon the annual flooding of the Nile, the behavior of its waters was carefully studied. The Nile in Egypt affords us the earliest known examples of river gauging. The annual flooding was accepted perforce as the gift of the gods. It was not indeed until the nineteenth century was far advanced that this water regime came to be understood and the source of the Nile itself discovered. With a total length of 4060 miles, the Nile is one of the world's greatest rivers. It ranks second in length only to the Missouri-Mississippi (4500) unless the Amazon can be found to be slightly longer than the 4000 miles commonly claimed. The basin of the Nile falls naturally into some seven major divisions.

THE LAKE PLATEAU. The Nile has several sources rather than one, but the farthest headstream may be regarded as the Kagera, which rises in the highlands of Urundi over 4000 miles from the Mediterranean, and flows into Lake Victoria. Lake Victoria is a huge though shallow lake. There is little variation in its level. Though it lies in the equatorial region of well-distributed rainfall, there is a great loss of water by evaporation. The Nile flows out of Lake Victoria at Jinja over the Ripon Falls, followed at a short distance by the Owen Falls, site of a large dam and power station. Known as the Victoria Nile it traverses Lake Kioga and then over the magnificent Murchison Falls before entering the northern end of Lake Albert.

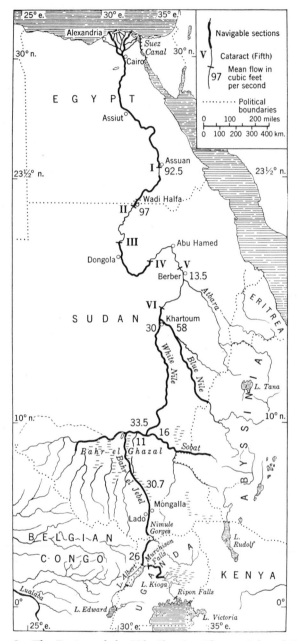

Figure 8.   The Regime of the Nile Showing Flow at Selected Points.

The waters which drain into Lake Albert form another source of Nile water, and, unlike Lake Victoria, Lake Albert is a deep narrow lake, with precipitous, mountainous sides. At its lower end it receives the Victoria Nile before the united waters pass on northwards as the Albert Nile. The great mid-twentieth-century plan for the regulation of the whole Nile basin envisaged the construction of a dam at Jinja which would raise the waters of Lake Victoria by about four feet, and would constitute immeasurably the largest storage reservoir in the world. A second dam to increase the storage capacity of Lake Albert would thus maintain an enormous reservoir of water to serve the whole basin.

THE BASIN OF THE BAHR-EL-JEBEL. This is a huge, almost level expanse of land lying some 1200 to 1500 feet above sea level through the center of which flows the main stream of the Nile, here called the White Nile, or Bahr-el-Jebel. The extreme flatness of the basin results in enormous areas becoming inundated during and after the rainy season, promoting the growth of enormous quantities of swampy vegetation known as sudd. The sudd is

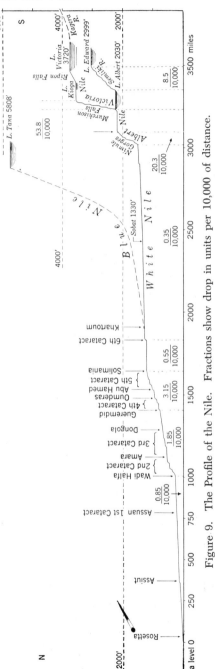

Figure 9. The Profile of the Nile. Fractions show drop in units per 10,000 of distance.

very likely completely to choke the main stream and to cause difficulties to navigation. Much more serious is the huge loss of water by evaporation from this great basin, with the result that the White Nile leaves the basin unenriched by the rainfall over this huge area, and possibly with a smaller volume of water than that which passed into it 500 miles farther south. Part of the scheme, therefore, for the regulation of the Nile is the cutting of a straightened channel through this basin and its maintenance as an open waterway.

Actually numerous streams, especially from the southwest (from the Sudan-Congo border), drain into this basin and join up to form the Bahr-el-Gazel, joining the Nile at Lake No. Other streams drain from the Ethiopian mountains to the southeast, collecting together as the Sobat which joins the White Nile a short distance above Malakal. The Sobat is a more important source of water than the left bank tributaries.

THE WHITE NILE VALLEY FROM MALAKAL TO KHARTOUM. Here the White Nile passes through the increasingly arid region of the central Sudan. Throughout the whole of this stretch it receives no tributary of importance.

THE BLUE NILE BASIN. The Blue Nile drains from the lofty snow-capped mountains of Ethiopia north-northwestwards, to join the White Nile at Khartoum. Whereas the White Nile at Khartoum is a river of almost constant volume, it is the Blue Nile which, receiving the monsoon rains as well as the melting snow from Ethiopia, contributes that volume of water in the high water season which is later responsible for the Nile floods in Egypt. The Blue Nile has in the heart of the Ethiopian mountains a natural reservoir in Lake Tana. Quite obviously the agreement of the Ethiopian Government is an essential part of a comprehensive regulation of Nile waters, yet there is little reason why Ethiopians should have any interest in what happens after the Nile leaves their territory. On the Blue Nile at Sennar has been constructed the magnificent dam which has made possible the irrigation of the Gezira (see "Sudan," Chapter 14).

THE DESERT CATARACT COURSE. Below Khartoum the united Nile flows at first northwards until it reaches the Sixth and highest Cataract and, after receiving the important but seasonal Atbara, commences the succession of descents to its lower levels over the Fifth, Fourth, Third, Second and First Cataracts, each of which marks the outcrop of resistant granitic rocks of the ancient African complex. This desert course of the Nile serves mainly to transport the life-giving water from Khartoum to the Egyptian border. The land on either side, for reasons which will be discussed at length in Chapter 14, is unsuitable for extensive irrigation, and so the water reaches the Egyptian border.

THE NILE IN UPPER EGYPT. Since this course of the Nile has already been described, no further comment is necessary, except to emphasize the utter dependence of Egypt on the waters received from Ethiopia even more than on the waters received from the Sudan and the plateau of East Africa. During the low-water season 80 per cent of the water is derived from the White Nile, but during the flood season only 14 per cent leaving 70 per cent at that season to come from the Blue Nile, 16 per cent from the Atbara.

THE DELTA COURSE. The map given above (Fig. 1) illustrates the existing and projected control points for the Nile waters. It emphasizes the discussion in Chapter 3 which suggested that the essential division of Africa for purposes of development must be on a basis of river basins. Unity of purpose within the whole Nile basin among all the peoples concerned is obviously a *sine qua non* for future African development and peace.

BIBLIOGRAPHY

H. E. Hurst and O. Phillips, *The Nile Basin*, Vol. 1, Cairo, 1931.
J. Ball, *Contributions to the Geography of Egypt*, Cairo (Survey and Mines Dept.), 1939.
C. W. Hallberg, *The Suez Canal*, New York, Columbia University Press, 1931.
C. Issawi, *Egypt: An Economic and Social Analysis*, London, 1947.
D. Warriner, *Land and Poverty in the Middle East*, London, 1948.

CHAPTER
II

Mediterranean Africa
or the Barbary States

In many respects the three principal countries, Morocco, Algeria, Tunisia, which together make up northwest Africa may be regarded as an island cut off from the rest of the world. To the northwest is the Atlantic Ocean, to the north and northeast the Mediterranean Sea, to the south the great wastes of the Sahara. But from earliest times the Mediterranean Sea has exercised a unifying influence on the countries by which it is bordered. It has permitted travel from one shore to another of peoples, of their religions and cultures, at times of their conquering armies. Northwest Africa was long called on the older maps "the Barbary States" from the name "Barbars" or "Berbers" then commonly used for the inhabitants. Northwest Africa of today bears the impress of several distinct cultures resulting from its geographical position. But the great developments of the present century have been under French influence so that the title French North Africa has become both usual and appropriate.

The basic substratum of the population, the Berbers, reached the area overland along the North African desert coastal routes. So too did the Moors, or Arab, conquerors, and the Moslem religion. The Moorish hoards found no reason to be stopped by the Atlantic Ocean when across the narrow Strait of Gibraltar, from one Pillar of Hercules to the other, they could see the lands of Spain which lay beyond. They extended their conquests and their influence over most of the Iberian Peninsula. But the Moors superimposed their culture and religion on a pre-existing pattern of life which had been brought across the narrow waters in the heart of the Mediterranean Sea. Carthage—the modern Tunis—was established by a sea power. When Rome overcame Carthage the Romans in their turn left their impress upon the Berber peoples. In due course when the great Arab domains gave place to the Ottoman Empire, northwest Africa

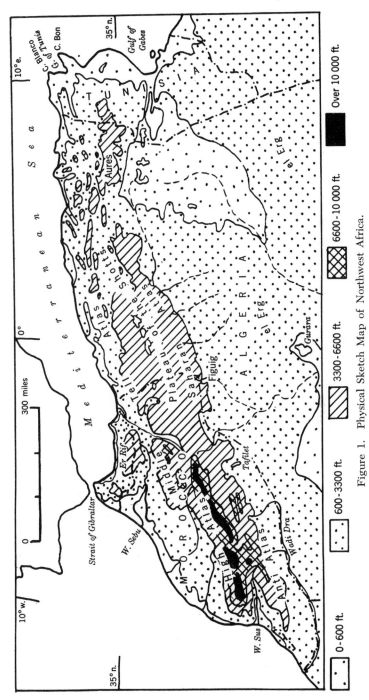

Figure 1. Physical Sketch Map of Northwest Africa.

became nominally part of the Turkish domain. Too remote to be under direct control of Constantinople, as the Turkish power waned the Barbary States became the prey of local upstarts of Turkish or other origin, and it was the piratical behavior of these local potentates in menacing harmless merchant shipping proceeding on its lawful way through the Mediterranean that led to interference in North African affairs by European powers. The task did not prove to be simple. Both British and American naval expeditions failed to

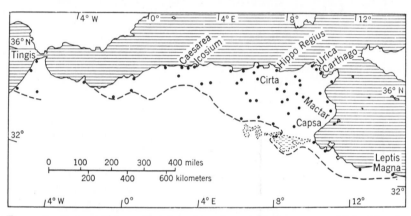

Figure 2. Roman Africa. The dots show the principal towns established by the Romans, and the broken line the limits of control.

produce decisive results in the suppression of the Barbary pirates, and it was for this reason that the French appeared on the scene. French influence began to be felt about 1830.

The territory now known as Algeria was proclaimed a French Colony in 1834, but seventeen years of guerilla warfare were necessary before the country came effectively under French control. The year 1951 thus marks the centenary of the real French hold over Algeria, but in the early part of that hundred years economic progress was slow. The railway line from Algiers to Oran was begun in the year 1860, and from that event the development of agricultural and mineral resources may be regarded as beginning and has, at first slowly, latterly more rapidly, continued to expand. French influence extended southwards over the great desert area now forming Southern Algeria. In 1881 the Sultan of Tunis transferred his allegiance from Turkey to France. But it was not until 1912, after a long period of dispute, that the appearance of German claims led the Sultan of Morocco to accept French protection, and Morocco became a French Protectorate. There remained Spanish interests and Spanish influence, rather naturally to the southern side of the Strait of Gibraltar, so that there a small tract has been recognized as Spanish Morocco, and the Port of Tangier came internationally under French, British and Spanish control.

The Physical Background

The Arabs called their great country of Arabia the Isle of the Arabs, recognizing that the desert isolates as much as the sea. They gave the name Djezira-el-Maghrib, or the Western Isle, to the area of northwest Africa isolated by sea, ocean and the great desert. Maghrib is indeed a convenient name and a better one than the Barbary States. The island, if we regard it as such, is structurally a part of Europe. The great folded mountain ranges which form such conspicuous features in the European lands bordering the Mediterranean Sea, the Alps, the Apennines of Italy, the Sierra Nevada of southern Spain, are continued in North Africa, where they form not one continuous mountain range but a succession of mountain ranges separated by lofty plateaus or at times by narrower mountain basins. Collectively this is the Atlas system, the alignments of which run, broadly speaking, from west-southwest to north-northeast, that is, roughly parallel to the sea coast, and are cut across by the political divisions of Maghrib. Perhaps the simplest way to regard the structure of the whole area is as a lofty plateau wider in the west, narrowing towards the east, with a corrugated surface, and flanked by great ramparts to the north overlooking the Mediterranean, and to the south overlooking the Saharan wastes. Thus a traveler, journeying from the north, from the Mediterranean shore southwards, will pass through a succession of mountain ranges and intervening plateaus from the relatively well-watered Mediterranean coastal slopes, across mountain ranges often capped with snow, to basins which become increasingly arid, until at last the real desert is reached. Such a traverse made by a geographer was described by him. A succession of east-west belts stands out impressively. The reference is to Professor Griffith Taylor's article entitled "Sea to Sahara: Settlement Zones in Eastern Algeria," *Geographical Review*, XXIX, 1939, pages 177–195.

The arrangement of the mountain ranges affords a natural division for the whole area, and it is usual to distinguish some ten regions for descriptive purposes on this basis. Starting in the west, in Morocco, the central and highest range is the Great or High Atlas, with a core of crystalline rocks, reaching in its highest points some 12,000 feet. South of the High Atlas lies the triangular depression known as the Sous, being broadly the valley and plain of the small river of that name. The Anti-Atlas range to the south is considerably lower and of less extent. To the north of the High Atlas is the parallel range of the Middle Atlas, and between the High and Middle Atlas lies the Moulouya depression. Both the Great and the Middle Atlas are separated from the Atlantic Ocean by a broad plateau roughly 1000 feet in elevation, dropping gradually to the coast. This largely cultivated plateau watered by snow-fed streams from the high mountains is a well-settled agricultural region, familiar to many travelers because it is traversed by the main road from the great port of Casablanca to Marrakesh, the capital of Morocco, which lies almost in the shadow of the High Atlas.

To the north the plateau passes into the plains, likewise well settled and cultivated, with the magnificent old walled cities of Rabat, Meknes and Fez, until a new mountain rampart is reached in the curved range of the Rif Mountains, lying mainly in Spanish Morocco (otherwise Er Rif). This range was obviously formerly continuous with the Sierra Nevada of Spain before the cutting of the Strait of Gibraltar.

Eastward into Algeria the High Atlas of Morocco fades out, and instead two parallel mountain ranges, the Tell Atlas, continue the line of the Rif in the north; and the Saharan Atlas continue the line of the Anti-Atlas in the south. Between them they enclose a broad plateau generally known as the Plateau of the Shotts. A "shott" is a shallow lake, frequently salt and frequently only semi-permanent. Along part of the Algerian coast the Tell Atlas drops steeply to the Mediterranean, the northward slope often being known as the Tell. A separate coastal range is sometimes developed, as near Oran, separated by a deep valley from the Tell Atlas itself.

Still farther east in Tunisia, the two main ranges of Algeria approach close to one another, thus almost eliminating the Plateau of the Shotts. The mountains reach the eastern shores of Tunisia in high cliffs, Cape Blanco marking the termination of the Tell Atlas and Cape Bon that of the Saharan Atlas. Between these two promontories is the Gulf of Tunis, which afforded such an attractive protected site to the builders of Carthage as well as to its successor, the modern town of Tunis.

Climatically the whole of the Atlas lands experience a Mediterranean climate of winter rainfall associated with cyclonic disturbances

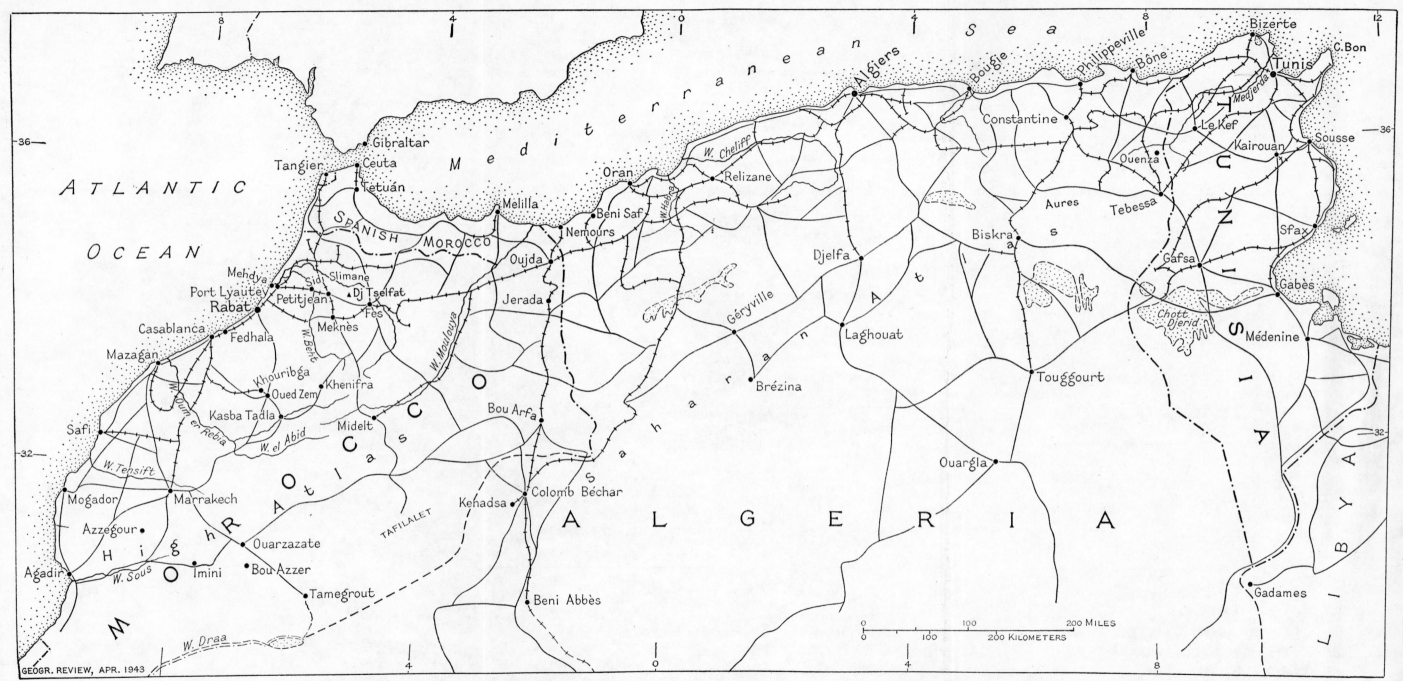

Figure 3. Northwest Africa. Main roads, railroads and towns. (From Jean Gottmann, *Geog. Rev.* 1943. Courtesy of the *Geographical Review*, American Geographical Society.)

and a summer when Saharan conditions spread over the whole, and a hot, sunny, rainless period results. Almost everywhere more than 80 per cent of the total precipitation comes in the winter half of the year. With such varied relief local variations in climate are very marked and often very sharp. The Moroccan coast is washed by the cold Canaries current flowing southwards, and the cool air from over it lowers the summer temperatures, resulting in considerable fog (as on the Californian coast) but only a moderate rainfall. The Moroccan coastal plain and plateaus are indeed dry and depend largely on irrigation water, but the lofty mountains attract a high relief precipitation of 60 inches and more.

The western coastlands of Algeria form a sort of rainshadow area, the bulk of the rainfall having been precipitated on the Rif Mountains, but farther east the Tell Atlas is well watered and contrasts strongly with the dry enclosed plateau, with only some 10 to 15 inches of rain. Despite nearness of the ocean in terms of miles the Plateau of the Shotts with an elevation of 2000 to 3000 feet is so cut off from maritime influences as to experience great extremes of temperature. Rapid changes in natural vegetation as well as of agricultural development reflect these climatic contrasts.

On the best-watered regions, as on the slopes of the High Atlas, the Middle Atlas, the Rif and in eastern Algeria, there are forests of cork oak, holm oak and conifers (the Aleppo pine, cedar and juniper) together with stretches of grassland. Much of the former forest cover, however, has been destroyed, leading to soil erosion and an arid appearance of the mountain sides which is not justified by the actual rainfall. In the drier areas, or where the soil is poor, the forests give place to that characteristically Mediterranean bush vegetation commonly called *maquis,* closely comparable to the Californian *chaparral.* It has stunted oaks together with numerous evergreen bushes and flowering shrubs, among which the heaths (*Erica*) are conspicuous. The *maquis* often forms very dense thickets. On such areas as the plateau of western Morocco and other dry areas, the *maquis* becomes impoverished, the shrubs are scattered, there are coarse wiry grasses, but small palms appear. With a still smaller rainfall we find a very stunted Mediterranean vegetation which is sometimes described as *steppe* or *dry steppe.* It is here that the wiry, tufted, drought-resisting grasses of the alfa or esparto types occur. The esparto is of some economic importance as a source of papermaking material.

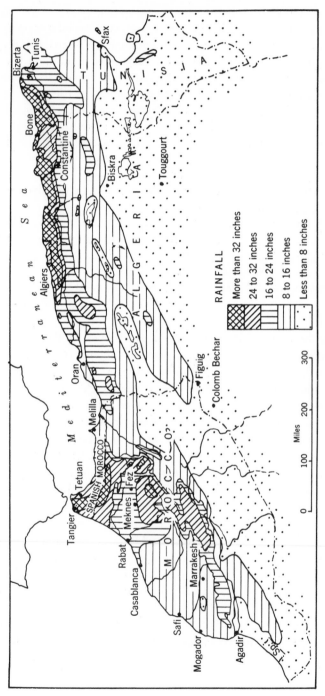

Figure 4. Annual Rainfall.

South of the Anti-Atlas and the Saharan Atlas the whole merges into true desert, often with considerable stretches of erg, or sand. A conspicuous feature is a line of mountain-foot oases, most of which are now reached by modern means of transportation and form the outposts of civilization from which the trans-Saharan journeys may be attempted. Throughout the whole area abundant and assured sunshine favors the ripening of cereal crops and fruits wherever adequate water is available. Wheat and barley are the principal cereals; and among fruits the grape, with very extensive production of wine, especially in Algeria, and the olive take pride of place with date palms in the oases. On the semi-arid pastures and maquis sheep and goats are numerous, especially the Merino and other wool-producing sheep. Though the irrigation works of North Africa are small rather than large and spectacular (there are no large rivers), irrigation has been practiced at least from Roman times onwards. The French in the last century did much to extend the cultivable area by their careful, systematic control of available water supplies.

Reference has already been made to the population of the Barbary States. A large proportion of the population is a mixture of Arab and Berber stocks, usually known as Moors. The more purely Arab population has come to be associated with the desert margins and the more arid areas, whereas the Berbers are the cultivators of the damper highlands. The Berbers even more perhaps than the Moors are European both in paleness of skin and cast of countenance, and it is not surprising that with the mixture of blood in Spain they should closely resemble Spaniards, or indeed the southern Italians. This alone marks off Maghrib from the rest of Africa, and yet the American or North European tourist to Morocco or Algeria is able to find in the flowing white robes of the people, in the characteristic architecture, in the prevalence of mosques, in the inevitable bazaars, with their mingling of camels, mules and donkeys, an oriental flavor far more distinctive than anything which he is likely to find in the Far or Middle East. The existence of the old Moorish walled cities and the occasional colorful uniform of an officer of the French Foreign Legion may be relied upon to add just that touch of romance which inevitably suggests the Arabian Nights. Northwest Africa is more truly oriental than the Orient.

Morocco (*Maghrib-el-Aksa, That Is, the Farthest West*)

Morocco is an Empire over which the Sultan, in theory, exercises supreme civil authority as well as, in his capacity as Commander of the Faithful, the supreme religious authority. The present dynasty has been in existence for some three centuries, and prior to that Morocco, from the time when Islam was introduced at the end of the seventh century, and more especially from the time of the great Arab influx of the eleventh century, had a colorful history, with the rise and fall of various Arab and Berber dynasties. Many rulers of

Figure 5. Moroccan Women Weeding the Wheat Fields. They work in gangs of thirty or forty, and later in the year they will work at harvesting beans, peas and other crops. (Copyright Geographical Publications Limited.)

the past have left their mark in the great cities. Fez was founded early in the ninth century, Marrakesh in 1062, and a number of other walled towns have remained well preserved to the present day. Perhaps one of the most colorful of them all, because of its situation on the seaboard, is Rabat. It is here that the Sultan normally resides, though occasionally also at Fez, Marrakesh or Meknes.

Actually, however, the Empire of Morocco is divided into three unequal zones, delimited in 1912. The French zone, by far the largest, has an area of approximately 200,000 square miles, and in it the effective authority is exercised by the French as the protecting power, represented by a resident general. With headquarters at Rabat, French administration is one of considerable complexity. With

Figure 6. A Glimpse through One of the Gateways of Rabat. A good example of the charming walled cities of Northwest Africa. (Copyright L. Dudley Stamp.)

Figure 7. The Main Entrance to the Walled City of Fez. (Copyright L. Dudley Stamp.)

Figure 8. Old and New in Morocco. A modern block of apartments behind an old Moorish arch. Notice the use of donkeys as pack animals. (Copyright Geographical Publications Limited.)

the French policy in other areas as a model, a School of Administration was established in 1950 in order to train Moroccans in the work of administration and to bring them into the comprehensive French Government machine.

The Spanish Zone, the Rif, is an area of about 8000 square miles. The Sultan's powers have here been delegated to a caliph, whom the Sultan chooses from two candidates presented by the Spanish Government. The Spanish High Commissioner resides at Tetuan. The Rif Mountains include some wild and inaccessible country where tribesmen were brought under effective control only in 1927.

A third zone is the International Zone at Tangier, only some 225 square miles in area, around the well-situated and well-equipped port of Tangier. Though theoretically Tangier should be the natural gateway from Europe into Morocco, in actual practice trade has passed to some extent to Ceuta in the Spanish Zone, but predominantly to the ports of the French Zone, which have gone ahead with amazing rapidity. From the point of view of its equipment as a port, its modern buildings in the new town, Casablanca has every claim to be considered one of the world's great ports. Its construction is a tribute to French enterprise and the strength of French commercial interests.

The Spanish Zone

The Spanish Zone, with a population somewhat over a million, has rather less than 100,000 Europeans and Jews and is an area of very limited natural resources. In the western coastal zone, especially around Larache, there are small areas of arable cultivation, but the country is not self-supporting and imports foodstuffs from Spain and France or French Morocco. The pastoral highland zones yield wool, hides and skins, mainly from sheep and goats, but such forestry resources and mineral resources as exist have been little developed except for the recent production of iron ore.

The short railways running inland from Ceuta and Rio Martin to Tetuan have become in recent years of little importance because of the construction of some good motor roads. Some of the latter were undertaken in the Rif Campaign. Mention may be made of Melilla, which serves as a port for iron-ore mines in the vicinity, some of the iron ore going to Britain.

Along the Atlantic seaboard in the extreme south of Morocco is an enclave of Spanish territory known as Ifni. The coastlands in the same latitude as the Canary Islands are designated officially by the

Spaniards as Spanish Morocco, adjoining Spanish Sahara or Cape Juby.

French Morocco

Excluding the rather indefinite area of desert in the south, the effectively occupied area of this country, some 90,000 square miles, has a population between 8 and 10 million, mostly Berbers, Moors and Arabs, but including some 20,000 Moroccan-born Jews, and a population of "foreigners," mainly from France and Algeria, which has been rapidly increasing. The French and other Europeans are mainly in the towns, more than a third of them in Casablanca alone, showing that the French and their colleagues have been little concerned in agricultural colonizations, and are mainly interested in trade and commerce.

The zones into which Morocco may be divided have already been mentioned—the inhospitable coastal plain, the plateau cultivated where water is available, the Atlas ranges, the inter-montane troughs and the Sahara with its oases.

The French have taken an active part in conserving what remains of the former more extensive forest lands, a conservation rendered necessary both from the shortage of timber and fuel and from the dangers of soil erosion where the forest cover has been removed.

Agriculturally Morocco is a country of considerable existing importance but of marked possibilities. To date crops have depended very largely on the winter rainfall, which is scarcely adequate, and the annual spring flooding of rivers controlled to a small extent. Not unnaturally yields, especially of cereals, fluctuate widely from year to year. This is important because cereal farming of barley and wheat takes leading place. The bulk of the agricultural land is in the occupation of Moroccans, and they have in the past had no effective weapon against serious locust plagues which play havoc with the crops from time to time. When I was working in Morocco some years ago, about the period of Easter, a locust plague occurred. The locusts were so thick and were killed in such numbers by one of the slow-moving railway trains that they formed piles before the engine large enough to stop the train. In the journey across by small steamer from Ceuta to Algeciras every passenger was mobilized to kill the locusts which had got on board ship and to sweep them overboard before permission to land in Spain was given.

There are some interesting points in connection with the development of agriculture in Morocco. Food is already produced in excess of home needs, and there is a surplus for export. Crops which pay the heavy costs of transportation are fruit and vegetables. Morocco can place these on the French market two or three weeks in advance of comparable Algerian products, but the bulk of the Moroccan harvest clashes with the harvest of Algeria. The Algerian producers object to this "unfair competition." Consequently in so far as the Moroccan output is from Moroccan farms a large increase in output is not to be encouraged, whereas if French farmers are to be established in Morocco, as they have been in Algeria, they need help and encouragement. If large-scale irrigation is extended there could be a greatly increased output of cereals, vegetables, of fruits, of wine and olive oil, as well as of cotton and possibly also of silkworms, . dependent upon mulberry plantations. Casablanca and Rabat offer attractive local markets, and more intensive development has naturally taken place around these centers.

In the drier areas Morocco has a very large number of sheep and goats, as well as considerable numbers of cattle, mules, donkeys, horses and camels. Among the hill peoples transhumance is commonly practiced, and the same is true on the intermontane plateaus where seasonal growth of vegetation is followed to different levels.

Off the coast of Morocco are very valuable fishing grounds. Fishing vessels from France, Portugal, Spain and even from distant Britain fish in Moroccan waters, but the coastal fishing industry is largely in the hands of Moroccans, who have adopted European methods for sardines, anchovy and tunny fishing. The canning of sardines has become an important industry at Casablanca and the smaller ports along the coast.

Morocco has few metallic minerals but very extensive deposits of phosphatic chalk. Where the proportion of phosphate reaches a certain percentage the deposits form resources of immense actual and potential value. The workings are in pockets scattered over the middle west of the country, and an electric railway connects some of the most important with Casablanca. At Casablanca is a factory for the manufacture of superphosphates, and in a world hungry for fertilizers it is difficult to overemphasize the importance of Moroccan deposits. Between one-half and one-third of the total exports of the country are represented by phosphates going almost entirely to those countries of Europe where intensive agriculture is practiced, such as Denmark and Holland, or where poor soils benefit enormously by phosphatic dressing, as in Spain and Italy as well, of course, as to France.

The old Moroccan railways of narrow gauge lines which the French constructed for military purposes mainly between the years 1911 and 1915 have almost all been replaced by standard gauge lines, but it is the growth of the road network in this relatively dry country where road construction is easy that has been the outstanding development of recent years.

Although Tangier is reached from French Morocco through the Spanish Zone by excellent roads as well as by a railway built in accordance with treaty agreements, this has not succeeded in diverting the bulk of the traffic from Casablanca and Rabat. The main railways and some of the principal roads are shown on the accompanying map, Fig. 3.

Apart from towns already mentioned, the great inland market of Marrakesh, or Morocco City, is by far the largest, with over 250,000 people, though only a small proportion of Europeans. It stands in the midst of rich agricultural though rather dry country and is an ancient walled city, still an epitome of the life of the country, with large markets and an important fair, also with local industries such as carpet making, oil pressing, leather, silk, metal work and butter making.

Both Fez and Meknes are also large and again are walled cities acting as collecting and distributing centers for their regions.

Casablanca stands apart from all the other Moroccan cities not only because it is a great port, but also because it has modern electrical power stations, supplying electricity to the railways as well as to the town, modern factories for superphosphates, cement works, oil and soap factories, a sugar factory and numerous others.

Kenitra, the second port, handles only about one-tenth of the trade of Casablanca, and Agadir, the port for the Sous basin, is a development dating only from 1930.

Algeria

The vast territory shown as Algeria on the maps of Africa, and as covering more than 850,000 square miles, falls clearly into the vast stretch of the Sahara Desert, or Southern Algeria, and the settled country of Northern Algeria. The line of oases along the Saharan foot of the Atlas ranges is broadly the dividing line between the two. Northern Algeria, some 80,000 square miles, has a population between 8 and 10 million.

In contrast to Morocco, Algeria is a French possession. In fact it is rather more than that. Northern Algeria, divided like metropolitan France into *Départements* (Oran, Algiers and Constantine), ranks as an integral part of France for purposes of government. The three *Départements* are organized into *Arrondisements* and *Communes,* with administration on French lines, the inhabitants electing representatives for all local and national assemblies.

In the century of French occupation Algeria has become a field for French settlement and colonization. More than one million Euro-

Figure 9. Home of French Settlers at Guyotville near Algiers. Along the fertile raised beach are carefully cultivated plots with "primeurs" or early vegetables, including tomatoes, potatoes and beans, also grapevines and fruits. (Copyright G. M. Hickman.)

peans, mainly French, reside in Algeria, and these immigrants from Europe and their descendants constitute between 10 and 15 per cent of the total population. Since 1871 the numerous Jews have been regarded as French citizens.

Five parallel zones may be distinguished in the country. These, as already mentioned, comprise the Tell, the Tell Atlas, the Plateau of the Shotts, the Saharan Atlas and the Saharan Oases Zone. Algeria is essentially an agricultural country, and under the French occupation the cultivable areas have been greatly extended. There are no permanent streams in the country, but by drainage and improvement of the distribution of existing waters large areas, especially in the coastal plain, previously almost unoccupied, have been rendered attractive and support a large population. Attention has had to be paid to the elimination of salt from some of the former salt-encrusted soils, but over the wide lands rendered cultivable, cereals take the first place. A large surplus of wheat and barley is produced on an area over 10 miles across, though climatic conditions result in much

Figure 10.   Terracing on the Steep Slopes to the Mediterranean near Algiers. The steep slopes are planted with vines, various fruits and vegetables.   (Copyright G. M. Hickman.)

fluctuation in yield from year to year. Commercial agriculture, however, is attracted especially to the cultivation of the vine. There is an enormous production of wines to be broadly classed as *vin ordinaire*, and the value of the export of wine is five to ten times the value of the next most important export, cereals. Algerian red wines tend to be a little heavier than those of France and are often blended with French wines on arrival. Total production from Algeria is between one-third and one-half of that of the whole of France.

Most of the vineyards are in the *Départements* of Algiers and Oran. French growers have evinced some fear that Algerian output would seriously overtake French and world demand and lead to a depression in the wine industry in France itself.

Other exportable products include tobacco, olive oil, early fruit and vegetables, as well as dates from the oases. Much of this commercial agriculture is in the hands of French settlers.

The pastoral occupations which are dominant outside the Tell, especially on the plateaus, by way of contrast are in the hands of

Figure 11. Contrasts in the City of Algiers. To left and right are blocks of apartments of different stages of architectural development; in the background a building showing Moorish architecture. The traffic cop in French uniform contrasts with the women in white Moslem garb and the men in part Arab, part European clothes. (Copyright G. M. Hickman.)

native Algerians. Here again irrigation plays a part because, with the provision of fodder, a great improvement can take place in the livestock industry, especially of dairy cattle.

The mineral wealth of Algeria is by no means negligible. There are especially rich iron ores, free from phosphorus and so suitable for steel manufacture, which are mined at intervals along the Tell and exported especially from many of the coastal ports, notably Oran, Algiers, Bougie, Philippeville and Bone. This is an important source of supply to Britain and formerly to Germany. Phosphates in quantity are also produced and exported.

It is perhaps a little difficult to convey a right impression of Algeria as a country which is so strongly oriental in its general aspect and character, but has so many of the amenities of modern life—well-equipped railways, excellent motor roads and numerous good hotels,

Figure 12.   Rooftops at Bou-Saäda, a small town on the dry plateau.   (Copyright G. M. Hickman.)

both large and small. The hotels are frequently owned and kept by Frenchmen, who run them as they would in their native France. The French undoubtedly have a very remarkable way of impressing their civilization and their culture on alien peoples, as is very well seen in Algeria. It is of course most noticeable in the larger towns, such as Constantine, the largest inland town, where half the total population is European. This town is a natural fortress and the natural outlet for the grain-growing lands of the high plain of Setif.

Algiers, again with half its population European, is the largest town of the Atlas lands and the principal port. Its original harbor—not a very good one—has been so extensively modernized as to be almost entirely artificial, and it deals with a third of the total trade of the country. Notwithstanding that, its attractive situation makes it a tourist center also.

Oran is almost as large and has almost as large a trade as Algiers. Again more than one-half the people are European. It is from Oran that the railway to the Saharan oases (Colomb Bechar in particular) may be extended to form the trans-Saharan route.

Figure 13. Irrigated Seedbeds under Date Palms in the Oasis of Touggourt. The water is brought by the pipe in the background from an artesian well. (Copyright G. M. Hickman.)

In sum, it is scarcely too much to say that Algeria has become an extension of France on African soil.

Tunisia

Tunisia, like Morocco, is a French Protectorate. The ruler of the country, the Bey of Tunis, is a descendant of one who nearly 250 years ago came from the Isle of Crete to make himself master of the country, though acknowledging the Sultan of Turkey. The French are represented by a resident-general, and they have built up an administration gradually tending to absorb more and more the Tunisian people into the French administrative machine.

With an area of rather under 50,000 square miles and a population of some 3 million, about 90 per cent of the people are Moslems, born and bred in the country. Of those inhabitants of European stock the French are now the most numerous, but there are very large numbers of Italians and much smaller numbers of Maltese,

Figure 14.   A Trans-Saharan Bus at the Oasis of Touggourt.   It is bound for Zinder, Kano, Niamey and Fort Lamy—2000 miles.   (Copyright G. M. Hickman.)

Spaniards and Greeks, together with a large Tunisian-born Jewish population.

Tunisia, like its neighbors, is primarily an agricultural country, though mineral wealth, particularly of phosphates discovered in the Gafsa region in 1885, and reached by railway, supplies important exports.   As in Algeria, there are large areas sown with wheat and barley, but the development of vineyards and of olive groves is smaller than in Algeria, although some of the largest olive orchards in the world are inland from Sfax and Sousse.

Road transport is not as well developed as in Algeria, and the country has suffered from the passage of armies in the Second World

War. The experts say that the surpluses of cereals, of vegetable oils, of minerals and wine again suggest possibilities for future development, though not to the same extent as in the larger and richer territories of Morocco. The principal railways and towns are shown on the accompanying map, Fig. 3.

Tunis, the capital, is connected with its outport of La Goulette by a 6-mile channel across a lagoon. It stands in a favorable position relative to a wide hinterland, and this same nodal position was doubtless responsible for the choice of the near-by site for the ancient city of Carthage, the ruins of which lie just out of La Goulette. Only one-third of its population is European, and it far exceeds in size any other town in the country. Sfax on the northern side of the Gulf of Gabès is a phosphate port, though there is also a trade in olive oil and fish.

Bizerte, which became so well known during the Second World War, may be regarded as an alternative outlet for Tunis for some of the oils and agricultural products of the interior.

There are no inland towns of any size, though one of great interest is Kairouan, an old Moslem capital, and now a center of mineral working.

It should be noted that in addition to phosphates Tunisia has deposits of metalliferous ores, especially of iron, lead and zinc, and these are particularly at the edge of the Sahel around Kairouan.

The Economic Development of French North Africa

The foregoing descriptions will have made it clear that Morocco, Algeria and Tunisia, though situated in Africa, form a region so apart from the remainder of the continent that they might almost have been excluded from a book dealing with Africa, the tropical continent.

Whatever their future, the three chief countries of northwest Africa must remain a monument to the influence of French enterprise and French culture. That influence was especially marked over the first half of the present century and may be measured especially by some of the changes in the three decades of 1921 to 1951. In those thirty years the population of Morocco increased from 4 to 9 million; of Algeria from 5.5 to 9 million; and of Tunisia from 1.9 to 3.5 million —in all from about 11.5 million to 21.5, or practically double in 30 years.

In the first place the French brought peace to countries harassed for centuries by internecine strife. The pacification of the Saharan areas of Southern Algeria was only completed in 1934. The isolated forts on the desert routes—usually with their little cemeteries—bear witness to the patient, self-sacrificing work of many units of the French Army, as well as the glamorous Foreign Legion.

In the second place the French introduced Western standards of hygiene and medicine. It is doubtful whether there has been any great change in the crude birth rate, but the result has been a big drop in the death rate and greatly increased longevity.

In the third place there has been a great increase in agriculture. Co-operatives among the indigenous population and later "rural amelioration societies" have played a large part.

In the same period mineral working has increased from virtually nothing to a level of world importance, notably in iron ore and phosphates. From 33,000 tons of phosphate exported from Morocco in 1921 the total topped half a million tons in 1951. With this has gone the marked though localized development of manufacturing industry, itself linked with the settlement in North Africa of large numbers of French. The French population approached the 2 million mark in 1951. The settlement of small French farmers on a large scale was officially encouraged in many ways. Villages in expropriated land were often built in advance, especially after the dreaded phylloxera disease destroyed the vineyards of southern France and left so many small farmers without a means of sustenance.

Road construction and port development have given the area, Algeria in particular, magnificent roads and ports second to none of an equivalent size anywhere in the world.

In some ways social change and education have moved more slowly. The vast majority of the indigenous people are devout Moslems. The women are heavily veiled, and in general education is not for them. But by 1951 even the old Islamic university of Fez was demanding modern studies, and the University at Algiers was crowded.

Politically the absorption of Algeria as an integral part of metropolitan France is part of the concept of *France outremer* and citizenship of "greater France." Nationalist elements within the countries voice other, though probably minority, views of self-determination.

BIBLIOGRAPHY

There is a very extensive and detailed literature on French North Africa in the French language. The accounts in the *Géographie universelle* are naturally very

Mediterranean Africa or the Barbary States

full, and later material will be found in J. Blottière's *L'Algérie* (Paris, 1948). English there is A. H. Brodrick's *North Africa* (New York, 1943). The detailed studies on which Bernard based his account in the *Géographie universelle* were his own *Le Maroc* (Paris, many editions), his *L'Algérie* (Paris, 1931) and de Lanessan's *La Tunisie* (Paris, 1917). Later works include J. Célérier's *Le Maroc* (Paris, 1948).

The Sahara

The world's greatest desert, the Sahara, stretches right across the north of the African Continent from the shores of the Atlantic Ocean to the shores of the Red Sea. The long, narrow Red Sea serves only to interrupt the desert stretch, to be continued on its Asiatic side across Arabia and into Iran. Three thousand miles from east to west across Africa, the Sahara is nowhere less than a thousand miles wide so that in round figures the desert occupies more than 3 million square miles or between a quarter and a third of the whole continent. Not by any means the whole of this vast area is "true" desert. There are very large areas of "tame" desert or poor scrub and steppeland, where at least some vegetation can exist and the margins fade into steppeland supporting sparse nomadic pastoral populations.

Such an obvious unit geographically has no separate political existence. The southwest quadrant forms an integral part of French West Africa, the northwest forms the territory of Spanish Sahara along the coast and the southern extension of French Algeria inland. The northeast quadrant lies in Egypt and the former Italian Libya, now the Kingdom of Libya; the southeast section lies in the old Anglo-Egyptian Sudan and, suprisingly enough, in the Chad territory of French Equatorial Africa. Though the boundaries between these political units are but lines through the desert wastes, they are clearly defined by treaty and in some cases demarcated. The geographical unity of the whole is such that a general description seems justified.

Every traveler by one of the desert caravan routes is familiar with the spectacle of bleached bones showing through the sand, grim reminders of some unfortunate camel or ass which perished by the way, in a country where nature is hard on the weak and unprepared.

In somewhat the same way, on a gigantic scale, there appear at
intervals through the desert plains of sand and gravel rocky mountain ridges which are the bare ribs of once huge mountain chains
formed early in the earth's history. Some of these mountain remnants are still mighty masses in their own right, especially the Tibesti

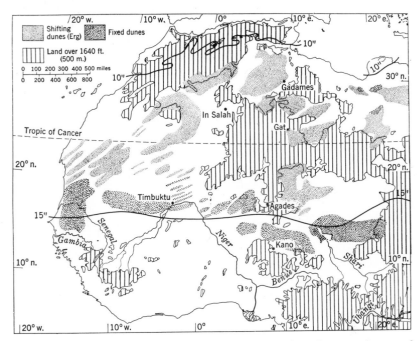

Figure 1. The Sahara. The Sahara may be regarded as lying between the annual
rainfall line of 10 inches in the north and 15 inches in the south; the true desert
within somewhat narrower limits. (Map in part after A. Bernard.)

and Ahaggar mountains, rising to heights of 10,000 feet in the very
heart of the Sahara. By the trend of the folds in the rocks and the
ridges to which they give rise, geologists distinguish the remnants
of several distinct periods of earth movement, at least two of which
are well marked. Much of the higher ground is actually of volcanic
material, and many of the peaks are extinct volcanoes.

The old idea that these mountain masses were once islands and
that the sands of the Sahara were of marine origin, and that its salt
lakes were the remnants of a once extensive ocean, is entirely without foundation. The features of the Sahara as they appear today are
the results of atmospheric weathering. Nowhere in the world are

there better opportunities for the study of the phenomena of arid lands. Although the desert is broadly the area with an average of less than 8 inches of rain a year, with decreasing average fall there is increasing irregularity. The regime along the Mediterranean border is naturally that of the neighboring lands, with the rare rains coming in the cold season, whereas along the Sudan border the season of possible rain coincides with that of the neighboring tropical lands. In the heart of the Sahara the mountain masses exercise a distinct influence of their own, and many storms of great violence have been observed, for example, at Tamanrasset in the Ahaggar massif. Short sharp storms may occur two or three times a year, or it may be that several years will pass without one. When such storms do happen the mechanical action of the rain on the unprotected ground is at a maximum, and the normally dry water courses are filled with turbulent muddy water.

With its normally cloudless skies and the consequent intense radiation, most of the Sahara is characterized by a great range of temperature from day to night. The range even of shade temperature may be over 60 degrees; it is double that on surfaces exposed to the sun. Consequently bare rocks are intensely heated by the sun and expand so that they crack away from the underlying cooler mass, often with a loud report like a pistol shot. Where rocks such as granite are composed of different minerals, each mineral may have its own coefficient of expansion, and the rock may be broken in small fragments by no other action than that of insolation—exposure to the sun. At night the temperature of the ground may be 15 degrees or more less than that of the air and so may record as much as 20 degrees of frost. The "skinning" of rock surfaces which results is clearly seen in the case of granite.

At least along the northern part of the Sahara the thermometer commonly falls below freezing in the winter, and every year ice forms at places like Touggourt or Biskra, much more frequently than along the Mediterranean itself farther north. In the summer the Sahara can lay claim to have recorded the highest known shade temperatures on the earth's surface. Azizia in Tripolitania recorded 58°C. or 136.4°F. in September 1922. There are other records at least as high as 133°F. These extremes of temperature are associated with a clear atmosphere and dry air; relative humidity may drop below 10 per cent.

Returning to the rocky deserts which form a large part of the Sahara, we may distinguish:

(1) The ancient crystalline rocks with associated granites and ancient volcanic rocks folded in pre-Cambrian times into the mountains known as the Saharides, trending roughly south to north.

(2) The older Paleozoic rocks grouped round earlier rocks but also folded by Hercynian movements into north-south folds—these are the Altaïdes.

(3) Sandstones and other rocks, especially the well-known "Nubian" sandstone of Cretaceous age, and also limestones, laid down in arms of the sea, not in the heart of the Sahara but in peripheral basins.

(4) Huge basins occupied by sediments of continental origin laid down by wind or in shallow fresh or saline waters.

It would seem that quite late in its geological history, probably at the same time as the formation of the rift valleys of East Africa, the Saharan area was rent by great faults. Some blocks of country were elevated, others depressed. Through the cracks great sheets of lava were poured out or volcanoes piled up to great heights. As a result of the differential uplift of the blocks, cliff-like scarps are of frequent occurrence.

The wind plays a very important part in sculpturing the desert surface. Apart from strong constant winds such as the harmattan, violent whirling storms produce the dreaded sandstorms. Particles of rock, already detached by insolation, are constantly rolled against one another, gradually rounded, reduced in size, and smoothed until, when desert sand is examined under the microscope, even the smallest grains are rounded and polished. But before this happens angular fragments are hurled against rock faces, undercutting them and sculpturing them into fantastic shapes. Some hard rocks appear polished by this action, but nature has here its own protection. The sun, bringing to the surface of the rocks, by capillary action, any moisture contained in the surface layer, causes the water to evaporate, and a thin hard skin of iron and manganese salts is formed to protect the rock surface. This desert *patina* or crust is often black in color and suggests that fire has passed over the rocks. The process is not fully understood, and it is probable that some of the moisture comes from dew.

Rock and gravel surfaces occupy the largest part of the Sahara. Sand dunes which have so fired the public imagination do not in fact occupy more than about an eighth.

In detail, the character of the desert is the result of a combination of several factors. There are, first, the character of the underlying rocks; second, the force of torrential water erosion produced by the rapid runoff after the occasional severe storms; and, third, the conflicting character of desert weathering consequent upon a rapid alternation of heat and cold, which results both in the formation of the protective hard crust or desert patina and also in the shattering of the rocks.

Broadly speaking, there are three main types of surface and resulting scenery. The *Erg* desert is the desert of shifting sand dunes, the distribution of which is shown in Fig. 1. A distinction is there made between those areas where sand movement is still active and what may be called "fossil" sand dunes, where movement appears to have ceased. The famous area of the Great Erg may be regarded as the most intractable part of the whole Sahara, and the area of sand which is most avoided by the cross-desert routes.

Then there is the *Reg* desert, a firm surfaced naked plain, where the surface is strewn with an accumulation of stones and boulders, representing the detritus from rock outcrops resulting largely from the sun's action.

Third, there is the *Hamada,* or rocky, desert, where bare rocks outcrop.

From the point of view of caravan movement preference is for the finer types of reg, or gravel plains.

In contrast to some of the deserts of Asia there are no great stretches in the Sahara of fine alluvium, and even if water were available there are not the stretches of land suitable for irrigation that we find, for example, in Iraq, or in Western Pakistan in the Indus basin.

A scanty vegetation is to be found over most parts of the Sahara except the erg. Naturally in the north it is a very stunted and attenuated representation of the vegetation of neighboring Mediterranean lands, whereas in the south it is the tropical grassland with scattered spiny shrubs, which fades gradually into the true desert. Both the coarse wiry grasses growing in tufts and the spiny bushes, and more especially the succulent plants, afford some rough pasture for camels, and few areas are completely despised by the desert nomads.

Oases occur wherever water is sufficiently near the surface for vegetation to be able to reach it, and often desert plants have amazingly long roots. It would be wrong to think of the typical oasis as a well surrounded by a clump of palms. Although the date palm is the characteristic tree of oases large and small, the oasis often has a margin of coarse shrubs and grass, the larger have tracts of land which can be cultivated by permanent settlers. Water is not always reached in depth from wells, but by striking horizontal channels into the surrounding country at a higher level and there reaching the water table so that the water flows into the oasis in the hollow by gravity. These horizontal channels are found especially in the west in Mauritania, and are known as foggara. They are similar to the karez of Baluchistan.

Most maps of the Sahara indicate the extensive water courses which may, on rare occasions, be occupied by surface water. Many

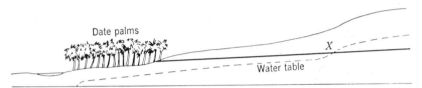

Figure 2. Section through a *Foggara*. The foggara, shown by a heavy line, taps the underground water table at X, and the water flows by gravity to the grove of date palms.

of them do mark the lines of underground streams, and from the air it is often possible to distinguish whole underground river systems by the sparse but nevertheless distinct lines of vegetation, plants with roots long enough to reach the water below. At intervals the vegetation becomes richer, and an oasis develops wherever the water table is near enough to the surface. The linear arrangement of oases is thus explained. Taking southern Algeria as an example, it would seem that water from the Atlas ranges drains as underground rivers southeastwards, water from the Ahaggar massif by a system of radial drainage. The underground water can of course be reached by wells and is usually cold, fresh and pure in contrast to the occasional scanty surface supplies impregnated with magnesium sulphate (Epsom salts) and other salts. There has been some discussion, as in deserts elsewhere, whether the water tapped by modern French wells is "fossil" water and therefore exhaustible, or is fresh water renewed from rainfall or snow on distant mountains and therefore inexhaustible. The water obtained along the French trans-Saharan routes discussed below suggests that the latter is true. The use of the water in irrigation has made possible a doubling of the size of the palmeries in several oases.

On the whole the numerous peoples of the Sahara belong to Euro-Asiatic groups rather than African. The core of the Sahara, with its focus in the massif of Ahaggar, is occupied by Berbers, a Hamitic group, of which the principal people are the Tuareg. The Tuareg are the "People of the Veil," so called because the men wear veils. The Tuaregs stretch right through the country of Air almost to the Nigerian border, and they are essentially nomadic camel men. Over the whole of the western desert and the northern area the people are of Arab stock, and are often called, very vaguely, Moors.

In contrast to the Tuaregs, who are nominal but unlettered Moslems, the Moors know and observe the Moslem religion, its history and Islamic law. They fall into three occupational groups—the camel nomads, the semi-nomadic cattle raisers of the northern Sudan stretch and the cultivators of the oases. Their habitation is essentially the tent; their connection with the peoples of northern lands is suggested by the appellation *Beidan*, or white, in contrast to the appellation *Sudan*, or black.

The Tibu (literally rock people from their home in the Tibesti Mountains) inhabit the southeastern desert, north and east of Lake Chad, and are obviously people with much Negro blood, though they too are Moslems. They may perhaps be regarded as Berbers who have intermarried with Negroes and adopted a Sudanese language.

It is natural that the French, who control such a large proportion of the Sahara, should pay particular attention to the problems of the desert and of its peoples. More than 100 pages of the great French *Géographie universelle* are devoted by Professor Augustin Bernard to a consideration of the Sahara. For details of the many regions into which the vast area can be divided, reference should be made to this work.

For both the French and the other nations concerned with peripheral areas, interest centers upon routeways across the Sahara. Those of importance in recent years have been discussed by W. E. Rudolph.[1] His map shows clearly the great east-west route lying to the south of the desert region through the grasslands of the Sudan, a route followed by Moslem pilgrims from the Islamized parts of West Africa through the Anglo-Egyptian Sudan on their way to Mecca. By way of contrast is the modern military road skirting the Mediterranean Sea, of such significance in the Second World War. The trans-

[1] "Strategic Roads of the World, Notes on Recent Developments," *Geog. Rev.*, XXXIII, 1943, 110–131. His map, reproduced as Fig. 3, uses anglicized spellings.

Saharan desert routes were thrown into fresh prominence by war-time conditions, with the need of communication for the Free French territories of West Africa at a time when communication by sea was impossible, or difficult.

In the years between the wars the French had built motor roads equipped with rest houses, refueling stations and a system of telegraphic communication to prevent the possible loss of tourist cars. One of these main desert highways (*piste automobile*) linked Colomb Béchar, at that time the railhead of the Algerian railway system, with Gao on the Niger River, and connected from there with Timbuktu and other points in West Africa. Another route, the Hoggar route, ran southwards from Algiers, through the remarkable center of Tamanrasset and Agades, to Zinder and so to Kano in northern Nigeria, thus linking with the Nigerian railway system. A third trans-Saharan route was from Tripoli across the southern part of Libya, through the oases of Fezzan, and thence across hundreds of miles of desert, virtually without water and pasture, to the neighborhood of Lake Chad. Other routes are shown on the map, Fig. 3. It is notable that the first follows along the course long proposed by the French for the trans-Saharan railway. This railway was constructed southwards from the Algerian system to Colomb Béchar, within desert territory but separated by 1400 miles from the proposed terminus of Gao on the Niger in French Sudan, whence an extension to Niamey lower down the Niger was also planned, while a branch line was intended to reach Timbuktu and the great irrigation area of the Niger inland delta.

The second, or Hoggar, route passes through Tamanrasset and skirts the Ahaggar massif—a remarkable region in the heart of the French Sahara—actually in the administrative area of Southern Algeria. In general the region is an immense plateau averaging more than 3000 feet high; more exactly a succession of platforms separated by abrupt edges and consisting of ancient schists penetrated by basic rocks. These are remnants of the pre-Cambrian (Algonkian) mountain chains known as the Saharides. Local peaks are formed of old volcanic necks and reach their highest point in Tahat (9840 feet). This island mountain mass in the midst of the Sahara is also a climatic island with violent thunderstorms which from time to time fill the deep water courses before the streams lose themselves in the surrounding desert. Bernard has described Atakor, as the highest part of the Ahaggar is called, as a formless mass, without harmony, without line; a skeleton robbed of its flesh yet transformed by its colors into country of wild beauty. Black basalt plateaus rest on a foundation of rose-colored granites whereas the volcanic peaks take on at sunset a lilac tint. The scene is so different from those to which we are accustomed that it appears entirely unreal. On the flanks of the mass lies the remarkable settlement of Tamanrasset, a town with poplar-lined avenues, electric light and a modern hotel where passing travelers mingle with the various French officials.

In 1941 the position of the Vichy Government was such that to tap the resources of West Africa by an overland route became vital, and active consideration of the railway scheme was decreed. However, the fortunes of war soon changed the urgency of this position. Details of the route are found described by R. H. Forbes in a paper entitled, perhaps rather prematurely, "The Trans-Saharan Conquest." [1] He notes that the great desert route to be followed by the railway has often been called the "Rue des Palmiers" from the numbers of date palms to be found in the favored locations along the route. He mentions the occasional floods and surface water, the wells operated by shadoof to supply water and also in places the use of foggaras. This old slave route had already become a well-traveled route with comfortable French hostels at convenient distances and even competing gas stations, though certain sections are waterless and cars were required to be equipped with radio and a competent operator, and certain points had been equipped with desert lighthouses to guide travelers.

In the early 'thirties I was planning to lead a small party of geographers across the Sahara by this route and to make halts on the way for geographical observations. A young couple who set out in a car to explore the position before our party made the attempt disappeared into the desert and were never heard of again, and it was largely in consequence of this that the later careful precautions were introduced. It may perhaps be claimed that the Sahara has not yet been fully conquered.

It may be of some value to terminate this chapter by some notes on the political divisions recognized in the Sahara.

1. Spanish Sahara (Rio de Oro and Sekia el Hamra)

This area of little over 105,000 square miles has a population of about 40,000, but some 30,000 nomads are estimated to enter with their flocks after the rains. The name of the southern part, Rio de

---

[1] *Geog. Rev.*, XXXIII, 1943, 197–213.

Oro, signifying River of Gold, must be an example of supreme optimism, fertile imagination or a facetious wit. To the north lies the Spanish protectorate of the Southern Zone of Morocco.

2. *Mauritania*

This territory is administered as a part of French West Africa and may boast altogether about half a million people. Economically, importance is centered on the salt obtained from lagoons along the coast, the fishing industry and the camels, dates and gum in those parts of the interior nearest to the savanna belt.

The vast tract of Southern Algeria has already been mentioned in connection with Algeria itself.

3. *The Kingdom of Libya*

Libya may be regarded as a wholly Saharan country. Along the borders of the Mediterranean Sea are those parts which enjoy a sufficient rainfall or can command sufficient water to make habitation possible. In the extreme south is the land of Fezzan, where isolated oases of considerable size are cut off by great stretches of desert. The Mediterranean coastal fringes fall into two main parts—Cyrenaica and Tripolitania. Cyrenaica includes Benghazi, Tobruk and Derna, towns which became familiar in the North African Campaigns of the Second World War. The western parts of the Mediterranean coastlands, likewise capable of settlement and some development, form Tripolitania, centering around the attractive town of Tripoli. Tripolitania came under Turkish domination in the sixteenth century, and, although the Arab population retained or later secured some measure of independence, the country in 1835 was proclaimed a Turkish vilayet or province. In 1911, when a quarrel had broken out between Italy and Turkey, the Italians occupied Tripoli, established an army there, and shortly afterwards the Italian Chamber passed a measure which decreed the annexation of the country, later confirmed by treaty. Though there had been earlier Italian settlements, this marks the beginning of a period of rapid development of Libya as an Italian colony.

By 1938 there were 90,000 Italian settlers in Libia Italiana, that is, in Tripolitania and Cyrenaica. The land hunger at home, the extreme pressure of population on the resources of the home country, had long resulted in a constant stream of emigrants from Italy to the New World, and in large numbers of Italian laborers seeking work in France and elsewhere. But there was still the great problem of

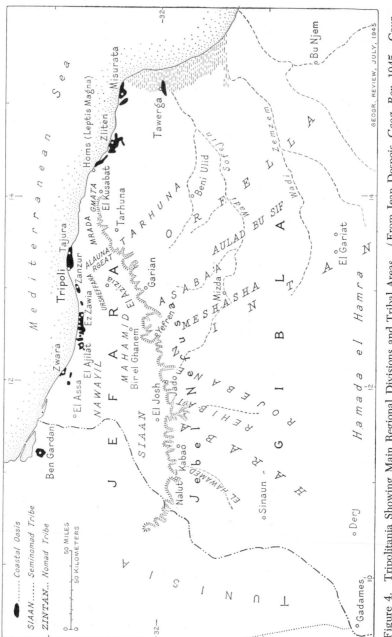

Figure 4. Tripolitania Showing Main Regional Divisions and Tribal Areas. (From Jean Despois, *Geog. Rev.* 1945. Courtesy of the *Geographical Review*, American Geographical Society.)

the need for land. In her colonies in Africa, all of them in desert tracts, Somaliland, Eritrea and Libya, it cannot be said that the Italians spared money or materials in their efforts to develop their new territories for settlement. The Italians are great road builders, and they gave Libya some excellent roads through areas capable of settlement. The buildings in the towns and the farms, if not on a

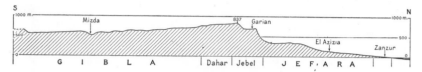

Figure 5. Section across Tripolitania from South to North. (From Jean Despois, *Geog. Rev.* 1945. Courtesy of the *Geographical Review*, American Geographical Society.)

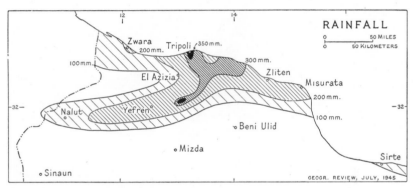

Figure 6. Tripolitania—Rainfall. (From Jean Despois, *Geog. Rev.* 1945. Courtesy of the *Geographical Review*, American Geographical Society.)

palatial scale, were ambitious. There was a touch of grandiloquence in some of the monuments which were erected rather in advance of successful colonization and development.

The whole of Libya has an area of approximately two-thirds of a million square miles, and the boundaries were fixed after agreement with Egypt in such a way that Italy secured the oasis of Giarabub (Jaghbub or Jarabub) in 1926, in exchange for which Egypt's claim to a rectification in the frontier at Sollum on the Mediterranean Sea was accepted. This vast territory has perhaps a million inhabitants, Arabs and Berbers as well as a considerable Egyptian population. The North African campaigns were fought through its deserts, and after a dingdong struggle the Germans and Italians were expelled in 1942. Tripolitania and Cyrenaica were placed under British military administrations and the Fezzan under French, with the idea that the future of the area should await development of events. The British Government recognized the Amir Mohammed Idris el Senussi

Figure 7. An Air View of the Ruins of Cyrene. The ancient Greek capital of Cyrenaica is a good example of early European influence in North Africa. (Copyright Aerofilms Limited.)

as Amir of Cyrenaica in 1949. Representatives from other parts of Libya met as the Libyan National Assembly in November 1950, and declared their desire to have the Amir as king of all Libya. Thus Libya became an independent kingdom, unifying the three traditional areas.

An interesting account of Tripolitania, in English, has been given by Jean Despois,[1] together with several instructive maps. The rain-

[1] "Types of Native Life in Tripolitania," Geog. Rev., XXXV, 1945, 352–367.

fall map shows at once the small area of the country which enjoys more than 8 inches of rain on an average, and how very tiny is the

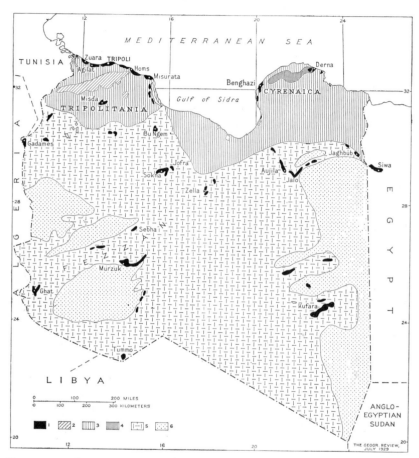

Figure 8. Libya. The boundaries are those that existed when Libya was an Italian colony. (1) Cultivated land and oases. (2) Dry farming with olives, figs and barley. (3) Steppes and scrub used for pasture. (4) Dense scrub. (5) Rocky desert (*hammada*) and pebbly desert (*serir*). (6) Sandy desert. (From S. Dainelli, *Geog. Rev.* 1929. Courtesy of the *Geographical Review*, American Geographical Society.)

area just around Tripoli itself which receives the not particularly large total of 14 inches.

Strung out along the sea coast between lagoons and the sands of the dunes are oases with numerous palms, dotted with villages. Their existence is possible through the thousands of wells from which water is constantly being obtained. Immediately behind are the plains of the Jefara, sandy steppes with stunted vegetation and occasional muddy depressions into which water seeps at times. The Jefara is

Figure 9. An Air View of Benghazi. Most of the modern buildings were constructed by the Italians during their occupation—a good example of modern European influence in North Africa. (Copyright Aerofilms Limited.)

bounded on the south by the bare rock cliff known as the Jebel, or the mountain. Its steep edge, which we may look upon as the beginning of the inevitable African plateau, is serrated by dry water courses. In places the Jebel is 2500 feet in height but falls eastwards.

On the heights of the mountain, altitude has resulted in an increased precipitation, and some dry farming is possible in a land with stunted Mediterranean plants; but otherwise from this area—

known as Dahar or "the back"—the country fades quickly into the desert itself.

Cyrenaica has points of comparison. There is a main coastal plateau and the southern zone or depression of the Kufra. On the coast Benghazi has about 10 inches of rain a year, and the Italian population was concentrated in the agricultural zones of the oases at the foot of the hills along the coast. Once again the area capable of settlement and development is extremely limited. A brief but lucid account of Cyrenaica is found in the *Report of the Proceedings* of the International Geographical Congress held at Cambridge, England, in 1928. Along the coast, sometimes called the Marmarican coast, are one or more systems of terraces ending seawards in cliffs, diminishing in general from west to east. A few miles from the coast is a water parting, south of which are the flat, bare surfaces of the highlands region tilted slightly southwards and consisting of a limestone *hamada*. This gives southwards to a depression in part below sea level, in which are found the Siwa oasis (in Egypt) and the oases of Jarabub and Jalo. Finally, to the south, is the great Libyan erg with long lines of sandhills. The Jarabub oasis is described as occupying a rock-girt basin some 350 square miles in area in which there are three large intercommunicating irregular basins, each in turn subdivided into small *hatiya*. A hatiya has a flat bottom with a salty alluvial soil, covered with halophytic vegetation and sometimes with a salt lake. There are occasional springs which give potable but bitter water, and all the numerous wells have a high proportion of magnesium and calcium salts. A few hundred people at most live in the *zawiya* enclosure focusing on a small mosque; there are palm groves and some small vegetable gardens.

Such a description might be applied widely to the oases of the Sahara.

CHAPTER

13

West Africa[1]

West Africa forms a well-marked division of the continent, whether it is defined geographically or politically. Geographically it may be defined as stretching from the westernmost point of the continent, Cape Verde near Dakar, for some 1750 miles eastward to the Cameroons mountains. There in the east the natural limit is a line of volcanic mountains and uplands trending along fault lines from northeast to southwest, including the mighty volcanic peak of Cameroon Mountain itself (13,350 feet) and extending out to sea to embrace Fernando Po, Príncipe, São Tomé and Annobón. The southern limit of West Africa is undeniably defined for all purposes by the Atlantic Ocean, or that large section of it commonly called the Gulf of Guinea. Speaking generally, the coast trends east and west and, roughly parallel to the coast, there exists in West Africa a succession of vegetation zones. Forest and swamp of the coast give place inland to savanna and scrub, until some 600 or 700 miles from the coast cultivable West Africa fades into the Sahara Desert. This is the geographical limit, and where the rainfall drops to 15 inches or less the desert may be said to begin. This great block of country, offering a variety of environmental conditions to its human inhabitants but broadly all permanently inhabited or capable of supporting a settled population, has an area of about a million square miles.

Politically West Africa comprises the vast lands of French West Africa (Afrique occidentale française) with the four enclaves of British Colonial territories (the Gambia, Sierra Leone, Gold Coast and Nigeria), Portuguese Guinea and Liberia. On the eastern limit the islands of Fernando Po and Annobón are Spanish, São Tomé and Príncipe Portuguese. French West Africa does not, however,

[1] I am greatly indebted to my colleagues Dr. R. J. Harrison-Church and Keith M. Buchanan for comments on this chapter.

recognize the existence of the Saharan Desert, and the territories into which it is divided stretch across the barren wastes, there to adjoin the southern boundaries of French North African territories (especially Southern Algeria). If, therefore, one uses the boundaries of French West Africa to define "West Africa" one includes another million square miles of desert to the north of what is geographically West Africa.

Geographical West Africa consists of a succession of strips running east and west. This is clear at once from Figs. 3 to 6. The lowland coastal strip gives place to a rolling plateau; the normally wet coast gives place to parallel bands merging into one another, but becoming steadily drier inland until the desert is reached. Equatorial rainforest is succeeded by deciduous forest, savanna, scrub and then desert, each with its own characteristic products.

Historical Background

Whoever may have been the original human inhabitants of West Africa, perhaps people of pygmy stock, the West African Negroes came early on the scene and penetrated to the coasts, taking their system of shifting cultivation in forest clearings wherever they went. From the Barbary States, from Egypt and from what was until recently the Anglo-Egyptian Sudan successive waves of adventurers came, helped greatly from Arab times onwards by the possession of camels. They included Hamites and Semites. Especially noteworthy were the Hamitic cattle-keeping Fulani who, like the other cattle keepers, rarely penetrated the tsetse-infested forest belts. The nomads mixed freely with the Negro peoples, often adopting their language and sometimes their customs, but it was the nomads who brought Islam to West Africa. The marked distinction between the agricultural, pagan, pure Negro, coastal peoples and the inland pastoral-agricultural Moslem mixed peoples is thus very old and very fundamental. For knowledge of West Africa in the Middle Ages we owe much to a Moor, Leo Africanus, who was born at Granada in Spain in 1494 or 1495, but was brought up in Fez (Morocco) and subsequently traveled extensively and left written accounts of the great Negro empires of his day.

The first great empire was the Ghana Empire, which reached its zenith about A.D. 1000. Its capital was at Ghana, now in the desert some 250 miles west of Timbuktu. This empire was succeeded by the great state described by French writers as the Mali Empire (from its thirteenth-century capital Mali on the left bank of the Niger

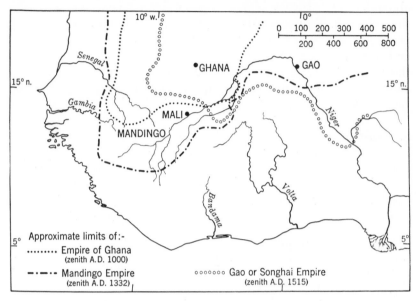

Figure 1. Ancient Empires of West Africa.

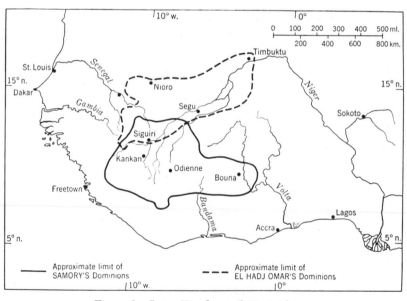

Figure 2. Later Kingdoms of West Africa.

above the modern Ségou) but more commonly from its ruling race
the Mandingo Empire. The Keïta family, to this day providing small
chiefs in the Bamako area, can be traced back to the seventh century,
and in the fourteenth century ruled over the greatest Negro empire
the world has ever known and one of the world's great empires. In
1660 the last Mandingo emperor was forced to abandon Mali, the
site of which is now a waste of scrub.

The Gao or Songhaï Empire lay to the east of the Mandingo Empire, with its capital at Gao on the Niger. It came to an end in 1591
by conquest from across the desert by a Moorish Army largely composed of European mercenaries and equipped with cannon. The
Songhaï and Mandingo empires gave place to many small kingdoms,
some ephemeral, some like the Mossi Empires or the Fulani Kingdoms
of remarkable and lasting stability.

The story of these Negro Empires is important for at least two
reasons.[1] In the first place they demonstrate beyond doubt the governing abilities of the African; in the second place they were based
on a mixed economy in areas which today have become semi-desert.
Does this prove the desiccation of Africa?

The foregoing descriptions make it clear that the natural geographical divisions of West Africa run east and west. In sharp contrast the majority of modern political divisions run north and south.
Each major political division thus tends to be a transect of the
whole. Political boundaries cut right across environmental zones
and in fact take no notice of human distributions. Frequently a single
tribe, such as the Ewes discussed later, is divided by an Anglo-French
boundary.

The Physical Background

Using West Africa in the geographical sense, we see that this great
section of the continent partakes of most of those features common
to the whole continent south of the Sahara. There are the usual
huge plateaus with level or gently undulating surfaces, though the
general elevation is here less than most parts of tropical Africa—500
to 1000 feet above sea level. The desert country of the north lies

---

[1] The Ghana Empire is believed by some to be the origin of the word Guinea
(as a corruption), later applied to the whole west coast. The British gold coin,
the "guinea," took its name from the fact that it was minted from gold from the
Guinea coast. The guinea, equivalent to 21 shillings, is still used in Britain by
some trades and professions as a unit of price, though no coins or notes have been
issued for a very long time.

mainly at about 1500 feet above sea level, with occasional hill masses rising above the general level. South of this lies the shallow depression or basin, an ancient sea and later lake bed, through the

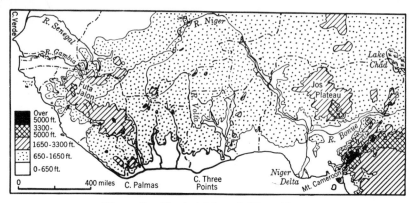

Figure 3.   Physical Map of West Africa.

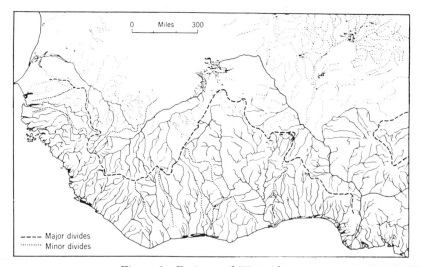

Figure 4.   Drainage of West Africa.

heart of which the River Niger makes its great northward bend via Timbuktu. Westward a low divide separates the basin of the middle Niger from the basin of the Senegal; to the east a somewhat similar divide separates the Niger from the basin of Lake Chad. Southward of the central Niger basin the land rises again to rolling country 1000 to 1500 feet above sea level, and this higher country forms the divide south of which are rivers, mainly short, draining direct to the Gulf of Guinea. At both ends this higher land rises to considerably greater heights. To the west are the Futa Jallon—Guinea Highlands; to the east the Jos (formerly Bauchi) Plateau. The three maps here reproduced show respectively the relief, the physical regions and the drainage.

Reference has already been made to the inhospitable, harborless character of much of the African coasts. West Africa is no exception.

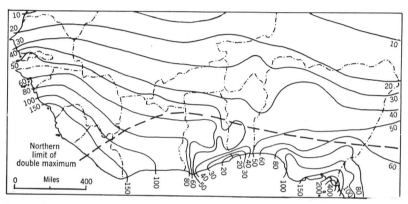

Figure 5. Average Annual Rainfall of West Africa. The figures are in inches.

Where the desert reaches the sea, north of St. Louis and Cape Verde, longshore drifting has caused long curving sandy beaches offering no shelter, with dangerous offshore shoals and heavy surf. Cliffs are rare on much of the African coasts so that those of Cape Verde, behind which Dakar seems to hide, call for comment. Southward the coast is largely one of mud flats with mangrove forests intersected by innumerable channels, but a number of estuaries, though with variable channels and impeded by sandbanks, offer shelter and access to the interior. Most important of these are the mouths of the Gambia, Casamance, Cacheu and the Sierra Leone rivers—respectively in British, French, Portuguese and British territory.

Geology

In common with the greater part of the continent, West Africa consists essentially of an ancient crystalline complex, widely exposed, with various groups of overlying sediments in certain regions. The basement complex includes great masses of granite-gneisses, ranging from true granites to ortho- and para-gneisses, and highly folded metamorphic rocks which show trend lines broadly termed Huronian, from north to south. Sediments, usually gently folded and only slightly if at all metamorphosed but believed to be pre-Cambrian, rest on these and are sometimes important because of the inclusion of gold-bearing conglomerates (as in the Gold Coast). There are also groups of Paleozoic sediments, likewise gently folded but into northeast to southwest folds. Later sediments include Mesozoic and Tertiary. The sediments of the lower group, known to the French as *Continental intercalaire* and broadly contemporary with the Nubian Sandstones of Egypt and Libya, were probably laid down in an inland basin over a very long period of time from the Permian to the Lower Cretaceous. Later a shallow sea invaded the interior or occupied gulfs extending from the eastern part of the present Gulf of Guinea. At a later stage there were the huge inland Quaternary basins, such as those of the Middle Niger and Chad, in which were deposited various lacustrine, fresh-water and terrestrial deposits. Volcanic rocks of various ages add the final major feature to the long geological story.

Although substantial mineral deposits are known to lie in French West Africa, many localities are remote, and not all the ores are high grade or worth exploiting. The impressive output up to the First World War was essentially from British West Africa. Though the gold-bearing "bankets" of the Gold Coast are not known in French territory, there are valuable alluvial and eluvial deposits, especially in French Guinea. Alluvial diamonds, probably derived from some ultrabasic rocks but not yet traced to their source, are widespread and industrially important in the Gold Coast, Sierra Leone and French Guinea. The local exploitation of highly ferruginous laterite as iron ore has long been widespread, and such ores are now of commercial importance near Conakry in French Guinea. Hematite iron ores of international significance worked in Sierra Leone are now known to exist elsewhere, as in Liberia and northern Mauritania. Bauxite is widely distributed, and some is of high grade and now being exploited in the Los Islands off Conakry and in the Gold Coast. Though the working of manganese ore up to 1950 was restricted to the Gold Coast, there are known deposits in the Ivory Coast and Niger. Mineral-bearing sands with ilmenite, zircon, rutile and titanium ores occur along the Senegal, Sierra Leone and Ivory Coasts. There are phosphates which rank with the lower grades of Morocco now being exploited near Thiès in Senegal, and deposits occur elsewhere. Unfortunately limestones suitable for making cement or agricultural lime are rare, and thus the works near Dakar are of special significance. Rock salt and saline earths by contrast are common and worked in Mauritania, the French Sudan and Niger.[1]

Natural Regions and Political Divisions in West Africa

The relief features shown in Fig. 3, which afford a series of strips roughly parallel to the coasts, are reinforced by the character of the

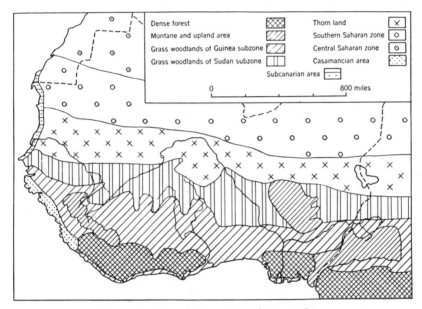

Figure 6. Natural Vegetation of West Africa.

natural vegetation—itself dependent upon climate—shown in Fig. 6. The general arrangement of vegetation belts is agreed, but several different detailed schemes have been proposed. It is indicative of the isolation in which each national group worked in Africa before the Second World War that even the scientists and technical officers such as foresters and agriculturalists in the French and British spheres rarely met, scarcely ever collaborated. Even in the study of natural vegetation it is difficult to correlate the work of the British [2] and the

[1] P. Légoux, *Esquisse géologique de l'Afrique occidentale française.* Bull. 4, Service des Mines. Gouv. Gen. de l'Afr. O.F. Dakar, 1939. Colored map. Reviewed at length in *Geog. Jour.*, CV, 1945, 129–133.

[2] T. C. Chipp (Editor), *Aims and Methods of Vegetation Survey,* 1928.

French.[1] In general terms, however, there is a *coastal belt* of mangrove woodlands and sand-bank grass forest with coarse grasses and screw pines. Floristically the French have distinguished a Casamancian area of forest in the west, where the coast trends northwest to southeast. Inland the *evergreen rainforests* extend as a broad belt except where interrupted by the Gold Coast dry belt and are succeeded inland by *deciduous forests* with much grass—the *Guinea Zone*—which gives place to the drier savanna or *Sudan Zone* with the conspicuous Bombax. On the higher plateaus the natural vegetation

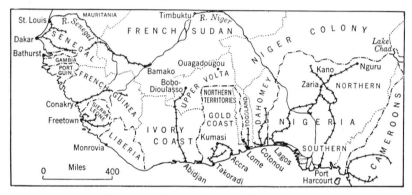

Figure 7. Political Map of West Africa.

is of somewhat different type, and *montane forests* may be distinguished. The Sudan Zone fades into thorn scrub and desert.

The important point is, of course, that each of these zones forms a distinctive environment to which the human response has been very different. The shifting cultivation of the formerly pagan or animistic Negroes of the coastal zones contrasts utterly with the life of the Moslem Fulani cattlemen or the sedentary Hausa of the northern zones. Yet political divisions cut right across all these natural zones.

Politically West Africa may be regarded as French territory occupying the whole vast interior and reaching to the coast in four main areas: (1) Senegal, (2) French Guinea, (3) the Ivory Coast and (4) Dahomey with Togoland, separated by enclaves not under French control.

The first enclave is the narrow British territory of the Gambia; Senegal and French Guinea are separated by the enclave of Portu-

[1] A. Aubréville, *Climats, forêts et désertification en afrique occidentale,* 1949.

guese Guinea; French Guinea from the Ivory Coast by the broad enclave of British Sierra Leone and Liberia; the Ivory Coast from Dahomey by the British Gold Coast and the trusteeship territories of Togoland.

The French approached and approach West Africa both by sea and by land, and French West Africa administratively meets Southern Algeria in the heart of the Sahara. The British and Portuguese approached West Africa from the sea, and Liberia too was established by coastal settlements. From the coasts there was gradual penetration inland, but the four British enclaves of the Gambia, Sierra Leone, Gold Coast and Nigeria, like Portuguese Guinea and Liberia, are based essentially on coastal settlements. The same was true of the former German Togoland and Cameroons. The fact that French West Africa forms a continuous area has encouraged unification of the territories whereas the British areas, cut off from one another, have each developed along individual lines.

French West Africa at the Midcentury

The reorganization of the former French Empire into the French Union (Union française) completed after the Second World War had certain important effects in West Africa. The seven former "colonies" of Senegal (Sénégal), Mauritania (Mauritanie), French Sudan (Soudan Français), French Guinea (Guinée), the Ivory Coast (Côte d'Ivoire), Dahomey (Dahomey), and the Niger Territory (Niger), all became "territories" within the Federation of French West Africa with its capital at Dakar. The trusteeship territory of Togoland remains outside the Federation. Each territory is administered by a governor assisted by the heads of the various departments, and each governor is responsible to the High Commissioner who is at the head of the Federation at Dakar. In each territory is an Assembly of Africans and Europeans elected by popular vote which gives advice to the governors, makes recommendations, approves the territorial budget and makes decisions on matters affecting the patrimony of the territory. The Grand Council of French West Africa, which meets at Dakar at least twice a year and is composed of members elected from the territorial assemblies, similarly advises the High Commissioner.

The High Commissioner is responsible to the Minister in Paris, no longer known as the Minister of the Colonies but of "Overseas France" (France d'Outre-mer). This title gives the key to the concept of the French Union, which is entirely different from that of the British Commonwealth. It was crystallized at the Brazzaville Conference of 1944. Each territory elects its deputies (African or French) whose duty and privilege are to reside in Paris and sit in the National Assembly, there to legislate both for French home affairs and for African or other territories. The African deputy thus can and does play an important part in the government of France itself. The Africans settle down to European ways of life in Paris; conversely, French settlers have established themselves as private traders, shopkeepers and craftsmen in large numbers in tropical Africa. They take with them French ways of life and give a remarkable atmosphere of metropolitan vitality and racial co-operation to the towns of French West Africa where they have settled. By 1950 there were 30,000 Europeans, mainly French, in the unique city of Dakar (12 per cent of the population) and 10,000 in the Ivory Coast capital of Abidjan. Between 1945 and 1950 new building and modernization took place in Dakar on a scale unparalleled in Africa, and the changes in Abidjan, especially with the opening to traffic of the deep-water lagoon port in July 1950, were almost equally staggering. In contrast to the system of marketing boards in British West Africa, the produce of French West Africa is freely marketed. There is keen competition for the African farmers' groundnuts, coffee, cocoa, palm kernels, palm oil and bananas; keen competition among middlemen and exporters. The big jump has been in coffee growing— 80 per cent on African farms and less than 20 per cent on European-owned plantations—with a ready market in France. There is proportionately less production of palm oil than in British West Africa. Some of the oil is made into soap locally in Senegal and the Ivory Coast. The same post-war period was marked by such industrial growths as oil seed crushing of peanuts on a large scale in Senegal, cement and lime making, brewing, boot and shoe making. These industries are run both by Africans and by French.

The development of iron ore and bauxite mining in French Guinea is large-scale private enterprise, but the social services and public works are financed by the Metropolitan Government, through the organization known as F.I.D.E.S., comparable with the Colonial Development Corporation of Britain.

The French system in Africa is designed to make the African a good citizen of Greater France, to bring him into partnership even to the extent of governing France. There is no place in the scheme for the conservation of any indigenous African social structure. The British system is designed to bring the territories gradually to the point when they can govern themselves and remain, if they so elect, members of the British Commonwealth. The conflict between the development of "democracy" as it is understood in America or Europe and the maintenance of the authority of chiefs and tribal assemblies we have already seen.

Which policy is destined to survive? In 1950 the African seemed content under the French system, restless and anxious to get on under the British, though loyal to the Commonwealth idea. Subsequently unrest in some areas tended more and more towards an assimilation of French and British policies.

British West Africa at the Midcentury

Thus the trends in British West Africa after the Second World War offer some remarkable contrasts to French West Africa. The introduction of universal franchise leading to democratic self-government would seem the quickest way of completing the disappearance of the British Empire, which indeed it is. Whereas the French hold up the ideal of citizenship of Greater France—just as the Romans did 2000 years ago, by the lure of the magic words, *civis romanus sum*—the British hold to the ideal of a Commonwealth of Free Nations. But as we have already seen, the rise of democracy seems destined to destroy the very system of indirect rule which has been such a feature of British African colonial administration.

Progress has been rapid. Before 1939, broadly speaking, the administrations of the British colonies were largely bureaucratic and almost entirely white. The governors were appointed by the Colonial Office in London, and ultimately policy was the responsibility of the British Parliament acting through the Secretary of State for the Colonies. Not unfairly the British colonies were described not as countries but as collections of tribes in a steel framework of British administration.

It was during the Second World War that Africans entered in large numbers the higher circles of administration, notably in financial committees, but in an advisory capacity.

In the post-war period the rapidity of African cultural and political development was recognized by the successive establishment in each colony of entirely new constitutions based essentially on democratic principles as understood in Anglo-Saxon countries. The form varies slightly from one area to another, but the principles are the same—a large Legislative Council, elected direct by universal adult (or adult male in Northern Nigeria) suffrage or through electoral "colleges"; African ministers in charge of departments and forming a cabinet in complete control of the countries' affairs, except for the governor's right of veto—the governor appointed as before. The changes have been accompanied by the development of a party system, the rapid Africanization of the civil service and the development of local government. It follows that the old distinctions between "colony" and "protectorate" have largely gone.

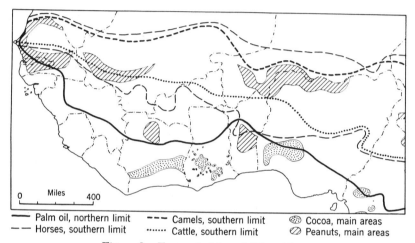

—— Palm oil, northern limit	– – – Camels, southern limit	⊛ Cocoa, main areas
— — Horses, southern limit	⋯⋯ Cattle, southern limit	⊘ Peanuts, main areas

Figure 8.   Economic Map of West Africa.

Obviously many difficulties remain—linguistic, racial and religious. For example, can a Yoruba or Ibo minister of Southern Nigeria command the confidence of the Moslems of the north if he is put in charge, say, of agriculture?   In Sierra Leone the Westernized African of Freetown had the same attitude towards the "natives" of the interior as the Americo-Liberians of Monrovia had towards the "natives" of the hinterland.   They refused the new constitution, which was accordingly imposed.

General satisfaction with the new constitutions is tempered by one consideration.   Africans have no direct representation in London, where the Colonial Office appoints governors and where Parliament determines policy.

In the Gold Coast the 1951 elections (see page 157) under universal adult suffrage for the House of Assembly put into power Kwame Nkrumah, leader of the Convention People's Party, who at the time was in prison for anti-government activities.   He was immediately released and took office as Leader of Government Business.

Thus according to the logical French system the goal and the steps thereto are known and clear, though not necessarily always adapted to local circumstances. According to the British system each territory is considered and treated separately in the advance towards self-government. Although theoretically this means that full consideration is given to special local conditions, it also may mean that jealousy is created between one territory and another. There is an interterritorial council designed to consider matters of common interest.

In 1945 the British people elected a majority of Labour (that is, Socialist) members to its House of Commons and a Labour Government took office for six years, until 1951, when a Conservative majority was returned. In general Labour politicians look upon the African as occupying the position of the masses of the workers and so are favorable towards giving them the reins of government. The system of indirect rule which upholds the authority of tribal chiefs savors too much of rule by an hereditary aristocracy. At the same time the British Labour Party, working towards its ideal of a social Welfare State, came to regard the profit motive as wrong, putting work and loyalty to the state as the alternative. It is by no means certain that human beings in general are capable of sustaining this high ideal; it is by no means certain that it will appeal to the African. Herein lies another contrast between British and French policies in West Africa.

Although political divisions between French and British territories cut indiscriminately across tribal areas, there is little if any tendency for mass migration one way or the other. Young men often come to reside in British territory to avoid the military conscription of the French areas; there are seasonal movements of labor such as the "strange farmers" into the Gambia. In general there is little restriction of movement across the frontiers.

In contrast to the system of free bargaining between producers and traders in French West Africa, the British have developed, notably in Nigeria, a system of government-controlled marketing boards for the chief export crops. In Nigeria there are such boards for cocoa, groundnuts and palm oil products. The boards (including African members in all cases) fix the price to be paid to the African producer, who therefore knows in advance what he will receive. It is held that this is conducive to an even spread of wealth, to a balanced cropping and to fair prices in depressions. There is no lure of a sudden high price to tempt the cultivator to neglect to grow food, nor in times of boom is there danger of the rise of a "Kulak" class. The marketing boards use the "profits" they make on world markets for the benefit of the industry; it is in fact a form of taxation. But, like other socialist measures, it minimizes the profit motive and leaves little incentive to the progressive individual. In the Gold Coast the Government likewise fixes the price paid to the farmer for his cocoa so that "constant and violent price fluctuations shall not again play havoc with the lives of the peasant farmers." [1]

The Gambia

The Gambia River as a natural routeway into the West African hinterland early attracted the attention of British traders. The "Company of Adventurers of London Trading into Africa," which received its charter from King James I in 1618, later in the century (1664) built Fort James on an island some 17 miles from the mouth of the river. In the wars with France in the eighteenth century the Fort changed hands several times and was finally destroyed. The Treaty of Paris in 1814 recognized British sovereignty over the banks of the Gambia River, although there was no longer a British post in the area. After the abolition of slave trading by the British Parliament in 1807, the British Navy had used Gorée as a base against slave carriers in the Gambia. The restoration of that islet to France by the Treaty of 1814 led Britain to select the site where Bathurst now stands. In 1816 the chief of neighboring Kombo ceded an island—little more than a low, uninhabited sand bank—on the south bank of the river, where the mouth is only 2 miles wide. Renamed St. Mary's Island, a military post was established in 1819 following a traders' settlement in 1816. Linked with the mainland by a line of sand banks, bordered on the south by a large area of mangrove swamp, well sheltered from Atlantic storms, it was an excellent defensive site for the original purpose but a poor one for the location of a capital from which to develop an extensive colony. Because the island is liable to flooding, especially in the low ground between two original higher parts, the drainage problem (there are insanitary open sewers) has never been solved. An adequate water supply remained an additional problem until 1951. As usual with African rivers, there is a bar at the entrance to the intricate channel. Although Bathurst harbor is sheltered, it had only shallow-water wharves, and vessels of more than 2000 tons had to load and offload by lighter. A deepwater wharf was provided in 1952.

[1] *Annual Report on the Gold Coast for the Year 1946* (1948), p. 35.

Technically only St. Mary's Island and certain other islands and settlements—a total area of 96 square miles—constitute the colony, the remainder of Gambia being a protectorate ruled by its own chiefs— in all 4101 square miles. This British protectorate takes the form of a long narrow strip on either side of the river, at most only 20 miles in total width, though extending more than 200 miles eastward into the interior. A century and a half of effective British control has resulted in considerable differentiation from the surrounding French

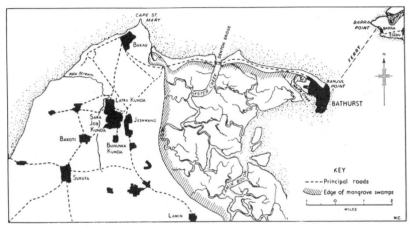

Figure 9. The Site of Bathurst at the Mouth of the Gambia River. (After H. R. Jarrett.)

territory with which the Gambia forms an enclave. The local differentiation into the Upper River, Middle River and Lower River has a justification geographically. The *Upper River* is a region of light sandy soils devoted especially to the cultivation of groundnuts as a cash crop and millets (especially coos or kous) for food. Groundnuts constitute over 95 per cent of the exports of the Gambia, and in the Upper River the pressure on land resources is such that food is brought in; only small tracts by the river are liable to flood, and these too usually have sandy groundnut soils. The *Middle River* has tracts of alluvium liable to river floods along the Gambia (known as *banto faros*) flanked by sandstone terraces yielding sandy soils. The flood lands have been reclaimed by building "bunds" or banks of mud and reeds, and the fields so formed are cultivated year after year for rice by the women. The men work the higher ground by the usual African system of bush fallowing, with an emphasis on groundnuts. In the *Lower River* there is the same distinction into the low-lying areas liable to flood and the uplands. Here, however, the flooding is by brackish water; there are extensive mangrove

Figure 10. Air View of Typical Mangrove Forests. Niger Delta—the larger growth along the margins of the delta streams is characteristic. (Copyright Aircraft Operating Company of Africa.)

swamps, and the utilization of the banto faros depends upon the breeding of a rice which can withstand brackish water.

The whole protectorate has a population of about a quarter of a million, and it has remained a somewhat backward area. There are roads, but most of the movement of produce and people is by river, though the ferry services are inadequate. Georgetown may be described as the head of ocean navigation, but river steamers can reach the eastern boundary with French territory throughout the year and in the high-water season even beyond. The river serves as an outlet for a large area of French Senegambia.

As one of the underdeveloped areas of Africa, the Gambia called for special consideration after the Second World War. It became famous on account of the Field Working Party for scientific study and infamous for the expensive abortive Poultry Scheme. The latter failed

Figure 11. A Typical West African Lagoon. These stretches of inland water are invaluable where the surf-bound coast is dangerous. This is the lagoon at Lagos. (Copyright L. Dudley Stamp.)

through the prevalence of the disease known as "fowl pest" and cost the British taxpayers $2,500,000.

Portuguese Guinea

The Portuguese were early among the European explorers of the coasts of West Africa and claim to have discovered what is now Portuguese Guinea as early as 1446. Sovereignty was claimed by the Kings of Portugal from 1462 onwards. In 1669 a station was established on the Corubal, and by 1690 Bissau, or Bissao, was a flourishing slave port. The territory was separated from the governorship of the Cape Verde Islands only in 1879, and in 1886 a long series of disputes with France was ended by a boundary settlement. By this settlement Portuguese Guinea is entirely surrounded, except on the seaward side, by French territory—Senegal to the north, French Guinea to the south.

Although the area is 13,944 square miles and the total population (1950 Census) over half a million, Portuguese Guinea remains one of the least developed parts of West Africa. The coastline is here extremely intricate. The coastal plain devolves into a succession of low peninsulas and innumerable islands between which lie a maze of channels while the deep estuaries of the Cacheu, Mansôa, Geba (with its tributary the Corubal) and Cacine afford access considerable distances inland. Though less than in Sierra Leone, the rainfall is high, and mangrove swamps give place inland to dense forest and then savanna. Some of the delta lands are covered with rice fields; bananas and oil palms are grown on the slightly drier lands, giving place to groundnuts in the interior. There are few cattle, but some sheep and goats of low quality.

The Portuguese are a mere handful, mainly officials. Such trade as there is—with export of groundnuts, rice, wax, palm oil and hides—is mainly in the hands of French or Belgians, with the chief port at the capital Bissau. This port is on a fertile island and can be reached even at low tide by vessels drawing 36 feet through the Geba Canal; it has deep-water wharves. Both Cacheu and Bolama can be reached by comparatively large vessels. The main disadvantages of the coastal strip are the poor drainage and the bad health reputation.

Most of the people are Mandingos or Fulani, little touched by either Mohammedanism or Christianity, who are of course agriculturalists and pastoralists.

Sierra Leone

The West African coast from Portuguese Guinea to Cape Palmas in southern Liberia trends almost directly from northwest to southeast and thus at right angles to the rain-bearing air streams of the wet season. In the typical wet month of July, Sierra Leone and Liberia its neighbor receive the full force, and nearly everywhere the rainfall in that one month exceeds 15 inches. Both countries belong, therefore, to the wet forested regions of West Africa, with evergreen forests of equatorial type forming the natural vegetation cover over the greater part of the whole. On the coastal belt of Sierra Leone some 150 inches of rain falls in the rainy season from May to October. Rightly or wrongly this excessive rainfall was long regarded as particularly unhealthy for white people, and it was

Sierra Leone in particular which gained the name of the "white man's grave." In the interior the rainfall decreases, and orchard bush or savanna is reached.

Like Portuguese and French Guinea, Sierra Leone has a much-broken coastline and a series of rivers draining direct from the in-

Figure 12. The Plateau Escarpment in West Africa. This rise from the coastal plain is typical of many areas. (Copyright Aircraft Operating Company of Africa.)

terior highlands to the coast, with estuaries sometimes affording good natural harbors. By far the best of these is the mouth of the Rokel, with Freetown nestling under its protecting headland called The Peak, perhaps the finest natural harbor of the whole coast.

Although the inland boundary of Sierra Leone does not correspond strictly with the water parting, in general rivers rise either within its territory or only just over the border whereas a short distance farther inland over the mountains which continue the Futa Jallon southeastward the water drains northeastward into the headstreams of the Niger. In contrast to the Gambia or Nigeria, no great river gives access to the far interior.

The history of Sierra Leone has been briefly recounted in Chapter 2. If the British in early days took an active part in the African slave trade, they have every reason to be proud of their pioneer work for its abolition. Settlement was begun in Sierra Leone in 1787 with 400 runaway African slaves who were waifs in London, and for those rescued from slaveships. Though the first settlement failed, it was followed by others, and Free Town (later Freetown) was re-founded in 1794. Behind Freetown is a mountainous peninsula some 25 miles long; it was the roaring of the winds in the mountains which gave rise to the Portuguese name meaning "Lion Mountain." The history of Sierra Leone repeats many features common to the West African coast. For a long time British interests were restricted to the coast. It was not until 1896, more than a hundred years after the foundation of Freetown, that a British protectorate was proclaimed over the hinterland where about $1\frac{3}{4}$ million people, in tribes under their own chiefs, live on 27,669 square miles. Sierra Leone had a Legislative Council as early as 1863, but not until 1924 was there direct representation of the protectorate.

·Sierra Leone falls naturally into a number of tracts roughly parallel to the coast.

The coastal belt is one of swamps. They are built up to a large extent by eroded soil from the uplands. They develop into mangrove-covered swamps or *Raphia* swamps covered to a few inches by high spring tides and heavily flooded by fresh water during the rains. Back from the coast they may be flooded only by fresh water. More than half a million acres of reclaimable swamp exist; only 10 per cent are at present cultivated. Indeed a large proportion of the rice which is the staple food grain of Sierra Leone is upland rice grown in the interior. Much of the land actually used is along the lower reaches of the Great and Little Scarcies rivers. These potential ricelands could undoubtedly relieve the pressure on the existing food-producing lands and provide a surplus for export, but the necessary land reclamation is difficult and expensive.

Behind the coastal belt is one of undulating ground where shifting cultivation has caused the destruction of much of the original high forest. Here forest products include palm oil and palm kernels, providing up to half the total value of the colony's exports. Though the solid rocks of Sierra Leone away from the coastal plain are mainly granite and gneisses, there is usually a thick covering of laterite which hinders the discovery of minerals. Some of the lateritic deposits are sufficiently rich in iron to have provided the basis of an African smelting and blacksmith industry, but the iron ore deposits which have been opened up are hematites near Marampa, to which place a 50-mile railway was completed from Pepel 15 miles upstream from Freetown and on the northern side of the estuary. Chromite is mined near Hangha on the railway. Diamonds are very important near Sefadu.

Inland the country rises as a much-dissected plateau towards the Futa Jallon Highland. In the east are forest reserves in high forest country. Elsewhere are clearings growing cassava, yams, upland and swamp rice. In the north is sparsely populated orchard bush country supporting 25 persons or less per square mile in contrast to Sierra Leone's average of about 70 (a high figure for tropical Africa).

The focus of the whole country remains Freetown. The hills rising high above the African town stimulated the growth of a European quarter reached at first by street cars, later by motor roads. The importance of modern transport is well illustrated in Sierra Leone. A government railway of 2 feet, 6 inches gauge runs from Freetown to Pendembu near the Liberian border (227 miles), with a branch line leaving it at Bauya northward to Makeni 83 miles. Roughly 50 miles is the economic limit for human porterage, and so the development of commerce, notably the oil palm belt, is virtually restricted to the lands opened up by the now extensive road system as it was earlier to a belt on either side of the railway. Unfortunately maintenance costs on roads are high, and in view of the very heavy rainfall bridges need to be numerous and able to withstand swollen streams. In the years following the end of the Second World War many ferries were replaced by bridges built with the help of the Economic Cooperation Administration (E.C.A.).

Freetown is a much-used port of call. The airport at Lungi on the opposite side of the estuary is also well served. Fourah Bay College at Freetown is proud of the fact that it is the oldest university college in Africa south of the Sahara.

Liberia

The story of the establishment of Liberia—"Free land"—is well known and has been briefly outlined in Chapter 2. The high hopes which the American Colonization Society entertained in 1821 when they selected the present site of Monrovia as the new African home for freed American Negro slaves were not to be realized quickly.   In the first place the American Negroes had lived long in contact with Western civilization; they were just as alien to the untamed African jungle as a white settler might be.   Although after the establishment of the first settlement others sprang up along the coast, they were under the aegis of the American Society, usually with white governors, and relied on American aid for their continued existence. Apart from the "independent African State of Maryland" which had been established at Cape Palmas in 1833, there were by 1847 only about 3000 Americo-Liberians.   In that year the Society suggested that the settlers headed by an octoroon from Virginia, Joseph Jenkins Roberts, should devise a constitution on American lines.   This was done, and the constitution of the Republic has remained closely modeled on that of the United States.   The Liberian flag even follows the parent model, horizontal stripes of five white and six red with a blue field on the upper corner next to the flagstaff.   On that blue field there remains the original one single star.   Independence was declared in 1847, and Roberts held office as first president until 1856.   Maryland was absorbed the following year.

But Liberia stagnated.   There were doubtless some Americo-Liberians who, having been slaves themselves, were inclined to look upon the new country as constituting their turn and to regard the existing inhabitants as creatures of a lower order, if not to be slaves at least to be ruled over as menials.   On the whole, however, it is probably true to say that Liberia wished to develop on national lines and to cooperate with the native-born Liberian tribes, but that the latter had no desire for cooperation.   And so, after a hundred years, the Liberian Government exercised authority over a narrow strip of coast and was ignored 20 miles inland.   In 1925 it was estimated that there were only 25,000 Americo-Liberians, more than half of whom lived in the capital while the hinterland remained the least known region in all tropical Africa and the one where government control was nominal or non-existent.   This is despite the vigorous forward policy initiated by President Barclay in 1904 of offering concessions to American and European interests and of permitting their advisers and technicians full access to the country.   The turning point was really 1925 when a large land grant for rubber planting was made to the Firestone Company.   This was followed by something of a "boom" when a number of estates were laid out and big houses were built of timber imported from America.

With a coastline of about 350 miles Liberia has a total area of 43,000 square miles, roughly the same as the State of Pennsylvania. No census has ever been taken, and the population is variously estimated between 1½ and 2½ million. Apart from the Americo-Liberians some 60,000 of the coast Negroes have been in comparatively close contact with Western influences and in that sense may be called "civilized." Of the six main groups inhabiting the rest of the country the Mandingos are Moslems but the Gissi, Gola, Kpwesi, Kru and Graboes may be called pagans, except where they have been reached by Christian missions. The "Kru boys" of the coast—indeed the southeastern coast is called the Kru coast—are great seamen and are employed on ships trading to West Africa. Indeed all the coastal tribes like the water and make great use of it. They build their villages near high water mark and make extensive use of dugout canoes in the tidal estuaries. Some of their canoes (the Accra type) are fitted with sails and are thoroughly seaworthy. Only those who can handle a boat with skill would dare the work of handling cargoes by surfboat. Except at Monrovia and one of the river mouths which can be entered by small steamers, coastwise shipping depends on these surfboats just as elsewhere on the West African coast. Some of the coastal people have penetrated into the interior by river and settled on the banks, but broadly speaking behind the coastal belt live people whose only contact with the sea is to come at certain seasons to fish and take back home the smoked fish. Some such tribes, the De for example, have actually reserved narrow corridors to the sea. Inland are people who have never seen the sea, who avoid the rivers which they fear and dislike. Many are essentially hill people living in rough country. Their fear of water is not unconnected with the activities in days not very far past of secret societies, the "water people," "human crocodiles" and the like who sought victims for human sacrifice and cannibalistic rites by working under water with gourds of air over their heads, or traveling in canoes covered with crocodile skin.

With certain exceptions Liberia is still a land the bulk of which is accessible only by trails.[1] Although a low rounded hilltop near a stream is a favorite site for a settlement, the higher hilltops are avoided, being considered sacred or the abode of supernatural beings. The trails tend to go straight from village to village, over rather than

[1] G. W. Harley, "Roads and Trails in Liberia," *Geog. Rev.*, XXIX, 1939, 447–460.

around the shoulders of hills and, avoiding the river valleys, tend to be ridge roads. Most of the rivers of Liberia are streams rising in the interior and following roughly parallel courses to the coast, so that trails from the interior to the coast have relatively few streams to cross. Where a crossing is needed, elaborate swing bridges are constructed of vines woven into nets and suspended by long vine cables from trees on the two banks. Despite handrails the use of one of these bridges is a nerve-racking experience for the uninitiated. Bridges are sacred. Constructed only by special guilds of men working in secret, they may not be seen by women or children until complete. The trails from the interior to the coast cross zones of very different character and hence with different products, and the ·trails were essentially trade routes along which moved in days past slaves, wild rubber and pepper to the coasts, kola nuts to the north.

But this Liberia of the past is rapidly changing. The Firestone plantations brought a road into the interior as well as a demand for labor and for payment by money with which hut taxes could be paid. Theoretically the old trails could be used by bicycles and even motor bicycles, but many had previously never known a wheel. Presented with the fact of a vehicular road, the Liberian tribesmen soon realized its value; little or no compulsion was needed to persuade workers to help with road construction which went on (usually along old trails) under the direction of a local official.

Many writers have referred to what they describe as Liberia's "colonial system." By this is meant the contention among Americo-Liberians that a very sharp line exists between them and the aborigines whose function should be to pay hut taxes, contribute foodstuffs and cheap labor to the national economy. The aborigines regard the Americo-Liberians as intruders of foreign origin, often in council refer to them as "Americans" and regard the future of the country as being one of self-determination in which the Americo-Liberians will be excluded. However, two factors have here intervened. In 1944 President W. V. S. Tubman initiated a policy designed to secure equality of citizenship throughout the country. In the second place the ties between Liberia and the United States have become increasingly close. During the Second World War an American force was established in Liberia (later withdrawn), a large and efficient airport was constructed and maintained at Roberts Field, the construction of a commercial deepwater port at Monrovia by the United States Navy was begun, a health mission was maintained and a road was undertaken from Monrovia into French Guinea. On their part, the Liberians granted a concession to an American company to work rich iron ore at Bomi Hill about 40 miles north of Monrovia, and a mineral line was built to bring out the ore. On January 1, 1944, the Liberian dollar was raised to parity with the United States dollar. In November 1944 an economic mission under Professor Earl Parker Hanson started work in the western and central provinces. The leader of the mission has given a very valuable account of the conditions existing at that time.[1]

Liberia can readily be divided, as shown in Fig. 13, into five belts parallel to the coast. The first (1 on Fig. 13) is the coastal plain with rivers and lagoons navigable for small boats where clearings in the forest yield a few palm products and citrus fruits can be grown. Behind this is a belt (2) of rolling hills, 100 to 300 feet above sea level, adapted to rubber plantations where the forest can be cleared. The narrow belt marked 3 on Fig. 13 is the main rise to the inevitable African plateau—hills rising steeply to 600 feet or more. Beyond this lies a dissected plateau (4) at an average elevation of 900 feet which has a low density of population (much under five and most under fifteen persons per square mile according to Hanson's calculations in the Western Province) but has much commercial forest and is the home of the kola tree. The interior (5) is mountainous country with elevations up to 3000 feet in the northwest, 4000 feet in the center and even reaching, in Mt. Nimba on the frontier, 6500 feet. Like the remainder of Liberia this country too is forested.

At the mission station at Ganta (see Fig. 13) Harley has described the climate with care. The year begins with the dry month of January, with the harmattan blowing. This wind continues till about mid-February; it then reduces the temperature by promoting evaporation of residual moisture. Some rains then arrive, but it is not until about mid-March that the ground has been sufficiently softened for a heavy fall to be followed by a flight of termites (flying ants). This is taken as a sign for bush cutting and the planting of cassava on the uplands, rice in the swamps. The harvest of rice—of which at least thirty-five varieties are known—begins in July, main crop in August, late varieties in December. In July and August the harvest is helped by a decrease in rain, the "little dries." October and No-

[1] E. P. Hanson, "An Economic Survey of the Western Province of Liberia," *Geog: Rev.*, XXXVII, 1947, 53–69.

vember have heavy dews and are best for growing vegetables, cotton and tobacco.

Rice may be called the staple food of Liberia. Not enough is produced, however, for the town population of the coast, and the

Figure 13. Liberia, Showing Main Trade Routes and Physiographic Regions. (1) Coastal plain. (2) Rolling hills, 100 to 300 feet elevation. (3) Hills rising steeply to 600 feet or more. (4) Dissected plateau, average elevation 900 feet. (5) Mountainous country. (From G. W. Harley, *Geog. Rev.* 1939. Courtesy of the *Geographical Review,* American Geographical Society.)

Firestone Company imports thousands of tons. Hanson's mission secured the cooperation of Liberian Government agriculturalists and reports how ready the people in the Kpoh Valley copied ideas demonstrated to them—use of fertilizers, compost heaps, new crops such as wheat, cabbages and corn, insecticides. In particular they appreciated the long-suffering donkey as a beast of burden. This gives a glimpse of Liberian possibilities at a time when 90 per cent of the exports came from the Firestone rubber plantations with gold making up most of the remainder. Development moved apace. The free port of Monrovia was opened on July 26, 1948, the road to the Bomi iron ore mines with a fine bridge over the St. Paul River was completed in November 1949. The same period saw the road completed from Monrovia to N'zérékoré in French Guinea; a motor boat service on the St. Paul River from Monrovia to White Plains came into operation as well as regular coastal services. The Roberts Field airport came to be used regularly by at least three international services.

The Gold Coast

Despite the absence of good natural harbors and the dangerous surf which pounds everlastingly along the sandy shores, the Gold Coast exhibited a combination of geographical factors which rendered it particularly attractive in the eyes of the early European explorers and traders. It is here, east of Cape Three Points, that the coast departs from its normal West African direction and trends west-southwest to east-northeast. The rain-bearing winds of the rainy season, coming from the southwest, thus blow almost parallel to the coast. In contrast to the totals exceeding 120 inches of the Sierra Leone and Liberian coasts, the seasonal fall drops to less than 60 inches, over a long stretch to less than 40 inches—at Accra to less than 30—and at Lomé on the eastern border it is only 31. Instead of a coastline of mangrove swamp backed by evergreen lofty forests the savanna zone reaches the coast. To the coast came Africans with gold dust; along the coast were occasional headlands offering defensible sites for forts or fortified trading posts.

The Portuguese were the first to establish permanent stations, starting in Elmina in 1481. In the seventeenth century the Dutch ousted the Portuguese but had to share with the British. Denmark and Brandenburg (now part of Germany) were there too. The abolition of slave trading in 1807 caused the British to reduce their forts from twelve to four, and even those would have been given up had they not served a useful purpose—by the irony of fate—as bases for the British Navy *against* slaving. An early attempt at government taking a hand in trading was unsuccessful, but a handful of merchant traders refused to leave the coast. George Maclean, their leader, was probably the first man to adopt indirect rule, encouraging the chiefs to apply their own laws to the orderly control of their territories, provided they were "in harmony with civilized ideas of justice."

When the British Government realized the determination of those interested in the Gold Coast to remain they reluctantly appointed a governor, and in 1850 a charter established a separate government

Figure 14. A Fishing Village on the Gold Coast. Copyright Aircraft Operating
Company of Africa.)

from that of Sierra Leone of which the Gold Coast had been nominally a dependency. Even then the object of the British Government was ultimately to withdraw. But there was no turning back. The great legend of Queen Victoria as the mighty mother protector was growing. In 1844 the Fanti tribes had voluntarily made a bond renouncing human sacrifice and agreeing that all cases of murder and robbery should be tried by British officers according to British law. So in 1865 a Report to the British House of Commons advised against any extension of sovereignty but stated: ". . . it is not possible to withdraw the British government wholly or immediately from the West African coast." But the little British territory could not remain static. The Fanti tribes threatened the remaining Dutch

ports, and in 1871 the Dutch asked the British to take them over
—at the price of the few stores they contained. So the British took
on a war, the Ashanti war of 1873. By this time the French had
been active. Their main object had been to consolidate their interest
in the Ivory Coast and its hinterland and to prevent the British in
Sierra Leone from linking up with the Gold Coast. Germany secured

Figure 15. Takoradi Harbor, Gold Coast. An entirely artificial, well-equipped
modern harbor to be contrasted with the lagoon harbors of Lagos and Abidjan
and the open roadstead of Accra. (Copyright Aircraft Operating Company of
Africa.)

the long narrow strip running inland of Togoland adjoining the Gold
Coast on the east simply by hoisting the German flag at Baguida, Lomé
and Porto-Segouro in 1884, and notifying Britain that a protectorate
had been established.

Thus the British colony of the Gold Coast (capital Accra) was
defined by the actions of France and Germany. It was not until
1901 that Britain finally settled a protectorate over Ashanti (capital
Kumasi), the Northern Territories having been delimited in 1897.
Part of Togoland was placed under British mandate after the First
World War and under trusteeship in 1946. The Gold Coast in that
same year became the first African dependency to secure a legisla-

ture with a majority of elected members (18 against 12), Ashanti and the Northern Territories being specifically represented.

The rapid recent political growth is closely bound up with economic development, which in turn is closely bound up with cocoa. It was an African worker returning from Fernando Po in 1879 who

Figure 16.   Adult Mealybugs Magnified Many Times.   These are the cause of the dreaded swollen shoot disease of cocoa.   (Courtesy of Pest Control Limited.)

brought half a dozen cocoa beans and planted them on his farm. There were later importations, and in 1891 there was the first recorded export of 80 pounds. The cultivation of cocoa spread rapidly through the Gold Coast Colony, and in 1898 was introduced into Ashanti, where it spread with equal rapidity throughout all parts of the country having suitable physical conditions. Within a few decades the Gold Coast as a whole was producing between 200,000 and 300,000 tons, two-thirds of the world's total output. It is not commonly realized that cocoa is grown entirely on African farms by Africans. It is not a plantation crop as is commonly believed. The

European's part is in buying the crop and also in helping with research, control of pests and diseases, provision of best seed and fertilizers, and, where needed, Government supervision. The cocoa is bought by the great international cocoa firms through the Marketing Board. Yet the swollen shoot disease which assumed alarming proportions in the nineteen-forties threatened the whole industry and with it the economy of the country.

Cocoa has made the Gold Coast rich, but it has brought problems. As a source of wealth the Government has encouraged planting, but in Ashanti the Confederacy Council (the supreme African authority) has wisely shown itself afraid of a single-crop economy. Every second chocolate, from every candy box in the world, comes from the Gold Coast. In fancy we may visualize running from the chocolate boxes everywhere in the world a constant river of money that seeps and percolates into the humblest homes of the country, and brings a standard of living scarcely known elsewhere in tropical Africa—bicycles, radios, clothes and homes. It is easy for a government to see in cocoa a crop readily salable and the country's most efficient dollar earner. The problem of the supply of food can surely be left to look after itself. But what of the virus brought by mealy bugs and threatening the whole industry? Is it not possible that for this or other reasons the African may one day face hunger if he forgets his traditional farming?

The success of cocoa production has brought increased population, especially to Ashanti by immigration from the Northern Territories and French West Africa. The population of Ashanti jumped from 406,000 in 1921 to 578,000 in 1931 and 824,000 in 1948. Thus the pressure on the 24,379 square miles increased from 17 to 34 per square mile in that period which, if not unduly high, involves much adjustment. Urbanization is also most marked; Kumasi jumped from 35,800 in 1931 to 78,500 in 1948 and mining centers trebled. The towns have to be fed by food imported from other areas; many even of the cocoa villages no longer have enough land to grow their own food. The pressure on the land has involved destruction of much forest. Runoff of rainwater is increased, soil erosion encouraged, protection from the drying harmful harmattan lost.[1]

The total area of the Gold Coast—colony, protectorate and mandated territory—is 91,843 square miles, with a 1948 census population

[1] These and other problems are discussed by R. W. Steel, "Some Geographical Problems of Land Use in British West Africa," *Trans. Institute of British Geographers* (1948), No. 14, 1949.

of 4,111,680. The whole is roughly rectangular, having a coastline of 270 miles and an extent from north to south of 300.

In its relief the Gold Coast repeats the usual West Coast features. There is coastal plain, though in the center this gives place to higher ground with cliffs. Behind lies an undulating upland rising gradually to the wedge-shaped Ashanti plateau with its exposures of ancient crystalline rocks. From the crest of this upland short streams drain southward straight to the coast, but northward from the crest the land falls again to the broad valley plain of the Volta and its tributaries. Two-thirds of the whole country lies in the basin of the Volta, the main stream of which, the Black Volta, rises far to the northwest in French Sudan.

Although not ranking with the Niger or the Congo, the Volta is one of Africa's major rivers; and though the river is of small use for navigation, a gorge course on the lower Volta offers possibilities of large power development. The Volta River dam as envisaged in the 1950 scheme would be bigger than Boulder Dam.

Both the relief and the climate prevent the Gold Coast from exhibiting the simple zonation of environmental conditions parallel to the coast seen in other parts of West Africa. It does, however, fall into a number of well-marked climatic-vegetation regions, each with characteristic human response. In the extreme southwest, west of Cape Three Points, is a coastal plain enjoying almost equatorial rainfall and temperatures where swamp rice can be grown. Its focal point is Axim.

Inland in the southwest is undulating country covered naturally with evergreen forest. This yields cabinet woods of the mahogany, ebony and teak types exported from Takoradi. This country and its extension eastward form the oil-palm belt. The production of kernels and oil has, however, diminished in face of the greater attraction of cocoa cultivation.

Over the plateau of crystalline rocks which makes up the greater part of the west of the Colony and the adjoining parts of Ashanti, the rainfall is sufficiently heavy and well distributed through the year for the natural vegetation to be that of a dense equatorial forest. Here are the words of a Fanti whose home is at Sekondi: [1] "I have walked mile after mile through narrow meandering paths bounded

[1] Joseph S. Annan, "The Gold Coast Colony," Scottish Geog. Mag., LIX, 1943, 55–59. For a detailed survey of a cocoa area, see Geog. Jour., CX, 1948, 155–160.

on either side by great forest lands, primeval forests in whose depths are the farms and cocoa plantations of the African farmers and cocoa planters . . . only here and there could I see streaks of sunlight penetrating through the branches and the leaves to lighten our paths . . . in these forests the most prominent tree is the silk-cotton, which rises like a column to a height of over 100 feet and measures 8 to 10 feet in diameter. . . . The forest is the home of wild animals . . . the elephant has been almost exterminated by ivory hunters . . . the forest growth is gradually being cleared in order that the land may be reclaimed for agricultural purposes and also for the building of new townships."

This word picture conveys the essential idea that the great cocoa region is still one of untidy African farms (averaging only about 3 acres in extent), largely hidden by forest—untidy but thus escaping the evils of soil erosion. But here conservation of appropriate areas of forest is vital to maintain an essential resource, maintain even flow of water and afford a protection against the drying harmattan. The preservation of the native fauna is another world-wide problem.

The areas of densest production of cocoa are around Kumasi. Though head porterage is still used, the development of cocoa production has depended largely on a growing network of roads and a considerable mileage of railways. It is the presence of mineral deposits, however, which has necessitated the construction of railways. Northward the cocoa-equatorial forest area gives place to forests where leaf fall in the hot season is marked; this is the region of kola nuts. Northward the forest merges gradually into savanna.

Gold is second in value to cocoa among exports. Gold-bearing conglomerates are widely distributed, and the gold is both panned from streams—as it has been since long before the Gold Coast earned its name—and mined. The chief workings lie along the Takoradi-Kumasi line and its branch to Prestea. Diamonds with stones of industrial quality were first found in quantity in 1919 in the Birrim Valley, reached by the Central Proyince Railway. The industry here has some advantage over an industry depending on stones of gem quality; the industrial demand is steadier. Large deposits of manganese ore have been found and are worked opencast at Nsuta near Tarkwa junction. The Gold Coast ranks as a leading world producer of this metal vital in the steel industry. Bauxite is worked at Awaso, having there been reached by a branch line, the opening up of other deposits awaiting the completion of hydroelectric power works.

The northern part of Ashanti and the Northern Territories are savanna, relatively sparsely populated but with some production of shea nuts, from which shea butter is produced.

For long the chief outlet of the Gold Coast was Accra, an open roadstead where all goods have still to be taken to and from the shore by surfboats while the ocean-going vessels ride at anchor in the heavy swell. Despite the consummate skill with which these surfboats are handled—I once watched a grand piano successfully lowered on to two surfboats lashed together—delay, damage and expensive handling are inevitable. Nevertheless, since the construction of the railway, the port and city have gone ahead. The western railway reached the coast at Sekondi, which was also an open roadstead until the construction and completion in 1928 of a fine harbor at Takoradi a few miles away led to the abandonment of Sekondi. Takoradi is a deep-water harbor protected by long breakwaters built of local gneiss and has commodious wharves so that more and more trade goes to the port—cocoa, manganese ore, gold, bauxite and timber. The other old roadstead ports along the coast not served by railway—Axim, Cape Coast, Saltpond and Winneba—have diminished in importance. A modern port is being built at Tema, a few miles east of Accra.

Kumasi has grown to be a focal point of Gold Coast communications, of railways and roads. Two roads from Kumasi reach the northern borders of the country, one in the west, the other through the heart of the Northern Territories and continuing to Ouagadougou in French Upper Volta.

The economic and political advancement of the Gold Coast is matched by a lead in education, with the University College of the Gold Coast at Achimota near Accra playing a leading role. In contrast, the old Danish fort of Christiansborg—a white castle crowning a sea cliff at Accra—is now used as the Governor's residence.

Nigeria

Nigeria is the largest and most populous of the British Colonies in Africa. Its area of 372,674 square miles (including the parts of the former German Cameroons under British trusteeship) make the country comparable in size to Texas and Arizona together or six times the area of New England. The population of about 30 million, although giving a density of only about 80 per square mile, is distributed in such a way that locally Nigeria faces serious problems of overpopulation at least with the existing system of cultivation. Pressure on the land has in turn led in the south to such a shortening of the period of rest in the system of shifting cultivation as to induce serious soil erosion, in the north to such overstocking as also to encourage soil erosion.

HISTORICAL DEVELOPMENT. Nigeria, although roughly the basin of the lower Niger, has little claim to be considered as a unit apart

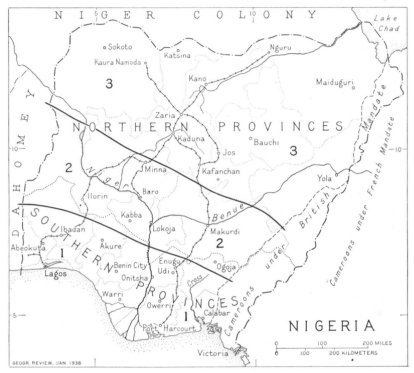

Figure 17. Map of Nigeria Showing Three Agricultural Belts. (1) Southern Belt of shifting cultivation: beans, yams, cassava, maize, oil palms and cocoa. (2) Middle Belt of orchard bush. (3) Northern Belt of open savanna merging into scrub, with cultivation of guinea corn, millet, groundnuts and cotton; cattle and goats. (From L. D. Stamp, *Geog. Rev.* 1938. Courtesy of the *Geographical Review*, American Geographical Society.)

from the almost fortuitous association of diverse territories and diverse peoples under one British administration since Northern and Southern Nigeria were joined together in 1914. The country lies between the equatorial latitude of 4° North and 13° North, and there is little to link the coastal peoples of the hot, wet, forested south with the Moslem Hausa and Fulani of the northern savannas.

Under the name of the Oil Rivers (from the association with palm oil) the channels of the Niger delta had been known for 300 years to European traders before H. L. Lander in 1830 proved their connection with the Niger. Wilberforce, who headed the anti-slavery movement in Britain, was succeeded in the eighteen-thirties by Dr. J. F. Buxton, who argued that naval or military force would never crush the slave trade but that profit from legitimate trade must be offered to the African chiefs in lieu of what they might lose by the suppression of the slave trade. A Niger expedition was organized in 1841–1842 to establish trading posts, but the climate proved fatal to nearly all concerned. Later attempts to establish permanent trading stations likewise failed.

Farther west Lagos had long been a headquarters of the slave trade. The British enthroned there in 1851 an anti-slaving King, but he did not prove strong enough for the task. It was his son who, in 1861, ceded Lagos to Britain, and so Lagos became an anti-slaving base. In the meantime British trading interests established firmer holds in the Niger delta and were consolidated into the United Africa Company in 1879. When West Africa was debated at the Berlin Conference of 1884–1885 British interests in the Niger coastlands were established and by the agreement of 1886 delimited from French Dahomey to the west and German Kamerun to the east.

British trading interests received a charter from the crown and became the Royal Niger Company in 1886, with extensive powers. Lagos remained a British colony and protectorate. The Royal Niger Company established stations on the Niger and Benue until its advance brought the British into contact with the powerful Moslem Emirates of the north, especially of Kano and Sokoto. Because there were differences to be settled with France, in 1899 the Company's charter and governing powers were withdrawn and its sphere of operations reorganized into the Protectorates of Northern and Southern Nigeria. In the succeeding years Lugard, as High Commissioner of the Protectorate of Northern Nigeria, slowly and steadily forced the Emirs to abandon slavery and accept Western ideas of law and order.

In Southern Nigeria there were pagan kingdoms where a rule of fear yielded slowly to the system of indirect rule under Britain. In 1906 Lagos was combined with Southern Nigeria, and in 1914 they were united with Northern Nigeria to form the Colony and Protectorate of Nigeria with Lagos as the seat of government. There followed a period of steady development in which the building of railways played an important part, later the building of roads. The enormous importance of modern transport in African development has been repeatedly emphasized in this book. Nigeria affords many examples. The prosperity of the southern coastlands has long depended largely upon palm oil, and the oil-palm belt can be reached to a large extent by navigable channels of the delta. But the production of tin ore from the Jos (Bauchi) plateau, permitting Nigerian output to reach a fifth or a quarter of the world's total, would not have been possible without the provision of rail access. The same is true of the coal deposits at Enugu.

The autocratic pagan kingdoms of Southern Nigeria with their colorful and picturesquely styled chiefs felt the full force of the political movements which reached their peak in the years following the Second World War. Large numbers of West Africans served in the armed forces in many theatres of war (including Burma) and came back critical of much in their homeland. Serious rioting took place in several places such as Abeokuta and Benin. The ruler of the former, the Alake of Abeokuta, went into exile, to return amid scenes of triumphal splendor some two years later. Again Western concepts of democracy came into conflict with the traditional African tribal organization.

In general terms throughout this book considerable emphasis has been laid on the sameness of conditions throughout tropical Africa. Although there are important differences between the major regions —such as West Africa and East Africa—and divergencies which increase under the varied European influences, naturally some parts stand out from others in social, economic or political development. It is in this regard that Nigeria, despite the diversity of its parts, is outstanding. Nowhere have the Moslem emirates retained their distinctive character so well as in the north of Nigeria; nowhere have the erstwhile pagan, now largely Christian, Negro kingdoms retained the individuality and the pageantry that they have among the Yoruba of the south. A description of the ancient city of Benin in 1951 referred to the pageantry whereby a new local chief in traditional garb of starched white linen skirt, coral necklet, anklets and wristlets, supported by a young man on whose shoulders he rested his arms, preceded by sword bearer and followed by a band, received confirmation of his office from the Oba or King of Benin. The sprawling palace of the King, partly of mud and partly of sheet iron or brick, was still lit only by an occasional hurricane lamp, yet the Oba speaks English perfectly and makes not infrequent visits to England. His son was educated at Cambridge University. Benin is the city which has produced some remarkable carving and brass work over several centuries.

The return from exile of the Alake of Abeokuta was the occasion for a thanksgiving service in the Church of St. Peter which lasted for three hours. The chiefs wore elaborate brocaded silk or satin robes and crowns. With attendant court officials they greeted one another in dignified ceremony before listening to a sermon lasting more than an hour and delivered in Yoruba by an African bishop.

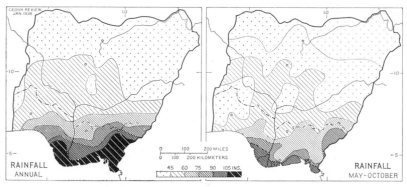

Figure 18.   Rainfall Maps of Nigeria.   (From L. D. Stamp, *Geog. Rev.* 1938. Courtesy of the *Geographical Review*, American Geographical Society.)

These indigenous cultures in a country where land-loving peoples have great traditions may play an important part in shaping the future. But how will they fare when, as one writer puts it, modern politics sweep through the kingdoms like epidemics in a walled city?

THE PHYSICAL BACKGROUND. These human contrasts between north and south in Nigeria do but reflect the climatic conditions which have resulted in a series of climatic-vegetation-agricultural zones roughly parallel to the coast. Before, however, the railroads and later motor roads came to link north and south, the Niger and its great navigable tributary, the Benue, played their part. Broadly the coastal swamps of the Niger delta give place inland to high plains in the Yoruba country and to the Udi Plateau reaching 1000 feet above sea level. In the lower Niger-Benue basin Cretaceous and Tertiary sediments obscure the ancient crystalline rocks, and the coal seams in the Cretaceous sandstones of Enugu are economically significant. It is north of the Niger-Benue that the Jos Plateau of crystallines averages 4000 feet and has the tin ores and gold of great importance. North-

West Africa   309

ward the plateau descends by steps to the Chad basin. The eastern margins of the country are marked by a great line of disturbance, with volcanic rocks culminating in the huge pile of Cameroon Mountain. Climatically the almost equatorial belt of the south enjoys in places over 100 inches of rain, with a double maximum (April–July

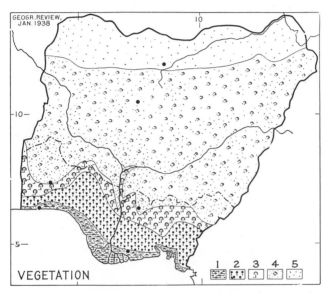

Figure 19. Natural Vegetation of Nigeria. (1) Fresh-water and salt-water swamp forest. (2) Equatorial-type rainforest. (3) Deciduous forest. (4) Savanna. (5) Thorn scrub. (From L. D. Stamp, *Geog. Rev.* 1938. Courtesy of the *Geographical Review,* American Geographical Society.)

and September–October) and a very equable temperature ranging throughout the year only a few degrees on either side of 80°F. Northward the amount of rain decreases, the length of the dry season increases (reaching as much as 9 months), there is a single rainfall maximum but the total fall varies greatly from year to year, and the daily and annual ranges of temperature increase. In the coastal belt some very heavy rainfalls are recorded, 150 inches over much of the delta and up to 400 inches on Cameroon Mountain. Storms of hurricane force tend to occur at the beginning and the end of the rains.

Mangrove forests cover large areas of the delta and coastlands, the trees ranging from 5 to 60 feet in height. Inland is the equatorial rainforest with its great buttressed lofty trees, some of which yield timber of mahogany type. This is the oil-palm belt, and it is the Guinea oil palm wild or cultivated which still provides a third of Nigeria's exports. The rainforest is a belt of poor sandy soils, badly leached in the east, and affords ample proof that the luxuriant forest growth is no criterion of soil fertility. How much of the forest is

Figure 20.   Yam Stacks in a Village of the Cross River District, Southeast Nigeria.
(Copyright C. Daryll Forde.)

"primeval" is an interesting problem. Traces of human settlement under the longest trees when felled have demonstrated that much is in fact second growth. Some African plantations of Hevea rubber have been established in Benin and Calabar. The succeeding "monsoon" or deciduous forest belt yields mahogany and bamboo but is more significant as the home of the kola nut. The great heart of Nigeria is savanna land with acacia, *Terminalia* and baobab, and this gives place northward to thorn forest and scrub.

AGRICULTURE. Agricultural belts follow those of natural vegetation. Gradually subsistence farming is giving place to farming where subsistence crops are combined with one or more cash crops. In the coastal and wet belts common crops in the temporary forest clearings (often with basin cultivation described on page 99) include yams, cassava, maize, sugar cane, plantains, bananas and oil palm. Cocoa cultivation is very important in the west, but it is difficult to dry the beans before they become moldy. It is only in the former

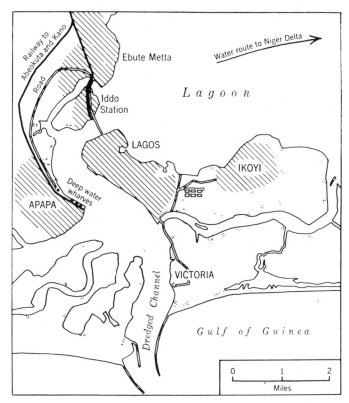

Figure 21. The Site of Lagos.

German Cameroons around Victoria that there are extensive banana plantations.

In the intermediate forest areas cultivation is similar, with kola nuts as a cash crop. Over the savanna or plateau areas the agricultural Hausas practicing permanent or shifting cultivation cultivate millet or guinea corn, peanuts, cassava, tobacco and cotton, together with shea nuts. On the irrigated lands around Sokoto rice is grown. The Hausas share the land with the pastoral Fulani, with their 10 million cattle and many sheep and goats. Local varieties of cotton have long been cultivated, but improved types, with staples up to one inch, as well as American long-stapled cottons have become general along the Lagos-Kano railway line. Zaria is a leading center. But the great cash crop of the north is the peanut. The introduction of light steel plows to replace the traditional hoe was found to induce soil erosion and was abandoned.

The minerals of Nigeria include the only worked coal fields of West Africa—the discovery of a British geologist—at Enugu on the

Figure 22. Street Scene in Lagos, with the African Church. The coast peoples of much of West Africa, formerly pagans, have been very largely converted to Christianity. The West African Church has become in many ways independent. · (Copyright L. Dudley Stamp.)

eastern railway to Port Harcourt. This same railway, after crossing the Benue by a great bridge at Makurdi, gives off a branch which taps the tin ore fields centering on Jos.

TOWNS AND COMMUNICATIONS. The Niger is navigable by flat-bottomed steamers all the year round from the sea to near the Kaduna confluence (460 miles), and in the high-water season (July to October) as far as the railroad crossing at Jebba. The Benue is navigable for 470 miles above its confluence with the Niger to Garua on the French side of the frontier. The Cross River is of great local value in reaching the palm-oil belt and has an oil-exporting port at Calabar. Behind the coastal sand spits navigable waterways connect the Lagos lagoon with the Niger delta.

Lagos, the seat of the central government, is situated on an island in a lagoon reached over a dredged bar from the ocean. Although Lagos has deep-water wharves most of the trade is handled at the

Figure 23. The Yoruba City of Ilorin, Nigeria. This is towards the southern limit of Moslem influence. Notice the city walls and the mosque contrasting with the thatched dwellings typical of the south. (Copyright Aircraft Operating Company of Africa.)

well-equipped railway wharves of Apapa on the mainland. Then the main line runs inland through the large, sprawling old Yoruba capital of Ibadan, now one of the largest cities of tropical Africa and the seat of a university college. The line reaches and crosses the Niger at Jebba, and beyond the modern administrative center of Kaduna (chosen as a healthy site) has to some extent replaced Zaria. It is at Kaduna that the eastern line to Port Harcourt (now Nigeria's second port) on the Bonny River joins the main line. Reference has been made elsewhere to the way in which in Nigeria railway and mineral development went hand in hand. Later motor roads have played an increasingly important part, and air transport is important both internally and internationally. A particularly fascinating ex-

Figure 24. The Emir of Kano. He is standing at the door in the characteristically decorated wall of one of the Palace buildings. (Copyright L. Dudley Stamp.)

ample of a major center surviving and adapting itself to change is afforded by Kano, which accordingly merits special study.

KANO. The walled cities which are the capitals of the Moslem kingdoms or emirates of Northern Nigeria and neighboring French territory are among the most fascinating features of West Africa. An excellent example is offered by Kano, though many others might be chosen—Sokoto or Katsina, for instance. Kano has been studied and described by Dr. Derwent Whittlesey.[1] It is the center of one

[1] "Kano: A Sudanese Metropolis," *Geog. Rev.*, XXVII, 1937, 177–199. Compare Sokoto.

of the major pockets of dense population in West Africa. In the area immediately tributary to the city within a radius of 30 to 40 miles live more than a million people, within the administrative division more than double that number. The *umland* or tributary area is well tilled: there are hamlets every half mile and about forty walled towns. The population of Kano City was recorded in the

Figure 25. A Typical Merchant's Town House in Kano. Notice the flat roof and elaborate decoration. (Copyright L. Dudley Stamp.)

1946 census as nearly 100,000, but this number is greatly increased at harvest time. Kano well deserves the title of "metropolis" as there is a constant stream of buyers and sellers into and out of the city; as many as 25,000 may pass inward through the gates in the wall during the day.

In contrast to most of Africa the Kano umland is continuously cultivated. The soils, derived from underlying granite, are light and easily worked and benefit greatly from manuring. The Hausa cultivators pay the nomadic Fulani who own all the cattle in the neighborhood to pasture their herds on the stubble fields during the dry season and thus to benefit the land by animal manure and "treading." The soil is enriched also by the manure of the sheep, goats and pack animals—especially asses and mules—which are kept by the farmers. The light land of the Kano area has also benefited greatly from the increased cultivation of peanuts, which, though they require other manures, add nitrogenous material made from atmospheric nitrogen to the soil. The field crops raised in the rainy half of the

Figure 26.   Decorated vaulting inside a house in the Kano area.   This was in the home of a wealthy young man; the designs were executed in bright colors.   Often decorated plates, saucers and fragments of china are let into the mud-cement.
(Copyright L. Dudley Stamp.)

year are chiefly Guinea corn (*Sorghum vulgare*), spiked millet (*Pennisetum spicatum*) and peanuts, with smaller proportions of cotton, manioc, sweet potatoes and sesame.   Where water can be obtained throughout the year from well or stream (by shadoof) gardens are found with onions, tomatoes, sugar cane, tobacco, peppers and indigo.

For more than a thousand years Kano has been a trading center, and for a long time the focus of Hausaland.   It may have been sited because of a locally usable deposit of iron ore; the city was long famed for the skill of the smiths and metal workers.   Within the mud walls which enclose an area of some 9 square miles is still much open land, intended to supply food in case of siege.   The mud

Figure 27.   Old and New Methods of Tin Working in Nigeria.   In the upper picture the tin-bearing earth is being dug by hand and the heavy baskets or basins carried by women.   In the lower picture the same type of ground is being worked by hydraulic sluicing, with a minimum of labor.   But the modern method has the disadvantage of affording little employment.   (Copyright R. J. Harrison-Church.)

houses are characteristic; modern dwellings faced with concrete usually follow traditional styles. There is an aristocratic section of the town where the Emir's Palace is a walled city within a city. When my wife and I were received by the Emir and entertained at tea within the thick-walled, color-washed adobe palace some rooms were furnished in Western style, notwithstanding the charming decoration afforded by colored china plates and saucers or fragments let into the arched roofs and walls. The Emir's ministers, the city ward headman, and rich merchants have houses in the neighborhood, and many rural headmen keep a "townhouse" in Kano. In the main part of the town are quarters devoted to cotton spinning, weaving, dyeing (with local vegetable dyes prepared in pits) and tailoring. Another leading industry is tanning of leather (goats, cattle, sheep, camels and asses all supply hides and skins, with goats easily leading), some tanning materials being derived from the seeds of a local acacia. Kano has a main market, well stocked, and many smaller ones, including one which before the British entry in 1903 was the slave market.

Outside the city walls is the township established by the British with government buildings, a European residential quarter and two African towns where many of the immigrants into the area reside. Though no longer the railhead, Kano has a large transshipping trade from camel caravans to the railway. The large trade in peanuts, cotton and skins is outward: the inward trade includes kola nuts from the south as well as a large range of imported goods.

Kano has become a great international and local airport as well as a focus of an increasing number of all-weather roads. The old city has been equipped with electricity, it has a good water supply, and some improvement has been made in sanitation. Its walls have tended to disintegrate; its old narrow gates have been widened to admit automobiles and the now widely used busses. Nevertheless, Kano retains much of its medieval charm.

Kano has been chosen as an example of a walled capital of an ancient Hausa state. There are others equally worthy of detailed study; a good example is Katsina.

NIGERIAN PROBLEMS. Despite the diversity between north and south and the arificial character of its boundaries, Nigeria is developing towards nationhood. Perhaps it is the country in tropical Africa nearest to the Western concept of a nation involving the federation of peoples of different speech and religion. In this the development of communications has played a major part, and the varied economic basis is important. Peanuts, palm kernels, palm oil, cocoa and tin ore all represent more than 10 per cent of exports. Other exports include hides and cotton. The possession of West Africa's only coal mines is also a valuable asset. Both Lagos and

Figure 28. A "Pagan" Village and Lands, Northern Nigeria. These are among the most primitive of African peoples. They go entirely or almost entirely naked, and the small round huts are used mainly for sleeping. Cooking is done out in the open, the smaller round mud structures being grain stores. (Copyright Aircraft Operating Company of Africa.)

Port Harcourt serve a large hinterland; the older ports of Forcados, Burutu, Warri and Sapele never did this. Nigeria, though a British creation, seems to have a future as a political unit.

Figure 29.   Details of a "Pagan" Village.   Showing sleeping hut on the right, granary on the left and protective stone walls.   (British Official Photograph.)

French West Africa (Afrique Occidentale Française)

The total area of the federation of French West Africa has been calculated at 4,675,700 square kilometers, or 1,815,768 square miles, with a total population estimated in 1949 at about 16½ million. The alterations of administrative boundaries after the Second World War included the erection of a new territory of Upper Volta and the incorporation of the former *circonscription* of Dakar and dependencies into Senegal so that direct comparison with earlier statistics is difficult.   A large part of the Sahara Desert—at least three-quarters of a million square miles—lies in French West Africa, in Mauritania,

French Sudan and Niger. The administrative divisions as constituted after the Second World War are as follows:

	Area, Square Kilometers	Area, Square Miles	Population (1949)
Senegal (with Dakar)	209,970	81,050	1,992,000
French Guinea	280,900	108,400	2,180,000
Ivory Coast	336,200	129,800	2,065,000
Upper Volta	315,700	122,900	3,069,000
Dahomey	115,700	44,650	1,505,000
French Sudan	1,195,000	461,300	3,177,000
Mauritania	943,000	364,000	518,000
Niger	1,279,000	494,700	2,029,000
Total	4,675,470	1,806,800	16,535,000

It should be noted that the Trusteeship territory of Togoland does not form part of French West Africa.

HISTORICAL BACKGROUND. French interest in West Africa really began in 1483 when Louis XI sent an expedition to Cape Verde in search of a remedy for the leprosy from which he died before the expedition returned. Although French vessels anchored off the site of Saint-Louis in 1558, the first French Company (the Norman Company) to receive a charter to trade with Senegal and the Gambia was founded in 1624, a few years after the British had established themselves on the Gambia. Within the next few years three French companies were granted rights by Richelieu extending from Cape Verde to the mouth of the Congo. In 1635 the first Christian mission was established; in 1658–1659 Gorée and Saint-Louis were founded. Although the French companies were established for purposes of trade, they soon became interested in territorial accessions, and the Compagnie du Sénégal (the successor of the Norman Company) undertook to provide 2000 slaves annually to the French possessions in America.

In 1698 the Frenchman André Brue built a fortified post on the Senegal 400 miles from the coast, the first attempt by a European to establish a permanent station away from the coast. The century which followed was one of constant strife between British and French; it was the Treaty of Paris in 1814 which marked the end of the struggle. At that time France was the only European power with any claims to possessions inland. France kept her possessions as they were in 1792—Arguin, Portendik, Saint-Louis, Gorée and its dependencies, Cape Verde, Rufisque, Portudal, and Joal. The British retained only trading rights.

Although the Revolutionary Convention of 1794 abolished the status of slavery in the dominion of France, slavery was not finally abolished throughout the Empire until 1848. But the concept of French citizenship grew gradually, and the French tried to reorganize the economy of Senegal on the basis of agriculture. The turning point was the beginning of the export of peanuts in 1840, and French development was concentrated in Senegal, based on Saint-Louis.

In 1845 the French possessions were divided into two governments—Senegal based on Saint-Louis and Rivières du Sud based on Gorée. In 1847 the French created a corps of African cavalry (Spahis); in 1848 the first Senegalese *Tirailleurs* were enlisted from freed slaves. The French military tradition was thus introduced very early into Africa.

A little later the French clashed with El Hadj Omar who had set up a Moslem state over a large area to the southwest of Timbuktu. French development at this time owes much to General Faidherbe, who was appointed governor of Senegal in 1854. He established schools, banks, and a survey organization, and he was the real founder of Dakar, where a military port was set up in 1857 and the first jetty built in 1863.

French interests in West Africa were well established at the time of the Berlin Conference in 1885. The same year France recognized German claims to Togoland, and boundary agreements with Portugal, Britain, Liberia and Spain followed gradually. Until the German occupation Togoland, with a seaboard of about 30 miles and a depth of 300, had not existed as a unit, and its status as a German colony from 1885 to 1914 was typical of the entirely artificial units created by European powers in Africa. On the outbreak of the First World War Togoland fell to British and French forces in the first month. Later the division of land between Britain and France was accepted by the League of Nations and the United Nations.

Senegal was thus the earliest area of French penetration into West Africa. France's rights in French Guinea were recognized by Britain in 1882, and Conakry was occupied in 1887. In the Ivory Coast the French had a factory at Grand Bassam at an early stage—lasting until 1707—and treaties with local chiefs were revived in 1842. The French were later concerned to maintain an access from the coast to the Upper Niger basin. In Dahomey they obtained rights to establish a trading post as early as 1669 at Ouidah, but it was not till 1851 that a treaty of friendship was concluded with the King of Dahomey. Porto Novo accepted the protection of France in 1863.

Consolidation of French West Africa came with the establishment of a central government in 1895, when the Governor of Senegal became Governor-General with his capital at St. Louis. The capital was moved to Dakar in 1904.

THE PEOPLES OF FRENCH WEST AFRICA. The people of French West Africa fall into the two main groups—the Islamized peoples of the north and the Negroes of the south. But northern religions, organizations and languages have invaded the south, Negro blood has penetrated far into the north. The lands are not neatly parceled out into tribal areas, but broadly the peoples of the north are Moslems of Arab, Berber and Fulani stock, the Negroes of the south are Animists. The Negro villages usually comprise "clans," each of families descended from a common stock, and there is no intermarriage between members of the same clan.

The French policy is to use native institutions only when they are the best instruments for rapid introduction of French civilization. Each territory is divided into "cercles" under a "commandant du cercle," who is often virtual ruler of his province. He appoints the village chief (after consultation with the village elders) and the canton chief, supervising a group of villages.

Senegal (Sénégal)

Both historically and actually Senegal is the bridgehead for French penetration into West Africa. Here the French established St. Louis on a remarkable sandbank site (obviously for defensive purposes) near the mouth of the Senegal River, an important highway into the interior. Although Dakar has replaced St. Louis as the capital of the Federation and chief port, and the railway inland from Dakar to Kayes on the Senegal (and then to Bamako on the navigable Upper Niger) has supplanted the old river Senegal highway, St. Louis remains a considerable town and capital of Senegal.

The town has spread from its congested sandbank island to the main sandspit (the "Langue de Barbarie") facing the Atlantic Ocean. A long road bridge spans the Senegal River to the railhead at Sor, whence a line runs to Dakar. St. Louis, like Bathurst in the Gambia (and to some extent Lagos), is a good example of a town site well suited to its original function as a European trading outpost but not permitting expansion to meet modern conditions.

French Senegal lies in the Sudan savanna, the "Sahelian Zone" of French writers, where the dominant vegetation is a sparse grass brush with spiny bushes. Much lies within the basin of that important navigable highway, the Senegal River. Floods permit the cultivation of millet and guinea corn in the river valleys, and along the coast between St. Louis and Dakar there is a line of oases behind the coastal sand dunes. Elsewhere settlement and cultivation are restricted to the more fertile pockets where water is available; it is the peanut which has made the fortune of Senegal. Commercially cultivation is important only where the crop land can be reached by river, rail or road. At the head of the estuary of the Saloum is the rapidly growing port and town of Kaolack linked by a branch line with the Dakar-Niger railway. The river Gambia, navigable through the British strip to the French border, also taps peanut country. The story is always the same—the dependence of economic development on modern transport.

Unlike so many of the political divisions of West Africa Senegal lies mainly in one vegetation zone. The exception is the southern part lying between the Gambia and Portuguese territory which is drained by the Casamance and falls in the wetter zone. That area is less well developed.

Dakar [1]

Dakar is unique among the settlements of tropical Africa, and as such merits special attention. Since it replaced St. Louis as the capital of French West Africa and seat of the Governor-General, it has become despite its situation near sea level well within the tropics— it is less than 15 degrees from the equator—a European city. This is true both because the European residential center with its tall apartment houses, its shops, cafés and hotels (run by Europeans) is unlike anything else in tropical Africa and because large numbers of French and other Europeans have settled there, to all appearance permanently. There are schools for their children, bathing beaches and yachting facilities for their outdoor recreation, cinemas and dance halls for indoor. The congested site on the peninsula, cut off by the African town, led to a closely knit city, but the European

[1] Derwent Whittlesey, "Dakar and Other Cape Verde Settlements," Geog. Rev., XXXI, 1941, 609–638. "Dakar Revisited," Geog. Rev., XXXVIII, 1948, 626–632.

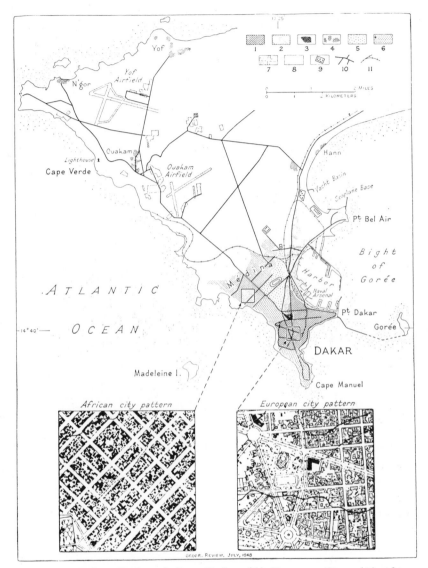

Figure 30. Dakar, Gorée and Cape Verde. (1) European City. (2) African City. (3) African market. (4) African village. (5) Sanitary zone. (6) Military reservation. (7) Airfield. (8) Factory district. (9) Tank farm. (10) Main roads. (11) Railroad. (From Derwent Whittlesey, *Geog. Rev.* 1948. Courtesy of the *Geographical Review*, American Geographical Society.)

suburbs have now spread toward the airport. The vast increase in sea and air traffic has concentrated much business in Dakar. With a magnificent natural harbor protected by Cape Manuel and extensively improved, the site is unmatched in West Africa, and the isolated rocky site supports Dakar's claim to be considered an "African Gibraltar."

The Cape Verde Peninsula behind which Dakar shelters owes its origin to the sheets of recent volcanic lava, partly covered with sand

Figure 31. Modern African Housing in Dakar. A blown-up balloon forms the "frame" over which the cement is poured. The result is a beehive-shaped home not unlike a traditional African pattern. (Copyright R. J. Harrison-Church.)

dunes. West Africa affords many examples of the importance of such geological "accidents"; Freetown is another.

It has been argued that, although Dakar is well within the tropics, the local climatic conditions link it with midlatitude rather than lowland tropical conditions. It is from Dakar or Cape Verde northward that the cool Canaries current with up-welling cold bottom waters tempers the air temperatures, and there are pleasant sea breezes, especially from November to February. The January average is 73°F. (with a mean of daily minima and maxima from 64°F. to 82°F.). There is no doubt that immediately to the *south* of Dakar the humidity becomes higher throughout the year, and the tempering effect of breezes off the sea is less where the Canaries current does not exist.

In the sheltered bay of Dakar is the tiny island of Gorée, so important in the history of French expansion in Africa but no longer of any significance.

Mauritania (Mauritanie)

Mauritania is essentially that part of the French Sahara which stretches to the Atlantic Ocean. Its southern boundary is the Senegal River, and in so far as the territory has any trade it is tributary to or lies in the hinterland of St. Louis. There is an African population along the Senegal in the south, but most of the half million people scattered over a third of a million square miles are nomadic Moorish Moslems who bring into St. Louis the gum and salt or cattle and skins which the country produces. Through Mauritania, linking eventually Dakar and St. Louis with French Morocco and Algeria, runs the Mauritania Road—more difficult and less important, however, than other trans-Saharan motor routes.

French Guinea (Guinée Française)

French Guinea stretches from the coast between Portuguese Guinea and British Sierra Leone inland to the headwaters basin of the Niger. The capital and chief port, Conakry, sheltered by the Îles de Los which were ceded by Britain to France in 1904, is itself on an island linked by a bridge with the mainland. Thence a railway runs through the territory to Kouroussa on the Niger, below which point the great river is navigable. Conakry is free from the sandbars which are a curse to so many African ports.

French Guinea in its 108,000 square miles comprises several very different regions. The coastal plain 30 to 50 miles wide is a very wet region inhabited by the Susu (Soussous). Cultivated plants include the Guinea oil palm, and there are European-owned banana plantations. Inland are rolling plateaus which form a foothill zone to the Futa Jallon. These are inhabited by the cattle-rearing Fulani living in villages of round huts surrounded by fruit trees. Crossing the Futa Jallon (Fouta Djallon on French maps), a considerable stretch of which exceeds 3000 feet above sea level, the land slopes toward the north, draining to the Senegal or to the northeast to the Niger. This part of French Guinea is linked naturally with neighboring parts of French Sudan—savanna country with peanuts and sesame. An important center and terminus of the rail from Conakry is Kankan. Finally the southeast of French Guinea is a forested region, much dissected and extremely difficult of access, lying behind Sierra Leone and Liberia which cut it off from the sea. It is now, however, penetrated by roads from Kankan as well as being linked by road with the Liberian port of Monrovia. French Guinea now has a large output of iron ore.

French Sudan (Soudan Français)

The huge area which forms the administrative territory of French Sudan comprises essentially, though the boundaries do not coincide, the basin of the Upper and Middle Niger from above Bamako, past Ségou and Timbuktu (Tombouctou of French maps) to below Gao. These towns are the main centers, and the French Sudan thus includes the great bend of the Niger, the heartlands of the old Mandingo and Songhai empires. For the most part the region is one of uniform and feeble relief. In the east and south the Archean peneplain is dominant, and its monotonous surface is varied only rarely

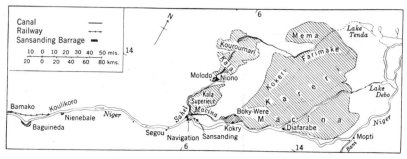

Figure 32. The Inland Niger Delta.

by small eruptive or granitic masses. Horizontal sandstones, resting on the peneplain, form a large plateau depressed in the center and with other broad valleys occupied by the Senegal, Niger and Black Volta. The sandstone plateau has a marked edge 1000 to 1500 feet in height—even reaching 3000 in the Hombari mountains—forming a great semicircle. Erosion has left flat-topped *mesas* such as the Manding plateau near Bamako. The sandstones are often covered, especially along the Niger, by flat stretches of alluvium, and toward the Sahara are stretches of fixed sand dunes.

THE INLAND NIGER DELTA.[1] Not only is this area of very great interest in itself but it also affords a practical example of what can be achieved in economic development with irrigation of a large flat area, and so points the way to possible developments in many other parts of the continent. Below Ségou in the French Sudan the River Niger once flowed into a large inland lake. When this dried up,

[1] R. J. Harrison-Church, "Irrigation in the Inland Niger Delta of the French Sudan," *Geog. Jour.* CXVII, 1951, 218–220.

the Niger split into a number of branches and meandered over the old lake floor, successive courses being abandoned because of silting. In 1941 the French completed a great barrage at the head of the delta at Sansanding with the object of raising the river level 5 meters (16 feet). The water could then be conducted through old channels, recut or deepened as required, to flood the lower lands (the area known as Macina) near the Niger for rice cultivation and also to irrigate the drier area of the Sahel for cotton and rice, sorghum,

Figure 33.   Large-Scale Mechanized Cultivation, Inland Niger Delta.   (Courtesy Office du Niger.)

peanuts and fodder crops.   The old lake silts afford good black soils with a high humus content.   The plan was eventually to benefit 2¼ million acres.   The sluice gates were not available until 1947, and the area immediately irrigated was about 50,000 acres.   The scheme includes the eventual settlement of 200,000 or 250,000 African colonists, each to work 8 to 13 acres.   With their families this would represent a million people.   On arrival each settler is provided with a hut, garden, three head of cattle, a plow and a well.   They market through a co-operative and purchase further equipment through the same channel.   What may be called a pilot scheme on a smaller scale was carried out higher up the Niger at Sotuba near Bamako.

Upper Volta (Haute-Volta)

In 1919 the colony of Upper Volta was carved out of the old colony of Upper Senegal and Niger, but later in 1932 the colony was suppressed, its territory being divided between the Ivory Coast,

Sudan and Niger. Then, in 1947, the separate division was re-established as a Territory, with an area of about 123,000 square miles and a population of about 3 million.

This territory lies in the same latitude as the populous parts of northern Nigeria. The French have made great efforts to counteract the disadvantages of its inland situation. There are numerous but not very good roads which focus on the two chief centers of Bobo-Dioulasso and Ouagadougou (Wagadugu), the capital. Both are served by air. The railway from the greatly improved port of Abidjan to Bobo-Dioulasso was extended to Ouagadougou in 1955.

Most of the country is a flat poor savanna land with numerous cattle, sheep, goats, horses and donkeys. Shea butter is produced, and cultivated crops include corn, millet, rice, beans, peanuts and manioc. Exports include cattle and peanuts.

Niger

The vast Territory of Niger with over 2 million people lies mainly to the north of the British territory of Nigeria and stretches roughly from the Niger in the west to Lake Chad in the east. The north is desert, the southern strip has sufficient vegetation to support large numbers of cattle, sheep and goats with smaller numbers of asses, camels and horses. The main difficulty of the country is absence of surface water. Indeed only three areas have sufficient water to permit settlement: the western districts watered by the Niger and its tributaries; the parts of the southern zone where the water table can be reached by wells and the water is potable; and the area near Lake Chad.

Dried or drying lakes yield salt and sodium sulphate (the latter in quantity for export near the Komadugu River in the east), and there is a demand for both in Nigeria. The Hausa cultivate millet, peanuts, beans and manioc, with cotton and locally rice near the rivers.

Focal points are Niamey, the capital, on the Niger and the terminus of a well-used trans-Saharan motor route. Zinder, north of Kano in Nigeria and linked with it by road, is another center from which the trans-Saharan Hoggar road passes northward through Air and the towns of Agades and Tamanrasset (see page 261).

The vast open savannas of Niger abound in game and form a favorite area for big game hunters—for lions, elephants, buffaloes and various antelope.

Ivory Coast (Côte d'Ivoire)
The capital of this territory of 130,000 square miles is the thriving town of Abidjan on the northern side of a large lagoon. As an example of French enterprise in Africa, Abidjan rivals Dakar both in

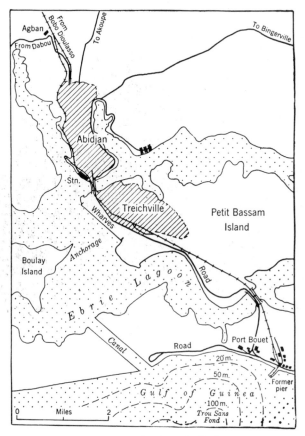

Figure 34. The Site of Abidjan.

interest and in importance. The whole orientation of the area was changed with the completion of the ship canal through the obstructing sandbar and the opening to traffic of the deep-water wharves in July 1950; the formal "opening" was in February 1951. Prior to that time Grand-Bassam at the mouth of the Comoé River and where the lagoon is connected with the sea served as an inadequate roadstead port. Later a port was established at Port-

Bouet (Petit-Bassam), where deep water (*Trou sans fond*—the "deep without bottom") approaches the coast, but the situation was obviously open and exposed. From the wharf at Port-Bouet a rail link was thrown across the lagoon to Abidjan. In the meantime the former administrative center of Bingerville had been gradually abandoned in favor of Abidjan. With the completion of the canal from

Figure 35. The Vridi Canal at Abidjan. This canal connects the lagoon with the open sea and has permitted Abidjan to develop as a modern ocean port. (Courtesy Information A.O.F.)

the lagoon to the Trou sans fond Grand-Bassam, Port-Bouet and Bingerville have all become ghost towns. From Abidjan the railway is the great highway to the interior. In the 375 miles to Bobo-Dioulasso it cuts through roughly the same zones as exist in the Gold Coast to the east, except that the coastal zone has the heavy rainfall of the Axim area of the Gold Coast and is naturally covered with equatorial-type forest.

This equatorial forest belt yields mahogany, and there is a production of palm oil, cocoa (first introduced 1904–1908), bananas and coffee. Inland in the savanna country there is a small production of cotton, but cattle, peanuts and millets form the mainstay of the African subsistence economy.

Though gold is known and worked, manganese deposits have been opened up, and there are small workings of copper, minerals play a smaller part in the country's economy than in the neighboring territory of the Gold Coast.

Dahomey

Dahomey lies between the trusteeship territory of former German Togoland on the west and the British territory of Nigeria on the east. With an area of 45,000 square miles and a population of some 1½ millions, its coastline is only about 70 miles long. From the old port of Grand-Popo through the chief port Cotonou (with an iron pier) a railway runs along the coast to the capital Porto-Novo a few miles away, and thence a short distance inland. The main line inland leaves this coastal railroad and serves the southern half of the country.

Naturally the vegetation and agricultural zones link with those of Nigeria and of Togoland and the Gold Coast. The forest zone of the south furnishes palm oil and kernels—the chief products of the country—but coffee and cotton have been successfully introduced farther north as commercial crops. Roads now render accessible the northern parts of the country.

Togoland

Togoland surrendered unconditionally to British and French forces in August 1914, shortly after the outbreak of the First World War. It was ruled under mandate from the League of Nations (approved 1922) until December 14, 1946, when the United Nations agreed on the terms of the Trusteeship. Of the total area of 33,700 square miles of the former German territory, the French control 21,893 square miles, including the whole of the coast. Lomé on the coast, with some 30,000 people, is the seat of administration; the total population of French Togoland is about a million. There are railways totaling 266 miles running inland from Lomé, which has a wharf handling the export of cocoa, cotton, coffee, palm oil and palm kernels, shea, peanuts and copra.

Togoland is entirely an artificial unit. Its people resemble those of neighboring lands, the Gold Coast and Dahomey. Its geographical divisions are those of its neighbors. There is a lagoon coast, somewhat arid as in the Gold Coast, succeeded inland by a terrace some 200 to 300 feet above sea level, which gives place to a marshy but fertile depression (with oil palms, bananas, maize and cocoa).

Northward is the zone favorable to cotton before the country of the Fulani and Hausa is reached.

Togoland illustrates many of the difficulties of the mandate or trusteeship system. It is not and cannot be part of the Federation of French West Africa and cannot share in any general advances the Federation may enjoy. Is the Trusteeship power justified in pouring in capital to an area whose future is at the dictates not of its people but of a distant council? Can private enterprise or individual settlers look upon such an area as they would Dakar or Abidjan? A Trusteeship power may do its duty by the trusteeship agreement, but can there be the personal, intimate interest in the territory? Togoland also illustrates the way in which African peoples remain divided by political frontiers. The Ewe people, for example, have occupied the same area continuously since the sixteenth century. But half of them now find themselves in French Togoland, about two-fifths in British Togoland and the remainder in the southern Gold Coast. Somewhat similarly placed are the Dagomba, who live partly in British Togoland, partly in the northern part of the Gold Coast.[1]

BIBLIOGRAPHY

During the Second World War the British Naval Intelligence prepared a series of geographical handbooks. Because they include copyright material they remain on the reserved lists, but may be consulted in such libraries as the American Geographical Society and the National Geographic Society. The two volumes on French West Africa being in English are especially valuable. Changes following the Second World War have been so rapid and important in West Africa that most older accounts are completely out of date, except where they refer to geographical conditions undergoing little change.

The accounts in the *Géographie universelle* must be read with this in mind.

For the British territories *Annual Reports* on each colony are issued by the British Colonial Office, and these contain extensive geographical accounts. A general survey of economic conditions is to be found in *British West Africa: Overseas Economic Survey* (His Majesty's Stationery Office, 1949). J. Carey's *Britain and West Africa* (London, 1946) is a useful general work dealing with history and administration up to that time. G. H. Jones's *The Earth Goddess* (London, 1936) deals with agriculture.

C. T. Quinn-Young and T. Herdman's *Geography of Nigeria* (London, 1946) is a geography written for the schools of the country.

See also *Handbook of Nigeria* (many editions), *Gold Coast Handbook* and *Handbook of Sierra Leone*. Detailed references are quoted above in the text.

[1] R. J. Harrison-Church, *Modern Colonization*, New York, 1951.

CHAPTER

14

The Sudan

The word Sudan is used in several different senses. Literally it is the plural of the Arabic word *suda*, meaning black; hence the Sudan is properly the land of the blacks. It has long been and is still frequently applied to the whole belt of country stretching approximately from the Atlantic Ocean in the west to the Abyssinian Mountains in the east, with the great Sahara Desert on the north and the hot, wet forest belt of the West African coastlands and Equatorial Africa on the south. In this sense it is essentially the belt of grassland, usually with scattered trees, constituting what is more frequently called the savanna country. The greater part of the west and center of the belt lies in French-administered territory. In the west are the French Sudan and Niger Territory, which are considered in Chapter 13. In the center the Chad Territory forms administratively a part of French Equatorial Africa.

A very important part of the belt lies in the east. In this chapter we are concerned both with the eastern Sudan as a geographical unit and with the political division of Africa known until 1951 as the Anglo-Egyptian Sudan. As this name implies, the Anglo-Egyptian Sudan was under the joint control of Egypt and Britain as a condominium from 1898 to 1951. The Anglo-Egyptian Sudan has a huge area, only a little under a million square miles, the closest calculation available giving a total of 967,500. The population is difficult to calculate because of the inclusion of large numbers of nomads; it is estimated to be between 8 and 10 million. Since the first printing of this book the Sudan has become an independent self-governing country—on January 9, 1954.

The Geographical Limits of the Anglo-Egyptian Sudan

The Anglo-Egyptian Sudan stretches from the heart of the great desert in the north where the boundary with Egypt is for the most part a straight line drawn across wastes of sand, to the borders of equatorial forest lands in the south.   In broad terms it coincides

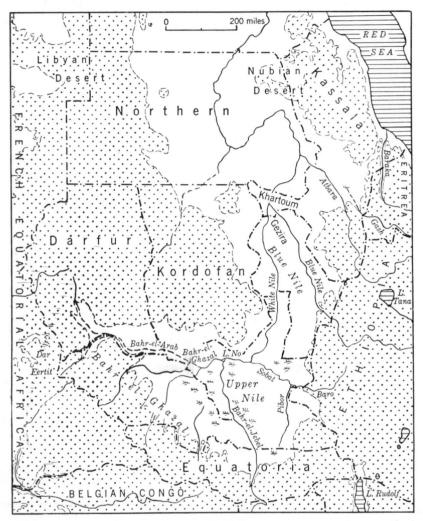

Figure 1.   The Relief of the Sudan.   All land more than 1000 feet above sea level is stippled.

roughly with the basin of the Central and Upper Nile, but excluding the sources of both the White and the Blue Niles.   Thus the Sudan as a whole, like Egypt, draws its life blood, the water of the great rivers, from territories beyond its control.   The waters of the White

Nile come from the plateau lands of Uganda, Kenya, Tanganyika and even to a small extent from the Belgian Congo. The source of the waters of the still more important Blue Nile, which below Khartoum supplies three-fifths of the total volume of Nile water, is among the mountains of Ethiopia.

It might be theoretically possible to divert the whole of Nile waters reaching the Sudan for purposes of irrigating lands in that country, in which case Egypt might virtually cease to exist. In Chapter 3 of this book, emphasis was laid upon the natural division of Africa into river basins and how existing political boundaries cut across the natural water partings or watersheds, with little regard for the ever more obvious fact that the future prosperity and development of the African continent must be based upon unified control of the waters in each of the great river basins. The unity of the Nile basin became a political slogan of certain sections of the Egyptians, culminating in October 1951 when the Egyptians abrogated the treaties with Britain and declared Farouk King of Egypt and the Sudan. The realization of unified political control of the whole Nile basin affects not only the status of the Sudan but, just as important, the position of the independent Kingdom of Ethiopia and all the East African countries already mentioned. It is very difficult to deal with the geography of the Sudan objectively when almost any statement is likely to have political implications, more especially as a very big factor is the natural aspiration of the Sudanese people for self-determination. The inhabitants of the Sudan are racially—though including many different groups—entirely distinct from the people of Egypt.

The Regions and Peoples of the Sudan

In broad general terms the Sudan consists of a succession of belts of country stretching from east to west, that is, from the margins of neighboring countries, French territory in the west to the Red Sea or the borders of Ethiopia on the east. Following a course from south to north and therefore cutting across these zones at right angles is the White Nile, entering Sudanese territory from Uganda in the extreme south. It will be convenient to consider these belts of country from the north, that is, from the Egyptian border, to the south.

THE DESERT BELT. The frontier between Egypt and the Sudan crosses the Nile just below the Second Cataract, that is, below the Sudanese town and railhead of Wadi Halfa. To the west lie the

great sandy stretches of the Libyan Desert, to the east the almost
equally arid wastes of the Nubian Desert, extending to the rugged
Red Sea hills and the shores of the Red Sea.

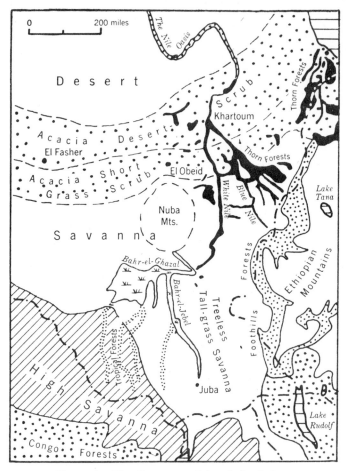

Figure 2.   The Vegetation Belts of the Sudan.

This desert belt extends southward roughly as far as Khartoum,
approximately in latitude 15° North.   Through this desert belt the
united Nile passes in its course, making a huge S-shaped bend.   To
the west the Libyan Deserts support a small number of nomadic
Arabs, to the east the desert nomads are Berbers who give place
toward the Red Sea to Hamites, known as the Beja.   The Beja are
tall people with a great mop of curly hair which has given them the

name of "Fuzzy-Wuzzies"—so well known to those who call at Port Sudan. In the great bend of the Nile are the Bayouda. Between the Nile and the Red Sea these various tribes possess a few camels and a few herds of sheep and goats. Both desert feed and water are scarce, oases are few, but it is to the west of the Nile that sustenance and water are even rarer.

It is perhaps to be associated with this increasing difficulty of life that the nomadic peoples of this western desert have long been guilty of raiding. The Numidians, mounted on their well-trained fast camels, able to descend with little warning even to the oases of Malik on the Nile, have kept the police forces busy for many years.

The Nile valley which passes through this desert belt may be described as an attenuated version of the Nile Valley in Egypt below Wadi Halfa. The Egyptian cultivators, the fellaheen, are not found south of the Egyptian border. Their place is taken by Berbers, who in Egypt may be found side by side with the Egyptian cultivators between the Egyptian border and Aswan, and who in the Sudan have established a chain of little agricultural villages on both banks of the Nile.

South of Dongola some of these little villages are occupied by Arabs who have taken to sedentary life.

Cultivation is carried out by using the shadoof, the Archimedean screw, and, though to a relatively small extent, basin irrigation from the Nile floods. The villages such as Dongola, Kareima, Abu Hamed, Berber, Atbara and Shendi have become markets to which the desert nomads come to provide themselves with grain and beans and peas and to sell a few of their animals or skins of goats and sheep. Because there are few oases in the desert belt outside those associated with the Nile little cultivation exists away from the river.

The stretch of the Nile between Khartoum and Wadi Halfa, being interrupted by cataracts, is not used for navigation, except to a small extent locally, but is served by railroad from Wadi Halfa to Khartoum, the railroad deserting the valley itself and cutting across the great desert stretch between Wadi Halfa and Abu Hamed. At Atbara is the junction from which the main line cuts across the desert and the Red Sea hills to the important modern port of Port Sudan on the Red Sea. It is at Atbara that the river of the same name draining from the northern hills of Ethiopia joins the Nile.

The Steppe Belt. Between latitude 14° and 15° the desert belt gives place gradually to one where vegetation though sparse becomes slightly more abundant. The number of people increases, and life becomes richer and more varied. North of El Obeid, now reached by rail from Sennar and Khartoum, are numerous Arab tribes, best described as semi-nomadic. They have camels and flocks of sheep and goats, and they follow the movement of the sun and of the associated rains toward the south, and then toward the north between June and October. In the dry months they remain near the oases, engaged in the preparation of skins or collecting the buds of gum from the small bushes which yield gum arabic. Gum ranks second to cotton among the exports of the Sudan. The acacia trees or bushes are cut with small incisions, from which "tears" of gum are later collected.

It will be seen that in this Steppe Belt there is no permanent agriculture, so that the well-cultivated Gezira, that famous triangular area between the White and Blue Niles before their union, depends for its prosperity entirely on the great irrigation scheme described below.

THE SAVANNA BELT. South of the latitude of El Obeid and Sennar summer rainfall increases, vegetation becomes more rich, one passes into the grassland with trees, or savanna, and agriculture becomes general.

The Nile seems to have provided a line of communication through this country in such a way that northern and southern influences have intermingled. So it is by no means uncommon to see side by side the little square hut of hard mud, so characteristic of the Nile Valley through its desert stretches, and the round hut with conical roof made of straw or grass and typical of the people of the savanna lands of so much of tropical Africa. Here the people are those we have considered previously as Nilotes, that mixture of Hamites and Negroes of widespread occurrence but among whom may be found Arab and other colonies.

In the typical savanna country the people combine hunting with herding and the cultivation of millet and sesamum. There is a certain amount of transhumance toward the great marshes of the south in the dry season; these people too are gatherers of gum, and market the hides of their cattle. To translate the words of Professor Maurette: "Nothing is more mixed than the population of these steppes and of these savannas, vast spaces without natural limits between the desert of the north and the forest or marshes of the south. There was the southern limit of the advance of Arab tribes and of the Nubians. The first Nilotics appear with the people known as the Shilluk. But above all, from Darfur as far as the region of the Blue Nile the Sudanese tribes are numerous."

A traveler by road in 1951 expressed the position in the following words: "Two hundred miles south of Khartoum we left the turbanned, long-robed Moslems behind and came into a different world, one of

Figure 3. Villagers Collecting "Tears" of Gum from *Acacia* Bushes. Gum arabic is the second export of the Sudan. (Courtesy Sudan Government.)

primitive people, who spoke no Arabic and for the most part wore no clothes. They carried spears, no longer for fighting, but for prodding their animals. Dura is their main food."

These open savannas have for very long periods been a line or belt of communication from east to west. As the peoples on the fringes of Negro Africa became converted to the Moslem religion, there followed the necessity of the pilgrimage to Mecca. Pilgrims who pass along the routeways do not always return, but sometimes remain to settle and form colonies amongst the indigenous peoples. In later times disturbed conditions in the Sudan led to much movement along this belt, and in still more recent times the movement of laborers, perhaps remaining to become settlers, has been equally marked. The study of migration, past and present, along this belt is one of fascinating interest, if of extreme complexity.

THE BAHR-EL-GHAZAL. The southern part of the Sudan is a huge shallow basin situated essentially on the great African plateau surface of crystalline rocks, through which meanders sluggishly the upper White Nile, or Bahr-el-Jebel, after it leaves the Uganda border. As already described, it is joined by the Bahr-el-Ghazal and the

Figure 4.   A Fishing Village in the Sudd Region of the Sudan.   (Courtesy Sudan Government.)

numerous tributaries which flow down from the watershed which lies between the Congo basin and the Nile basin. In the heart of the basin is that enormous marshy area, perhaps one of the most extensive in the world, known as El Sudd, from which the great masses of floating vegetation, or sudd, find their way into the river courses and into the Nile itself to cause both interruption to navigation and further flooding resulting from the obstruction.

In addition to the vast permanent swamps there are the "toich" areas, which are periodically inundated.

In the Sudd region there are immense numbers of fish in the shallow pools which attract vast flocks of fishing birds. The people of the region spear the fish in the early months of the year when many have been trapped in natural ponds by the fall of the flood waters. They are dried, and can then be used throughout the year.

The margins of the basin, including that division of the Sudan known as Equatoria, constitute remote, almost inaccessible regions where the Negro peoples practice their shifting cultivation and which are far beyond the influence of the Moslem religion. This is a vast area, and the population in sum is large, so that there is considerable truth in the assertion that the Sudan from the point of view of its human geography consists of two utterly different and contrasted parts—the Islamized north and the Pagan south.

The History of the Sudan

Such in brief outline is the physical background of the Sudan. Since claims to the territory are based in many cases on historical grounds, it is necessary to sketch with some care the historical development. Claims of Egypt and Britain may appear to be conflicting, and for that reason I proposed to use the brief historical account given by a Frenchman, as an objective view of one having no reason to side with any particular group. The following is an approximate translation of the account given by Dr. Fernand Maurette in the *Géographie universelle*, published in 1938, the year after the death of the author.

From the nineteenth century B.C. Egyptian Pharaohs had an interest in "Nubia." An inscription of 1879 B.C. found 40 miles south of Wadi Halfa forbids "Negroes" (without doubt the Nilotes) to pass farther down the Nile. From this time onward all the masters of the moment in the east tried, whether from the north or from the east, from the Mediterranean or the Red Sea, to put their hands on the country which was the source of precious materials—ivory, ostrich feathers, gums and, above all, slaves. In the time of the Emperor Julian the Roman power advanced as far as Ethiopia. The Coptic form of Christianity established itself at Khartoum and at Dongola, the foundation of which dates from this time. In A.D. 641 the Arab government of Egypt invaded Nubia, took Dongola, and demanded from the Nubian chiefs an annual tribute of slaves; the treaty was observed for the next 500 years. In 1169 the Turkish Sultan, Saladin, founded in Egypt a dynasty whose raids into the Sudan were numerous. Then there were Arab sultans from the Yemen, who, coming by the Red Sea and landing at Suakin, advanced as far as the Nile and to Darfur, which they Islamized, thus cutting off for a long time the Christians of the north from those of Ethiopia. After them and concurrently in the sixteenth century, the Islamized Negroes living between the Blue and White Niles, the Fung, founded a vast empire, with Sennar as its capital, which stretched from Ethiopia to Dongola. They systematically exterminated Christianity from all the low country lying below the Ethiopian massif. The Turks of Soliman themselves advanced from the other direction as far as Dongola. When the Fung disappeared a new Arab kingdom of Sennar succeeded them, and right from the sixteenth century up to the time of Mohammed Ali the Arab kingdoms of Darfur, that of

Figure 5. Arab Houses in the Old Red Sea Port of Suakin. (Courtesy Sudan Government.)

Sennar and the Turkish power divided the country between them. But they were concerned almost entirely with that lucrative trade, the supply of slaves to the Lower Nile or to the Red Sea.

In 1830 Mohammed Ali established an Egyptian government at Khartoum. His son, Ismail Pasha, obtained from the Turkish Sultan the right to establish himself at Suakin and Massawa. The whole of the eastern Sudan was in the hands of the ruler of Egypt. The temporary unification resulted in a sort of nationalism and an intensification of trade, but this was the time when the anti-slavery campaign reached its peak in Europe. Ismail, who needed Europe's support, was forced to accept a policy of reform. From 1869 to 1880 three European governors were named by him to the Sudan, Samuel Baker, then Gordon, then Emin Pasha (see Chapter 2). They suppressed the slave trade between Khartoum and Uganda. Economically, however, there was nothing to replace the profit, immoral and illicit but lucrative, and this spelt ruination for the country.

The revolt of the Mahdi which began in 1881 and which was an explosion of Mohammedan fanaticism undoubtedly gained strength by exploiting the discontent of the impoverished Sudanese chiefs. In four years, from 1881 to 1885, Mahdism conquered the whole Sudan. The evacuation of the Anglo-Egyptians was made by relatively orderly steps, only darkened by the murder of General Gordon at Khartoum in 1885. The Anglo-Egyptians kept only the Red Sea ports. For eleven years, until 1896, the country remained in the hands of the Dervishes or Mahdists. The commerce in slaves began again, although it was hindered by the Anglo-Egyptian occupation of the ports. This occupation was, besides, the base for a pincer movement for encircling the Dervishes. From 1885 the Berlin Conference had declared war by the whole of Europe on the slave trade.

In Uganda in 1893 a British company had given place to a Government Protectorate. In 1891 an Anglo-Italian treaty fixed the frontiers of Eritrea. Against the Dervishes, thus cornered, an expedition under the command of Kitchener was sent in 1896. It finished in 1898 with the complete conquest of eastern Sudan by the Anglo-Egyptians.

So it was that the Anglo-Egyptian Sudan as its name implies came under the governments jointly of Egypt and Britain. The treaty of 1898 laid down that the flags of the two countries should fly side by side; that the Governor-General of the Sudan should be named by the Khedive, like the Governor of Egypt, on the recommendation of the British Government.

This arrangement is, says Maurette, ". . . a sort of mandate, without the letter, and which lacked only the control of the League of Nations." The British Government guaranteed also to the Egyptian Government the defense of the southern frontier of Egypt and guaranteed to Egypt such volume of waters of the Nile as was necessary to the country. It was this question of the waters of the Nile which was the basis of the Anglo-Egyptian Treaty of 1898 and the subsequent development of irrigation in the Sudan.

A treaty between Britain and Ethiopia in 1902 guaranteed the interests of Great Britain and Egypt as far as the waters of the Blue Nile were concerned, and the tripartite agreement between Britain, France and Italy in 1906 extended a similar arrangement. A new agreement with Ethiopia in 1933 went into technical details in that it dealt with the construction of a dam at the exit from Lake Tana in Ethiopia, thus covering one of the points of a great plan for the control of the waters of the Nile which had been prepared after a long enquiry by the great British hydrologist, Sir William Garstin. The Garstin plan had five essential parts.

The first part of the plan was to preserve part of the waters of the White Nile for the period of drought following the flooding of the Blue Nile, and for this purpose a dam was to be constructed at Jebel Aulia, some 29 miles above Khartoum.   In the second place, in order to secure this regular volume of water, a large canal was to be constructed through the Sudd region.   In the third place a dam at the exit from Lake Tana was to be constructed to maintain reserve water for the flooding of the Blue Nile and to regulate its contribution for perennial irrigation.   These three parts of the plan concerned not only the Sudan but Egypt also, and the third required the agreement of Ethiopia.

The two final parts of the plan which concerned only the Sudan were the first to be carried out.   The one outside the Nile proper was the irrigation of the deltaic plains of Gash (below Kassala) and of the Baraka around Tokar near the Red Sea.   From 1929 the canals constructed resulted in the perennial irrigation and cultivation of 45,000 acres at Gash and 55,000 acres at the Baraka.   The much larger scheme was the construction of a' gigantic dam at Sennar across the Blue Nile for the purpose of irrigating part of the Plain of Gezira between the two Niles.   The dam was finished in 1925, and the canal works by 1929.

Economic Development of the Sudan

The economic development and present economy of the Sudan rest upon two bases.   The first is the production of traditional commodities, the second is the production of cotton, which is based essentially on the modern irrigation works.

The traditional production of the country is designed primarily for human consumption and consists mainly of cereals—wheat, and barley in the valley of the Nile, millet (dura) in the remainder of the Sudan.   The harvest has always been adequate for the population. A feature of the Sudan has long been the storage of grain in especially constructed elliptical silos in the ground known as *matmuras*. Later grain was stored in primitive elevators aboveground.   There are also the products of the herds of cattle, sheep and goats.

By far the most important Sudanese product for sale outside the country is gum arabic. The Sudan is the world's chief source of this substance, of which there are two kinds obtained from two different species of small acacia tree. With the low rainfall these trees may degenerate to mere bushes. The better gum is obtained from *Acacia verek*, the inferior but more abundant from *Acacia arabica*, and the

Figure 6. In the streets of Port Sudan. A Fuzzy-wuzzy brings a load of firewood on his camel. (Copyright L. Dudley Stamp.)

great source of the material is in the heart of the country in the Province of Kordofan.

There are inexhaustible supplies of papyrus which might be collected in the Sudd region, and with a world shortage of paper materials these are possibilities still to be explored.

Other agricultural products include sesamum and peanuts, both of which are exported in small quantities, and some of the millet also goes to Egypt for cattle and poultry feed. In the northern desert region dates are produced, and melon seeds are now important. By far the most important crop cultivated for export is cotton. Some American cotton is grown as a rain crop notably in the Nuba hills region of Kordofan and also in Mongalla and the Upper Nile Province, together with small areas around government pumping stations along the Nile. This is a development which took place almost entirely after the First World War.

The great development, however, is that of Egyptian varieties—sakel and types which have succeeded or replaced it and on permanently irrigated land. There are three major areas of production. The older are the inland deltas of the Gash and Baraka streams already mentioned, streams which descend from the mountains of northern Ethiopia and disappear in fan-shaped swamps. But the great area is that of the Gezira, irrigated by the Sennar Dam and

Figure 7. T.V.A. on the Nile in the Sudan. Although the great irrigation works of the Gezira are a government enterprise, everything is done to encourage the small tenant farmers. Much of the plowing is done by modern machinery, but some of the soft ground, as in this picture, is still best plowed by teams of bulls.
(British Official Photograph.)

its canal streams, and where the area under cotton has steadily increased to reach over 200,000 acres in the years following the Second World War. Much of the Gezira cotton is ginned locally at Wad Medani, that of the two delta regions at Port Sudan.

The development of the Gezira irrigation area is a fascinating story. It is the supreme example in Africa of a successful co-operative scheme between a European management and African cultivators settled in an orderly way on the reclaimed land. Until it was nationalized in 1950, the Gezira scheme was run on a unique system of triple partnership—between the Government, the two concession companies and the Sudanese tenant cultivators. It was in fact the largest peasant agricultural co-operative in the British Commonwealth and probably in the world, covering close to a million acres along

the banks of the Blue Nile. The land is now the main cotton-pro-
ducing area of the Sudan, it is irrigated by free flow from the Sennar
Dam. Before the construction of this dam the Gezira, a name which
applies to the whole doab between the White and Blue Niles, was
a flat clay plain with a precarious rainfall on which cultivators grew
an uncertain crop of dura (millet). They lived in scattered villages,
usually on the higher ground, and embanked small fields in an en-
deavor to conserve moisture. When the irrigation scheme was decided upon the land was surveyed and the owners' titles registered.
The Government then rented the land from the owners or purchased
that required for permanent works, about a quarter of the whole.
The railway reached Sennar in 1910, and the great Sennar Dam
built by the Government but delayed by the First World War was
completed in 1925. Two companies, Sudan Plantations Syndicate
Limited and Kassala Cotton Company Limited, were given concessions (which expired in 1950) to carry out subsidiary works and
generally to manage the land and market the crops. The third part-
ner, the Sudanese cultivators, grew their crops under guidance as
well as providing labor and sharing in profits of the whole scheme.
Although cotton is the cash crop, the crops are carefully rotated to
provide millet (dura) for food and a leguminous fodder, *lubia* (*Doli-
chos lablab*), for working bulls and other livestock. These food
crops occupy together considerably more land than the cotton. Of
all profits on the sale of cotton 40 per cent goes to the tenant cultivators, the remainder being shared by the Government and the
Companies. From a few acres in 1912 the area under cotton approached an average of a quarter of a million acres in 1940–1950.
Of the tenants about 20 per cent are also the owners of the land; 60
per cent are local peoples. Other tenants come from French Equatorial Africa and West Africa, especially Moslem pilgrims to or from
Mecca who have stopped to obtain work and funds and sometimes
settle.

The history of the Sudan Plantations Syndicate Limited is interesting. In 1904 the American philanthropist Leigh Hunt obtained an
option over about 11,000 acres along the Nile at Zeidab, but his plan
to settle American Negroes there proved a failure. An English company took over his option and it was this company which made a
new agreement with the Government in 1907, changed its title slightly
and took over the management of the Gezira lands. It is an example
of successful private enterprise co-operating with and approved by
the Government, but with a minimum of Government interference.

Transportation and Communications in the Sudan

It may be said that the million square miles of the Sudan fall naturally into two zones. The first zone can be reached by modern means of communications, the second zone is a vast hinterland within which life remains primitive, resources relatively undeveloped, primarily because of difficulties of access. The transportation routes, excluding airways, are shown in Fig. 8.

It will be noticed that the 2000 miles of railroad of the common African 3 feet, 6 inches gauge make the important irrigated tracts, including the Gezira together with Khartoum and the Nile Valley settlements, accessible to the modern port of Port Sudan, which has replaced the old Arab port of Suakin a few miles to the south on the Red Sea.

Over 2400 miles of river steamer routes exist, and apart from communication by air these provide the only permanent link between the northern and southern parts of the territory. Stern-wheel steamers of shallow draft are principally employed. The cataracts of the Nile result in three separated stretches of navigable river. There is first the connection from the Sudanese railhead at Wadi Halfa, down the Nile to Shellal in Egypt just above the Aswan dam, where connection is made with the Egyptian railway system. Between the Third and Fourth Cataracts there is a short stretch where the Nile settlements are connected by river services and linked with the terminus of a branch railway at Kareima. By far the most important navigation is that above Khartoum, from which steamers ply up the Nile itself to Juba, whence road motor services operate to the Uganda frontier and into Uganda as well as into the Belgian Congo.

The steamer routes up the Blue Nile from Khartoum as well as up the Sobat into Ethiopia and up certain other tributaries of the White Nile are possible in the high-water season only.

As in so many other parts of Africa road transport has increased enormously in importance. In the Sudan road construction and use are comparatively easy in the Steppe and Savanna Belts, and modern roads replace or parallel the old east-west migration roads. But the Sudd remains an impenetrable barrier which must be skirted by road transport. The road from Khartoum to Juba is open only in January and February and perhaps into March, when the melting snows in Ethiopia bring down freshets which wash away the flimsy bridges.

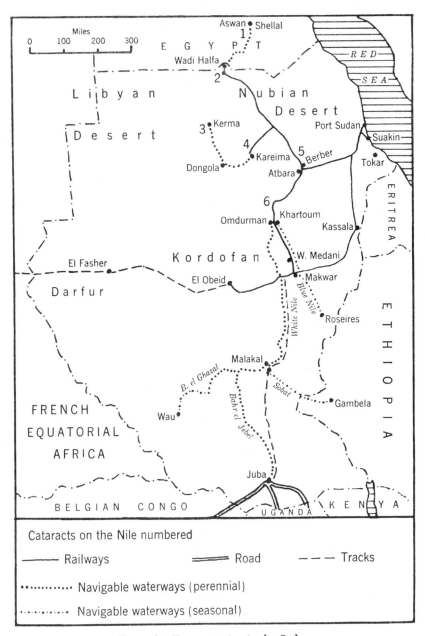

Figure 8. Transportation in the Sudan.

When the rains come in June grass covers the "road"; the grass is cut in December.

Very great use is made of air transport, with regular services, international and local, serving Halfa, Khartoum and Juba. The administrators at Khartoum are within 48 hours of London.

Khartoum, the capital, has of course become the focus of the Sudan. It is a modern town laid out to a design of the British general Kitchener. From about April to October the heat is often intense for long periods broken only by rainstorms with torrential and damaging downpours, frequently following sandstorms. From November onward days are warm and sunny but nights cold enough for Europeans to appreciate a warm coat, even if heating of houses is rare. The University College of Khartoum makes Khartoum the center of higher education.

Facing Khartoum on the other side of the White Nile is Omdurman, which, though a sprawling African town in great contrast to the modern Khartoum, is one of the largest market towns in Africa. It is of considerable antiquity, for long a capital and center of caravan traffic, and housing over 120,000 inhabitants.

The steady growth in importance of Port Sudan since its completion as a modern port in 1926 is reflected in the fact that it handles over 80 per cent of the foreign trade of the Sudan. To the casual visitor its coral gardens seen through glass-bottomed boats are perhaps the finest in the world to be visited thus easily.

BIBLIOGRAPHY

J. D. Tothill (Editor), *Agriculture in the Sudan*, New York, 1948. This is a veritable encyclopedia on the country.

CHAPTER

15

Ethiopia and
the Red Sea Margins

A glance at the physical map of the African continent reveals the presence of a great knot of mountainous country stretching from the shores of the Red Sea to the northern borders of the East African plateau in the neighborhood of Lake Rudolph. This great knot of mountains forms a continuous barrier cutting off both the Nile basin of the Sudan and the Sahara Desert from the part of the African continent which projects eastward for some hundreds of miles into the Indian Ocean, and which is occupied by the country of the Somalis, actually divided politically into French Somaliland, British Somaliland and Italian Somaliland, or Somalia.

Referring back to the rainfall map of Africa, we see at once that the mountain knot enjoys a heavy precipitation whereas the whole of Somaliland to the east is a continuation of the desert lands stretching across Arabia on the other side of the Gulf of Aden and the Red Sea. The mountain knot coincides in general extent with the ancient Empire of Ethiopia. This is another part of Africa to which the much-used adjective "unique" can also be applied.

The Ethiopian Empire

The whole area of Ethiopia (the people of Ethiopia dislike their country's being called Abyssinia) is one-third of a million square miles, the population is unknown, and, whereas official estimates place it as 15 million, more carefully based calculations suggest about two-thirds of this figure. The Empire of Ethiopia has the status of a sovereign independent state which has grown out of a combination of a number of kingdoms which used to recognize the King, or Negus, of Ethiopia as their King of Kings. The smaller kingdoms, such as Tigré, Gojjam, Gondar and Shoa, have become mere provinces, as have other parts which previously enjoyed at least some autonomy.

Haile Selassie I, who was born in 1891, was crowned king in 1928, proclaimed Emperor and crowned Emperor in 1930.

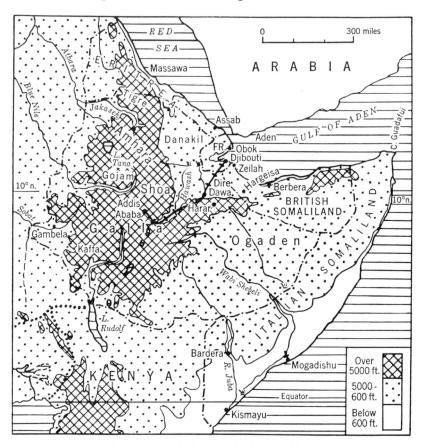

Figure 1. Ethiopia and the Eastern Horn.

It should first be made clear that Ethiopia is an empire and not a simple kingdom. The most important race in Ethiopia is the Amhara, who number about two million and who inhabit the Central Ethiopian Highlands. They were converted to Christianity in the early days of the Christian era and have always maintained close contact with the Egyptian Coptic Christians; in fact, the Abuna, or Metropolitan Archbishop of Ethiopia, had always been an Egyptian Copt appointed and consecrated by the Coptic Patriarch of Alexandria. The church is very strong in the country, the clergy numerous, the church holding large possessions of land. It was a natural consequence of recent events that Ethiopia should seek a greater degree of independence in this as in other directions. In January 1951, an Ethiopian became archbishop of the country.

To the north of the area which forms the homeland of the Amhara are the Tigréans, closely akin and also Coptic Christians. Both these races are probably of mixed Hamitic and Semitic origin. The most numerous of the people of Ethiopia are, however, the Gallas, constituting about half of the entire population. They are a pastoral people of Hamitic origin, some of whom are Christian, some Moslem, some Pagan. The Empire also includes Nilotic tribes in the southwest, Falashas of Jewish origin north of Lake Tana, and numerous tribes either of Somalis or allied to the Somalis live in the plateau country of the southeast of the Empire. Various Negro peoples live in the southwest, bordering the Sudan. As in East Africa, an Arab and Indian commercial element is found in the towns.

The importance of appreciating the racial complex within the Ethiopian Empire is great because of the widespread belief in America and Europe that Ethiopia is the supreme example of an African country where the people have determined their own destiny.

Between Ethiopia which nowhere reaches the seaboard and the southern coasts of the Red Sea lies Eritrea, which was part of the pre-1939 Italian African Empire. The people of Eritrea, who number more than a million, consist of Coptic Christians living on the plateau areas and Moslems, with few exceptions, on the lowlands of the western province and the Red Sea littoral. Italians settled at Assab in 1869, and Eritrea became Italy's first colony in 1889. When the time came for the future of the country, from which the Italians were driven by British Commonwealth forces in 1941, to be decided there was clearly opportunity for a difference of opinion as to whether Ethiopia should be allowed to extend its Empire over the whole of this country, on the grounds of uniting together all the Coptic Christians, despite the alien character of the coastal Moslem population. By virtue of the decision made by the United Nations it was agreed that Eritrea should be federated with Ethiopia—that is, should enjoy partial autonomy—by 1952.

With regard to its physical setting, if Ethiopia is examined in some greater detail it will be seen that the western half includes most of the lofty mountain area and where large tracts exceed 10,000 feet above sea level. This extensive mountainous western half is bounded by a great fault scarp overlooking the rift valley previously described. The rift valley in fact forms a great trench south of the capital, Addis Ababa, occupied by a succession of lakes, but northward it broadens out into the lowlands abutting Eritrea and the Red Sea. To the east of the rift valley trench in the south of the country there are other lofty mountains, but the country passes thence into a plateau, eventually fading into the lower elevation of the Somaliland desert plains. The highly mountainous character of Ethiopia is a direct result of an immense number of extinct volcanoes and huge piles of volcanic rock which cover so much of the country. Peaks too numerous to detail reach over 10,000 feet, many of them over 13,000 feet, and in consequence are permanently snow covered. This mountain massif enjoys a heavy rainfall, coming at the time of the Indian monsoon and associated with monsoonal influences. The rainy season is thus in the mountains the rainy season of India, June to October. This mountainous heart of Ethiopia is a land of abundant rainfall, of swiftly running mountain streams carving their way through deep and tortuous gorges, many of them eventually finding their way to the Blue Nile or to other Nile tributaries, the Sobat in the south, the Atbara in the north. The western rift valley edge is the main water parting of the country. Eastward the water drains towards the Somali deserts.

In the sparsely inhabited but well-watered mountain land the chief industries are pastoral and agricultural. Cattle, sheep and goats are numerous, the horses of the country small and hardy, donkeys sturdy and well adapted as baggage animals; mules are also available as pack animals. The immense range of environmental conditions has meant that Ethiopia is just as able to produce cotton and coffee as sugar cane and cereals like millet, wheat and barley.

From the point of view of agricultural production the Ethiopian highlands may in fact be divided into three zones. The lowest, called *Kolla*, comprising the lower slopes of the plateau itself and the deeper valleys up to 5000 or 6000 feet, is forested with a vegetation of tropical character for here frost is unknown. Here may be found rubber vines, ebony trees and bananas with coffee, which grows wild in abundance in the higher parts, date palms in the drier. There could be an enormous output of coffee of the Mocha type of Arabia from this zone.

Above the Kolla is the *Voina Dega*, or wine highlands, extending up to 8000 or 9000 feet, a healthy tract with numerous trees, where such Mediterranean fruits as the orange, fig and apricot as well as

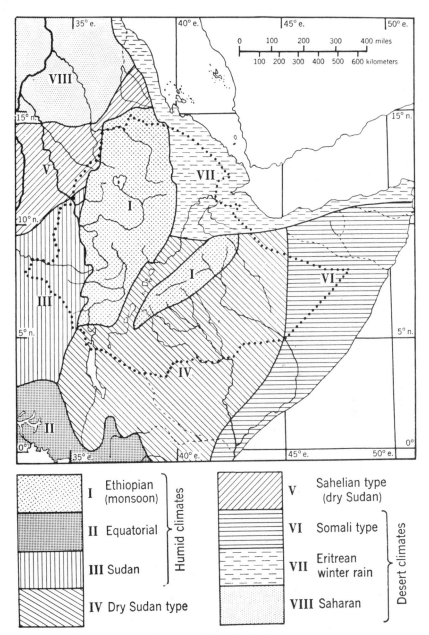

Figure 2. Climatic Regions.

the vine will flourish, where cereals can be grown and cattle and sheep are reared in large numbers.

Above the Voina Dega rises the *Dega* proper, extending from about 8000 to 14,000 feet. The degas are actually equivalent to Alpine pastures of open grassland with bushes, but there such cereals as wheat and barley can be cultivated and there is abundance of pasture for cattle and sheep.

In the arid regions gum arabic and gum tragacanth are collected and also those aromatic substances so prized by the people of former days, frankincense and myrrh. Beeswax too is obtained from the honeycombs of wild bees.

In Ethiopia there is obviously the possibility of vast mineral wealth, of gold and silver, known to exist, of the more mundane metals such as iron, or of resources like marble, mica, rock salt, coal, sulphur and potash. The discovery of oil on the Red Sea littoral of Egypt, and later in such enormous quantities on the Arabian coasts of the Persian Gulf, naturally suggests untold possibilities in the unknown Ethiopia.

Ethiopia has been described as the Switzerland of Africa, a description more apt of the mountainous western half of the country than the unkind designation of its arid northeastern plains in Danakil as the "hell-hole of creation."[1] Mountain Ethiopia shares some of its features with other mountain lands—its great scenic beauty, its invigorating mountain air and its sturdy independent peoples organized on a feudal clan basis, the clans long accustomed to fight, raid and pillage one another. A description of mountain Ethiopia today reads not unlike one of Highland Scotland a few centuries ago. One day it may well become a Mecca for tourists, a jewel in the great deserts protected by forbidding escarpments. If primitive by Western standards, Ethiopia boasts an ancient civilization. Its people, proud, intelligent and clever, yet face the bewildering modern world as a young nation.

Around the great mountain wall which encloses Ethiopia proper are wastes of rock and sand where existence in an environment of heat and drought is possible only when wells are known whose life-giving waters enable the desert nomads to keep alive their camels, donkeys and mules or their herds of wiry goats, lop-eared sheep and big-horned gaunt cattle. Wild and domestic animals alike live pre-

[1] L. M. Nesbitt, *Hell-Hole of Creation: The Exploration of Abyssinian Danakil*, New York, 1935.

cariously on the scrub vegetation under the eyes of the ever-watchful vultures. Captain Angus Buchanan, who led a body of Abyssinians re-entering Ethiopia from the direction of Khartoum shortly after the Emperor had followed the same route on his restoration in 1941, counted 9 dead camels in a 25-minute march. His party had 400 camels, but in the defile on this route entering Ethiopia every pack-

Figure 3. The Blue Nile amid the Mountains of Ethiopia. It is in this region that the Blue Nile receives the monsoon rainfall, causing the river to rise and carry life-giving flood waters to Egypt. (Courtesy British Overseas Airways Corporation.)

age they carried had to be man-handled to the summit, a task which took three days.[1] He records that on reaching the top of the pass at an altitude between 6000 and 7000 feet: ". . . we could hardly realize the beauty of the wonderland before our eyes . . . we had passed abruptly from the African desert to a green-clad paradise of wooded hills and placid cultivated valleys." This country of Gojjam south of Lake Tana is well populated. There are groups of small round huts of baked clay and thatched roofs, the people owning small areas of arable land similar to Scottish crofts, plowing with wooden plows, and growing wheat, barley and oats. In the gardens fenced with

[1] "Some Impressions of Abyssinia," *Scottish Geog. Mag.*, LIX, 1943, 24–27.

thorn bushes are numerous vegetables. Despite the climate the children who tend the sheep, goats and cattle on the hillsides go naked. Much meat is eaten, raw or served highly seasoned with pepper; goats and sheep are milked, and a home-brewed beer or rough wine helps the diet. The mark of a grown man, tall, lean and wearing a draped cotton *shama* over the shoulders, is the possession of a rifle and a well-polished cartridge belt to be worn around the waist. Though the men do the heavy work, most of the domestic chores fall as elsewhere in Africa to the voluminously clothed women. In Ethiopia, however, the women exercise considerable authority and are far from shy or unassertive. Here and there, as in Debra Markos, the former capital of Gojjam, are walled forts and the rifles carried are not for show, but demonstrate the continued existence of tribal and personal feuds. As a result, rifle fire is by no means an unusual sound even in Addis Ababa.

Addis Ababa is an attractively sited town on a plain sweeping upward to an escarpment to the north. There are many steep, narrow, winding streets, and some excellent modern buildings stand side by side with shacks—of the old mud walls or rusting tin—just as finely paved streets, lined with eucalypts, fade into muddy byways. Loose sheep and horses wander about jostling with horse buggies or a few modern automobiles.

Recent Developments

Overpopulated Italy's Colony in North Africa, Libya, her Colony along the Red Sea in Eritrea, and the large area of Italian Somaliland were all virtually desert. But the establishment of Italy in both Eritrea and Somalia not unnaturally brought Ethiopia into the sphere of Italian interests. At a time when the Negus of Ethiopia was consolidating his hold over the surrounding peoples from bases in Amhara, Tigré and Shoa in the period of 1880–1900, the Italians were consolidating their position on the Red Sea coast, and the French were already in possession of Jibuti (Djibouti), which they had annexed in 1884. An Italian force, invading from the Red Sea coast, was annihilated by the Ethiopians at Aduwa in 1896. Undoubtedly this resounding defeat rankled in the minds of Italians for many years. Although the three European powers concerned, Britain, France and Italy, reached an agreement with Ethiopia in 1906 confirming the independence of the Ethiopian ruler and acknowledging his right over the territories he had conquered in consolidating the Empire, the Italians accepted this settlement with the memory of the past defeats still in mind.

It was in 1936 that Benito Mussolini, the Italian dictator, felt himself sufficiently strong and independent of adverse European opinion to invade Ethiopia and to annex it to the Italian Empire. The Emperor fled to Britain and there lived in exile until, with the outbreak of the Second World War, British Imperial troops drove the Italians from Ethiopia and gave the country back to the control of Haile Selassie, who re-entered his capital, Addis Ababa, in 1941.

In the brief five years that the Italians occupied Ethiopia they carried out some remarkable work in road building and left Ethiopia with a legacy of motor roads which have since proved of great value. Previously the only other modern means of entry into the country had been the French-constructed and French-owned railway from the port of Djibouti in French Somaliland to the Ethiopian capital of Addis Ababa. This railway was constructed between 1897 and 1926 on a meter gauge, but since the Second World War there has been no through-running, and previously two trains a week in each direction were sufficient to cater for the meager traffic over the 500 miles. The Italian roads, over 3000 miles, are extensively used, but elsewhere the ox wagon, mules and camels remain the principal means of transportation in extremely difficult country.

It was not until 1947 that the country was linked with the outside world by wireless telegraph. The easiest way today of reaching Addis Ababa is by plane via Aden. The only other outlets for Ethiopian trade are westwards to Gambela on the Sobat River, from which steamers run in the high water season to Khartoum; to Berbera mainly through the Harar district of the northeast; or to the Red Sea ports, now Ethiopia's own ports, of Massawa and Assab. It is interesting that many Italian technicians remain in Ethiopia and are helping in the modernization of the country.

Almost the only town of any size in Ethiopia is Addis Ababa, with one-third of a million people. It stands in the highland zone at 8000 feet so that the three hottest months (before the rains break as in India) are March, April and May, but they average only a little above 60°F. In winter nights temperatures drop to 40°F. and even below, but the average is 58°F. for the coldest month. These figures of small range compare closely with the figures for Nairobi. In contrast to the old walled cities Addis Ababa is modern. It was deliberately selected as a site for his capital by the Negus Menelik II only towards the end of the nineteenth century.

Harar, the ancient walled city and center of the coffee district, is the starting point for caravans to the coast. It is a Moslem stronghold and the former commercial capital with a large Arab and Indian population. The old city is on a plateau; a new city has grown up at a lower level on the railway.

Eritrea

Eritrea consists of two regions. The first is the narrow coastal plain, backed in the north by the wall-like fault scarp of the Ethiopian highlands and in the south by the uplands of Danakil. The second region, the highlands, drain westward to the Nile plain. The population is mostly nomadic, engaged in the occupations of animal rearing and the collection of gums and resins. The Italians sought to develop irrigation agriculture, especially for cotton and food grains in the coastal plain. In the highlands agriculture is possible only in a few more favorably watered parts.

Most of the trade passes through Massawa, the largest port, and Assab, and it will be interesting to see how far these ports will serve to help an increase in the foreign trade of Ethiopia now that they come within the Empire. A railway runs from Massawa to Asmara, the administrative center, and thence to Agordat. From the latter there are roads southward and to the Sudan frontier.

French Somaliland

A small French Colony on the Somali coast has very little economic importance apart from the port of Djibouti, which replaced the original French port of Obock, acquired in 1867, but replaced when Djibouti was chosen as the terminus for the railway to Addis Ababa. French Somaliland would seem to occupy an important strategic position at the narrow entrance to the Red Sea through the Straits of Bab-el-Mandeb. Actually in the Straits there are several small islands. The chief—Perim—is British but too small to continue to serve as a naval base, a function carried out by the fortified British possession of Aden on the Arabian coast. Aden has the advantage of a magnificent natural harbor.

Somaliland Protectorate (British Somaliland)

This Protectorate (dating from 1882) consists of a narrow coastal plain only about a dozen miles wide, backed by a steep fault scarp. The highlands rise abruptly to a height between 4000 and 7000 feet, and then the surface of the plateau slopes gradually southward. The whole country is extremely arid, the population almost entirely nomadic, with a dependence upon sheep and goats and a few cattle. Some gums and resins of different kinds are collected from the bushes of the semi-desert, and there is a small production of salt.

The administrative center is Hargeisa and the principal port is Berbera. Berbera has long acted as an outlet for products of the Harar and the Somali plateau.

Some idea of the difficulty of economic use of the arid east of Africa is illustrated from the island of Socotra, lying 150 miles east of Cape Guardafui. It is a British Protectorate and has a population of perhaps 12,000 nomadic or semi-nomadic pastoralists. Though the flat-topped island is a familiar sight to the many thousands who travel by ship to India every year, the island cannot be reached by any regular steamship, nor is it even served by air.

In desert and semi-desert country vegetation patterns are often clearly visible from the air which are not readily visible on the ground. The commonest pattern is of course that which picks out underground water courses. Scrubby bushes which seem to have no pattern on the ground are seen from above to follow the windings of a hidden flow of water, often complete with branching tributaries. In Somaliland a curious rhythmical arrangement of vegetation in arcs has been noticed at first sight like ripple marking on sand, but on a huge scale—apparently due to delayed runoff in slight hollows. In the same country are relatively straight water lanes simulating a gigantic plowed field. The study of these patterns has been found useful in locating water supplies.[1]

Italian Somaliland or Somalia

This very large area has a population of probably about one million and consists essentially of a plateau 2000 to 3000 feet above sea level, sloping gradually eastward and presenting a series of steep scarp faces toward the coastal plain and Indian Ocean. Much is absolute desert, but from Mogadiscio (Mogadishu), a roadstead port, formerly part of the domains of the Sultan of Zanzibar, a fair road runs inland to a cultivated belt along the Webi or River Shebeli. The Juba River is navigable, and at its mouth is Kismayu.

[1] W. A. Macfayden, "Vegetation Patterns in the Semi-desert Plain of British Somaliland," *Geog. Jour.,* CXVI, 1950, 199–211.

The pastoral people of the country gain a little financial return from the collection of gums and the sale of hides of their cattle. A little cotton and sesamum oil are produced by the agriculturalists in the oasis settlements.

Italy's first concession dates from 1889, largely extended in 1901, and later by treaty with local chiefs. The Italians, who invaded British Somaliland on the outbreak of the Second World War in 1940, were driven out the following year, and the British took Italian Somaliland. After nine years of British administration Italy was allowed to resume control, on a Trusteeship, on April 1, 1950.

CHAPTER

16

Equatorial Africa

Equatorial Africa coincides in general with the great basin of the Congo, together with a region between the Congo mouth and Cameroon Mountain drained directly to the Atlantic Ocean. Politically it thus includes for all practical purposes the whole of the great state of the Belgian Congo and the very large section of French Equatorial Africa draining southward or westward. French Equatorial Africa as a whole covers an area of well over a million square miles, but we must exclude from this the 400,000 square miles which lie in the inland Lake Chad basin and belong properly to the Sudan, sharing many features with neighboring parts of Nigeria. The parts of French Equatorial Africa with which we are concerned are thus the coastal regions, Gabon and the trusteeship territory of the French Cameroons, the whole of the territory known officially as Moyen Congo (Middle Congo) and a large southern part of Ubangi-Shari (Oubangui-Chari).

Through the heart of the great area runs the line of the equator but equatorial Africa in the sense generally understood does not stretch right across the continent since to the east lie the high plateaus occupied by Tanganyika, Kenya and Uganda, with a very markedly contrasted character. The Congo Basin is essentially an enormously broad flat basin in the great African plateau. Although there are considerable differences from one part to another over such a huge area, there are many features common to the whole drainage area of 1,600,000 square miles.

The heart of the area enjoys an equatorial climate with no dry season, and this extends to the coast and the Cameroons. The so-called rainfall equator lies about 3° North of the true equator, and along this line rainfall is well distributed throughout the year; the total reaches 60 to 80 inches. The range of temperature between day and night does not commonly exceed 10 or 15 degrees, and the difference between the mean of the hottest and coldest months is not more than 3 to 5 degrees. This is the region of the hot wet forests so closely associated with true equatorial regions.

To the north one passes into a subequatorial region of northern type, with rainfall maxima in June and September, and an appreci-

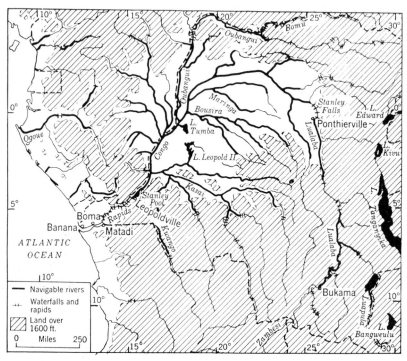

Figure 1.   General Map of the Congo Basin.

able dry period in December and January. Southward from the rainfall equator the southern type appears, with rainfall maxima in March and November, and a distinct or relative drought in June, July, August and September.

Where the southern margins of the basin are reached in the Katanga the daily temperature range has become considerable (15 to 20 degrees), and the annual as much as 15 degrees. The rainfall regime has become that of the southern tropical areas, with a rainy season from November to April.

There are fascinating local differences. Where the heights of the Cameroon mountains are reached there is a rapid rise in rainfall so that stations on a slope of the mountain itself show an average fall of 400 inches a year. Circumstances closely associated with the up-welling of cold water and offshore winds bring the arid coastal belt of South West Africa and Angola almost to equatorial latitudes in the neighborhood of the Congo mouth, where the fall is only 30 inches per year.

Equatorial forests of the evergreen type naturally occupy the heart of the basin, but give place as the land rises to a high savanna type of forest where trees lose their leaves in the dry season, though evergreen forests stretch as long tongues up the river valleys. Drier types of forest succeed towards the margins of the basin and pass naturally into the African savannas.

Along the coasts there are extensive mangrove swamps, especially north of Cape Lopez. It should be noted that the true equatorial forest is of much more limited extent than was supposed in the early days of the African explorers, who rather naturally penetrated by rivers and were unaware of the relative open character of the ground between the main streams. How far the large areas of savanna are natural and how far they owe their existence to the long-continued system of rotation cultivation practiced by the widespread though not very numerous African peoples belonging to various primitive tribes is an open question. What strikes one in flying over the more populated parts of the Congo Basin is the amount of forest which has been destroyed and the numerous areas either under cultivation or recently deserted. It is doubtful how much of the high forest is original; even in the depths of the forest evidences of former human settlements are frequent. Unfortunately when the land is cleared of forest the soil is very rapidly leached by the heavy rainfall and recovery takes a long time.

In the early days of European penetration equatorial Africa was chiefly of interest as a source of slaves. Later under white influence the tapping of native rubber trees and the collection of palm oil from the wild oil palms attained large proportions, and so too did the trade in ivory, one of the few commodities whose value enabled it to stand the high cost of transport by human porters from the heart of the forest to the rivers, or the coast. Overtapping or ruth-less destruction of the rubber-bearing trees killed that trade. It be-came more profitable to grow oil palms in accessible plantations. Some of the more accessible parts of equatorial Africa have come to make an appreciable contribution to world commerce, with planta-tion rubber, plantation palm oil, cocoa and coffee. Though valuable timbers, mostly heavy wood of the mahogany type, have been worked, the great variety of trees in the equatorial forests makes the working of any one type difficult.

It is true to say that today vast areas of equatorial Africa still remain almost completely untouched by European contacts.

Three main ethnic groups are to be found in equatorial Africa. There are the pygmy tribes, who still live a semi-nomadic existence in the western part of the equatorial belt. They do not mix, though they are in friendly relationship with their Bantu neighbors. Some of the tribes have achieved a special notoriety in school textbooks in the English language from their habit of building temporary shelters among the branches of trees, away from the danger of floods and certain wild animals. Some of them do still depend to a considerable extent on animals which they can kill for food, or on fruits and roots which they gather, but the majority practice some form of agriculture.

In the north of the region are people of Negro-Hamitic stock, forming a distinctive group of agriculturalists. They are people who were formerly cannibals. Over the remainder of equatorial Africa the people are Bantus. They live for the most part in straggling villages, often of great size. These Bantu peoples for some centuries before European penetration had established and organized extensive empires. Indeed the Congo derives its name from the Congo Empire which covered much of this area in the fifteenth century when the first Portuguese discoveries were made.

The whole of equatorial Africa has good reason to remember its contacts with white civilization with very mixed feelings. It has been estimated that from the French area alone some 12 million slaves must have been obtained in the course of 300 years, and the number exported from farther south by the Portuguese was probably greatly in excess of this number.

It was Stanley who said that the Congo, without railroads, is not worth a penny. It is still true that any form of development depends upon the provision of access by river, supplemented by rail, latterly by road and, for specialized purposes, by air.

Flowing as it does through the heart of equatorial Africa the great Congo is a more constant stream than the Nile or the Zambezi. The tributaries from the south, such as the Kasai, have two periods of low water and two of high in the year, but the tributaries from the north such as the Ubangi have a single maximum. Consequently the regime on the main river varies from place to place; at Stanley Pool the river is at its lowest in July and August. The emphasis, however, should be on the relative constancy of the flow. Below Stanley Falls the river is unimpeded by rapids for a thousand miles to Stanley Pool. The central navigable channel is never less than 10 feet deep, though the river with its shallows and islands is often 8 or 10 miles wide. It should be realized that the Congo, with its enormous basin and huge volume, is probably the largest undeveloped source of hydroelectric power in the whole world. One must remember too

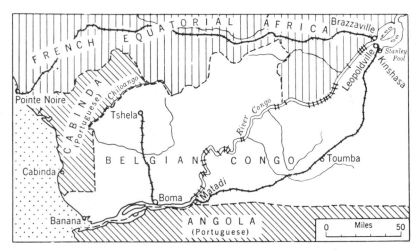

Figure 2. Countries at the Mouth of the Congo.

that the river in about 220 miles descends nearly 900 feet in a series of thirty-two rapids, known collectively as the Livingstone Falls, from Leopoldville to Matadi. What a dream for a water engineer!

The Belgian Congo

The Belgian Congo is the only European colony which lies almost entirely in equatorial Africa. Excluding the mandated or trusteeship territory of Ruanda-Urundi, formerly part of German East Africa and mandated to Belgium by the old League of Nations after the First World War and which has an area of 20,152 square miles, the Belgian Congo is estimated to cover 902,082 square miles. This vast area is nearly eighty times the size of the mother country of Belgium (11,775 square miles).

The Congo Independent State was set up in 1885 by Leopold II, King of the Belgians, and for more than 30 years was virtually the personal property of the King. It was only in 1907 that it was annexed by Belgium. The boundaries were defined by declarations dating from 1885 and by successive treaties with the powers interested in neighboring lands. An interesting adjustment took place as late as 1927 when Portugal exchanged 3 square kilometers—a little over a square mile—near Matadi in the Congo estuary for 3500 square kilometers in the extreme southwest.

Though the Belgian Congo lies almost entirely within the Congo Basin, it is much less extensive than the basin. Only over a few stretches does the political frontier coincide with the water parting. The whole vast area has but a tiny though immensely important coastline on the Atlantic—the deltaic lands of the river north of the main stream hemmed in between Portuguese territory to south (Angola) and north (Cabinda, which is administered as part of Angola).

For some 1500 miles the main river, and then its great tributary the Ubangi (Oubangui), and then the Bomu (which flows into the Ubangi) form the boundary with French Equatorial Africa. In the extreme northeast the water parting between the Congo Basin and the Bahr-el-Ghazal basin of the Nile is the frontier with the former Anglo-Egyptian Sudan, and in the extreme south the water parting with the Zambezi is in part the frontier with Northern Rhodesia. In the east the Belgian Congo stretches to Lake Tanganyika.

In general terms the Belgian Congo is a shallow depression on the surface of the great African plateau so that most of the heart of the country is less than 1600 feet above sea level. The geological structure is essentially simple. The basin is geologically very ancient. Recent alluvium borders the main river and stretches around Lake Leopold II; older alluvium—once the bed of a great lake—occupies the lower core of the basin. These give place on the higher ground to vast stretches of soft sandstone known as the Loubilache (Lubilash) Beds. Older than these are the famous Koundeloungou (Kundelungu) Beds, more localized in distribution. These are the oldest sedimentary rocks found resting on the ancient crystalline massif. They are probably Permian-Triassic in age and have been folded, not very severely, by the movements responsible for the folded mountains of the Cape in the extreme southwest of Africa. These beds include limestone, shales and sandstones, but the adjective "famous" refers particularly to the basement beds with great boulders scratched by ice. It would seem that at this period the whole of the heart of Africa was covered by great ice sheets, and it is held by many geologists that either the North or the South Pole of the earth was then over the heart of Africa.

Apart from the actual or potential value of the younger rocks as providing the material for agricultural soils, economic interest centers on the ancient crystalline rocks and mineralized ancient sediments. In the Katanga district in the extreme south on the Congo-Zambezi divide is one of the richest mineral-bearing tracts in the world.

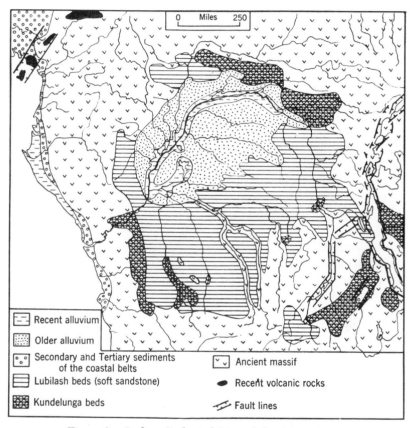

0   Miles   250

- ⊡ Recent alluvium
- ▨ Older alluvium
- ▣ Secondary and Tertiary sediments of the coastal belts
- ▤ Lubilash beds (soft sandstone)
- ▩ Kundelunga beds

- ⊻ Ancient massif
- ● Recent volcanic rocks
- ⚡ Fault lines

Figure 3. Outline Geological Map of the Congo Basin.

For long the population of the Belgian Congo was a matter for surmise, but according to the census of December 31, 1951, the African population numbered 11,593,494 and the white population 69,204, of whom 75 per cent were Belgian. Thus the overall population density is only 12.5 per square mile, in actuality very irregularly distributed. There are some pygmies in the forests and Nilotics in the northeast, but the bulk of the Africans are Bantu with some Sudanese. Most are fetishists and some 4000 missionaries (80 per cent Catholics) are scattered through the country. On the basis of the 1941 census, Pierre Gourou prepared a detailed population density map, published in color as one of the sheets of the *Atlas général du Congo* by the *Institut colonial belge* on the scale of 1:5,000,000. He used the 1047 administrative divisions known as *circonscriptions indigènes*, and apart from groups of forest pygmies who may have escaped enumeration the map may be accepted as an accurate representation of the facts. It shows some very remarkable contrasts in population density. Some 10 per cent of the Belgian Congo is truthfully a "forest desert" with fewer than 0.3 person per square kilometer—less than 1 person per square mile—and three-quarters of the whole Congo have less than 12 to 13 persons per square mile. By way of contrast most of Ruanda-Urundi has a density exceeding 125, and in the Congo itself Gourou finds an east-west belt roughly 5° south of the equator, including Kikwit and Luluabourg, of relatively dense population and a less pronounced one north of the equator. Surprisingly Elisabethville is an "island" of population in a sparsely inhabited area. The heavy population of Ruanda-Urundi is in line with that of neighboring Uganda and is closely related to elevation. The highlands are healthy because of the deleterious effect of height on the mosquitoes and flies which carry malaria and sleeping sickness. Local factors which influence the number and variety of these disease carriers are responsible, Gourou believes, for local population growth, and he instances the good health record of Coquilhatville right on the equator with the poorer record of Elisabethville nearly 12° South. Gourou believes the freedom of Coquilhatville from malaria is connected with the character of local waters which, draining from laterized surfaces, have a high content of aluminum hydroxide in solution. He believes that the well-populated belt south of the equator coincides with a belt where the forest, though of equatorial type, is sufficiently dry in some years to be burnt but where the fires do not become so intense as to damage the soil. Gourou's map affords an interesting example of a factual survey used as a starting point for an analysis of the influence of geographical factors.

The Belgian attitude towards the Africans of the Congo resembles that of the French, in that chiefs are accorded their authority by the government and are civil servants rather than the chosen of their own people. On the other hand, the Belgians encourage the use of local vernaculars rather than enforcing the use of French.

The Belgian Congo is divided for purposes of administration into six provinces, each of which includes several districts. The provinces and the chief towns are Katanga (Elisabethville), Leopoldville, Equator (Coquilhatville), Kivu (Costermansville), Eastern (Stanleyville) and Kasai (Lusambo). The capital was changed in 1927 from Boma to Leopoldville. Boma and Banana are now of little importance, but

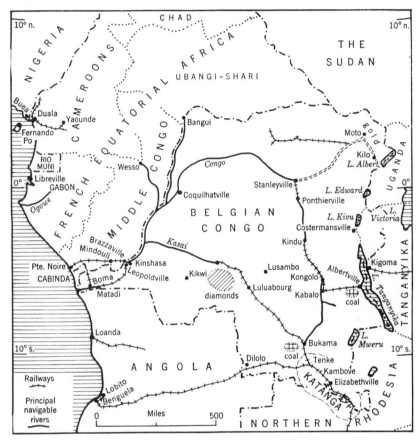

Figure 4. Communications in the Congo Basin.

Leopoldville with its adjoining river port of Kinshasa has become a great modern city. The same is true of Matadi, the chief ocean port, with its extension known as Fuca Fuca and the special oil port of Ango Ango, from which a pipeline takes fuel to Leopoldville for Congo river steamers.

The modern history of the Belgian Congo falls into several marked stages. When Stanley in 1877 came from the east and solved the problem of the Congo itself the whole territory had long been in the hands of scattered tribes, sometimes grouped into ephemeral and ill-defined Negro empires. It had been a reservoir of slaves going latterly eastward by Arab slave traders to the Indian Ocean, previously to the west and so eventually to America. Stanley found, in Europe, one man able to understand the importance of his discoveries and that man was Leopold II of Belgium. He thought out a comprehensive scheme of transport development to open up the whole basin, first a portage railroad from Leopoldville to Matadi on the estuary, second a combined rail-river route to the Katanga, which he secured, and third a direct rail to the Atlantic. All of these were eventually constructed. It was Leopold who had established in 1876 at the Brussels meeting of the International Geographical Union a Commission for the Exploration of Central Africa. After several expeditions Leopold established the *Association internationale du Congo*. This Association, under the active presidency of Leopold, rapidly followed political and economic rather than scientific aims, and, despite French and Portuguese objections, was "recognized" by the United States and Germany in 1884. Leopold granted numerous concessions to companies and, although the slave trade had ceased, there followed a period of exploitation in the companies' efforts to obtain, in particular, ivory and wild rubber. Gradually stories of harsh treatment of Africans came out but the stories were found to be exaggerated for political reasons.

In 1900 four-fifths by value of all the exports from Leopold's domain were represented by wild rubber from vines such as *Funtumia elastica*. But Leopold, being a far-sighted as well as an ambitious man, had secured control over a part of the plateau to the extreme southeast of the Congo Basin known as the Katanga. This he secured in 1892 at a time when local chiefs were considering asking Britain for protection. The mining period may be said to date from 1906, when the Katanga copper deposits began to be exploited, though there was but a small output until after 1911. Africa had, of course, shared with other continents the stories of fabulous wealth in minerals, but although copper, tin, iron and even gold were brought out of the interior the stories of the trackless forest and its perils had prevented anything approaching a "gold rush." The discovery of substantial copper deposits in the Katanga may be credited to the Belgian geologist Jules Cornet, who explored the area in 1890 to 1892. When I had the honor of studying geology under Cornet at Mons in 1919 he must have been the last of the geologists who worked in the field in striped trousers, a tail coat and carried a black umbrella!

Figure 5. Air View of Leopoldville, Capital of the Belgian Congo. A good example of an imaginative layout of a modern city in the heart of equatorial Africa. The large building on the left of the Boulevard Albert I is the Post Office. (Courtesy Office du Tourisme du Congo Belge.)

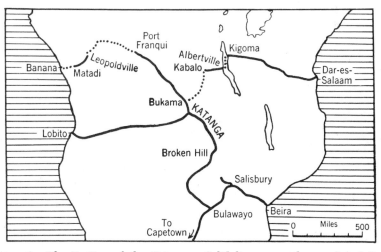

Figure 6. The Position of the Katanga. Solid lines are railways; dotted lines are water routes.

Vast concessions were granted by Leopold to land and mining companies, notably to the *Compagnie du Katanga* (1891) and its later subsidiary the *Comité spécial du Katanga,* and these had to be recognized when the territory became a Belgian Colony in 1908. Since that time the Katanga has become the focus of European activity in the Belgian Congo. Most of the mining activity is in the hands of the great combine formed in 1906 (involving Belgian and British interests), known as the *Union minière du Haut Katanga.*

At first production was restricted mainly to the vicinity of Elisabethville especially from the famous mine known as the Star of the Congo (Étoile du Congo), but later the center shifted a hundred miles north-northwest to Kambove. Rail access was first provided in 1910 from Northern Rhodesia, through which comes the coal from Wankie in Southern Rhodesia, but the completion in 1931 of the Benguela railway across Angola from Lobito Bay provided a convenient "side door" much nearer Europe. Three developments of great importance took place. One was the establishment of smelting works at Elisabethville and Jadotville so that nearly all the export is in the form of crude copper. Then, from 1925 onward, came the increasing use of coal from two fields within the Belgian Congo instead of from Wankie. The third is the growing development of hydroelectric power—first from the Cornet Falls on the upper Lufira River. In consequence of all these developments the southern Katanga has become the largest white settlement in tropical Africa apart from the Kenya highlands, and the industries are dependent on immigrant African labor drawn from many parts of the Belgian Congo as well as from Angola, Portuguese East Africa and even farther afield.

Apart from the great copper deposits the Katanga also yields tin and zinc as well as the greatest output of cobalt of any region in the world, and, for some time, almost all the world's output of radium.

There are other mining areas in the Congo, especially the Kilo-Moto region in the highlands northwest of Lake Albert which yields gold and the Kasai region which yields alluvial diamonds. Tin is found in Ruanda-Urundi.

A very interesting account of the Belgian Congo as it appeared in 1948 has been given by Professor R. L. Pendleton, whose wide experience in many parts of the tropics in southeast Asia and America gives him a natural standard of comparison.[1]

[1] "The Belgian Congo—Impressions of a Changing Region," *Geog. Rev.,* XXXIX, 1949, 371–400.

Figure 7. Potential Water Power in the Belgian Katanga. The waters of the southern Kalulo River plunge over a wall of horizontal schists over 260 feet high. Away from the mining centers there are few people in the Katanga, and only some of the many rivers have been harnessed to provide power for the mining operations. (Courtesy Office du Tourisme du Congo Belge.)

Like other recent travelers he stresses the amazing contrasts. He suggests that development in Central Africa has been by jumps rather than by slow stages; that Africans, who never used a wheel in their native culture, rapidly and unaided learned to operate railroads and river steamers and drive automobiles and trucks; that they had no draft animals and no plows and yet soon learned to run tractors, though many of them—perhaps wisely—consider the hoe a better implement.

Not far from the huge reduction works for the mines in the Katanga are to be found primitive charcoal furnaces for the smelting of iron and copper blown by means of skins tied over wooden funnels. Pendleton draws attention to the rapidity with which the forests, by being burnt, are giving place to savanna, and where the soil, thus exposed, deteriorates almost at once. There has been the need for extended production of foodstuffs, particularly manioc, upland rice, corn (maize) and beans, for feeding the new urban and mining population. The Europeans seem still unable to appreciate that north temperate methods of soil management and crop production cannot be applied in the new environments in which they find themselves.

Pendleton calls attention to the not altogether happy changes taking place among the African peoples. Formerly villages were essentially communal minded, sharing what they had; the men cleared the land and did the hunting, the women planted, tended and harvested the crops and prepared the food. Where a husband prospered he usually bought a second wife so as to have more labor for more food production. Where a young man in a community learned by some Western contact to be a better farmer, his relatives would immediately expect to share his better crops rather than copy his methods for themselves. Europeanization has resulted in the growth of individualism, the young Africans adopting European customs such as cutting their hair short and wearing some Western clothing. They have become virtually detribalized, but with no adequate substitute for the old established order.

The Belgian administrators are fully alive to the difficulties of the position. They seek to study and understand tribal and family organization and to graft a knowledge of better agricultural methods with higher yielding and better quality crops on the traditional crop rotation. As Pendleton says, the Belgians and their associates deserve great credit. Because of their relatively late start they are able to avoid many of the pitfalls which have brought such unhappy results in the colonies of the other governments.

Despite the developments in the Congo as a whole the Katanga forms a region perhaps without parallel in the world. In the heart of this busy mining area stands Elisabethville, the capital, with its magnificent skyscraper blocks of offices which would be a credit to

Figure 8. On the Shores of Lake Kivu, 4790 Feet above Sea Level. Costermansville has developed into a modern city and health resort. (Copyright Aerofilms Limited.)

cities anywhere in the world. The layout of the modern towns is on comparable lines. Much has been written of the importance of access in Africa, and the story of the opening up of the Katanga is well known. It is now reached by the Congo routes, where road and rail has shortened former long tedious journeys. It is reached by rail from the ports of Benguela or Lobito. It is reached by the South African railway systems through the Rhodesias; and the later link by railway to Lake Tanganyika, which, when Pendleton visited the Congo, was in course of construction, renders it accessible from that Lake and hence from Dar-es-Salaam on the Indian Ocean.

It seems strange to think of any area of the heart of Africa as one to be used as a holiday or health resort by Europeans. Yet the high country, largely open grassland, around Lake Kivu and especially the remarkable modern settlement of Costermansville are examples of what opportunities there are for European settlement even in the very heart of Africa. Ease of access by air to places like

Figure 9. Among the Hills of Ruanda-Urundi. In the center is a coffee plantation of an African chief. (Courtesy Office du Tourisme du Congo Belge.)

Costermansville has placed equatorial Africa within a couple of days' journey of the cities of Europe. The present means of communication in the Congo are clearly shown in Fig. 4 and do not require description here.

Ruanda-Urundi

At the end of the First World War Belgium as one of the Allies received under mandate from the League of Nations the territory of Ruanda-Urundi, a tract some 20,900 square miles lying east of the main western Rift Valley, that is, west of Lake Kivu and the northern end of Lake Tanganyika. Formerly part of German East Africa, it has formed administratively an integral part of the Belgian Congo since 1925—adjoining the progressive province of Costermansville or Kivu. A trusteeship agreement was approved by the United Nations General Assembly in 1946. It thus lies on the high plateau and adjoins southwestern Uganda on the north, forming in fact a continuation of that island of dense population in the heart of Africa. The census of 1949 showed 3,882,393 Africans belonging to three tribes, 3407 Europeans and 2894 Asiatics. The cattle-raising and agricultural Africans were not organized as fully as their neighbors in Uganda and planted only enough for the season, so that there is, or was, the usual "hungry" season before the harvest. The bean is the great food staple with peas and corn, but crop failure is an ever-present danger owing to the vagaries of the climate. The introduction by the Belgians of manioc and sweet potatoes, less dependent on the weather, did not prove immediately popular owing to the longer period taken to reach maturity. The development of cash crops is coming slowly.

Climatically there are five regions. First there are two long narrow belts running north and south parallel to Lake Tanganyika. This is in the tropical lowland of the Rift, with about 35 inches of rain. Here is situated Usumbura, the chief settlement, on the shores of Lake Tanganyika. High-forested mountains with heavy rainfall (and a double maximum) follow to the east and form the Congo-Nile watershed. The Central Plateau with about 50 inches occupies most of the heart of the country. Farther east is the warm dry eastern depression. Finally the volcanic district of the northwest forms a distinct area.

French Equatorial Africa

Afrique equatoriale française (or A.E.F.) is perhaps the least homogeneous of all the political divisions of Africa, stretching as it does from the Saharan margin around Lake Chad to the Congo River and Atlantic margins, actually as much as 5° *south* of the equator. What has been said about equatorial Africa in general applies thus to the southern half only of French Equatorial Africa. Despite its vast area the whole territory is without the proved mineral resources of the Belgian Congo and so remains for the most part as it has been for centuries past. French settlements on the Gabun or Gabon River date from 1839, and Libreville on the Atlantic coast was founded in 1848, as its name implies, for liberated slaves. From these settlements as bases the sphere of French influence was steadily expanded and limits defined by a series of treaties. The boundary between French Equatorial Africa and the Anglo-Egyptian Sudan was not fixed until February 1924, and the present organization into the four territories of Gabun, Middle Congo, Ubangi-Shari and Chad dates only from 1946. The Governor-General lives at Brazzaville, and there is a Governor at the capital of each of the four territories—at Libreville for Gabun; at Pointe-Noire for the Middle Congo; at Bangui for Ubangi-Shari; and at Fort Lamy for Chad.

Official estimates place the area of tropical forests at 300,000 square miles. The fact that wild rubber is still a significant output is an

Figure 10. Contrasts in Duala, French Cameroons. This view shows a modern hotel, an African store, an American automobile, a British bicycle and Africans in various stages of European dress. (Copyright R. J. Harrison-Church.)

indication of the continued underdeveloped character of the country. Ivory too continues as an article of export, but the fact that there is a production of copper, zinc, coal, lead, diamonds, corundum and tantalum is an indication of mineral developments which may be greatly extended.

In a direct line it is 1500 miles from the north to the south of French Equatorial Africa; sheer distance presents a tremendous obstacle to economic development. The railway from the fine modern and artificial Atlantic port of Pointe-Noire to Brazzaville on the navigable Congo enables the products of the Moyen Congo to reach the outside world. A road 600 miles from Bangui to the Cameroons port of Duala similarly enables valuable products to come out of Ubangi-Shari. Although roads now reach the cotton-growing lands of the far north, clearly haulage costs must remain very high. Port Gentil and Libreville serve more directly as the outlets of Gabun since this, the original French colony, is largely the basin of the Ogowe (Ogooué) River and oriented towards the Atlantic.

The total population of French Equatorial Africa, excluding the trusteeship territory of the Cameroons, is only between 4 and 5 millions, an overall density of about 4 per square mile. There are huge areas virtually uninhabited. There is thus no reservoir of labor to support a plantation system such as might naturally follow the system of granting concessions to land companies, which the French started at the end of the last century. Similarly railroad construction, road building and other public works start with the same handicap.

Trusteeship Territory of the French Cameroons

As briefly noted in Chapter 2, the Germans secured a hold on the Cameroons coast in 1884. British traders and missionaries had already established settlements in the country near the present Victoria and Duala within sight of the great Cameroon Mountain, but Britain had declined the request of the Duala chiefs to extend a protectorate over their lands.

The Germans were quick to appreciate the value of the highland zone, and in 1901 moved their administrative headquarters from Duala to Buea on the southeastern slopes of the mountains. On the healthy heights above the equatorial rainforest they looked to establish European settlements. In particular they set to work to study scientifically the problems of tropical agriculture and established a fine botanic garden at Victoria. Their buildings were constructed with double roofs for purposes of insulation and were built to last. At first the wealth of the country came from palm oil and rubber gathered from the forest, but they introduced plantation agriculture, notably of bananas, which were sent in large quantities from Victoria to Hamburg before the First World War. The Germans pushed their territorial claims inland to Lake Chad, passing thus (like neighboring Nigeria) out of the forest through the savanna zone to the Saharan margins. They adopted over the people of the grasslands a form of indirect rule, recognizing the integrity of tribal groups.

In 1911 the French were forced to cede to Germany 100,000 square miles, giving German Kamerun direct access to the Ubangi and to the Congo, thus cutting the French equatorial empire in half. Almost as bad was the inclusion of a strip of land reaching the Atlantic only a few miles north of Libreville. This was the price of Germany's non-interference with French plans in Morocco.

Early in the First World War British and French forces took the Cameroons; the French reincorporated the territory they had been forced to yield three years earlier and the remainder was divided— 166,000 square miles going to France and 30,000 to Britain, including Victoria and Buea. This was later recognized by the League of Nations under the mandate system, now trusteeships under United Nations.

To a considerable extent the French have built on the economic foundations laid by the Germans. The port of Duala has been progressively improved (formerly ocean vessels anchored 25 miles away); a railway has been constructed to Yaunde (Yaoundè) on the plateau which has been made the seat of government and the focus of an important road system. One road goes through to Fort Lamy, the capital of the Chad region, crossing the upper Benue at a point from which it is navigable through Nigeria. Though the European-owned plantations have advanced but little, the plantations for coffee, oil palm and cocoa which the Germans encouraged African chiefs to establish have now a considerable output. But the total population of the whole vast tract is only 3 million, and it is difficult to develop plantations without an element of forced labor.

It may be noted that on the whole economic development in the trusteeship territory is, largely for historical reasons, ahead of that in A.E.F. proper.

Spanish Guinea

This is a small and undeveloped territory covering rather less than 11,000 square miles and a total population of less than 200,000. These figures include the island of Fernando Po, of 778 square miles and about 40,000 people, with the town of Santa Isabel, where the governor resides. The islands of Annobón (7 square miles), Corisco (5½ square miles), Great and Little Elobey (less than a square mile) are also included in Spanish Guinea, so that the continental area, otherwise known as Río Muni from the chief settlement, has a density of only nine or ten persons per square mile.

Spanish Guinea is the sole tropical remnant of the once vast Spanish Empire. But to believe that Spain now neglects this remnan would be to harbor a very false idea. The mainland, it is true, of 10,163 square miles is, like the neighboring French territory, but little developed. There are however large and important timber, oil palm and coffee concessions and the Africans—besides growing their usual foodstuffs—also grow coffee and cocoa for export.

Tiny Annobón has some 1400 people, is heavily overpopulated and many seek work in fishing off Fernando Po.

Figure 11. The Agricultural Offices, Santa Isabel, Fernando Po. An example of modern Spanish interest in the development of Africa. On the right a Guinea oil palm; on the left a Traveler's palm. (Copyright R. J. Harrison-Church.)

Fernando Po (Fernando Póo to the Spaniards) is unique in West Africa. The volcanic line of the Cameroon mountains extends southwestwards. Fernando Po is thus a collection of extinct volcanoes rising from ocean depths to heights of 6000 feet above sea level. The fine harbor of Santa Isabel is part of an old crater invaded by the sea; elsewhere on the island are volcanic peaks rising from the ash and lava plains and fascinating crater lakes. The heart is forested or grassed, with some Dutch and Swiss cattle on the grasslands. On the west, north and eastern fringes of the island, up to about 2000 feet, are extensive plantations. Fine-quality cocoa is by far the most important crop and, with coffee, accounts for four-fifths of the cultivated area, the rest being occupied by African foodstuffs. Export crops are produced on plantations, some extending to about 2000 acres; these are owned and managed by Spanish settlers and companies. Europeans number between 3000 and 4000. These European plantations are but one of the contrasts to all other parts of West Africa.

Santa Isabel is essentially a Spanish town set in the tropics—fully as European as Dakar or Abidjan—in which Africans happen to live. It houses a quarter of the people of the island; its fine Spanish-type houses and public buildings suggest both prosperity and a lively interest in the island's welfare. There are excellent macadam roads, and there is even a pleasant hill station (Moka) with chalets, where conferences can be held, at 4500 feet.

The Spaniards were excluded from Africa by the Treaty of Tordesillas of 1494, and it was not till 1778 that Portugal ceded these territories and not till 1845 that Spanish occupation was really effective. The indigenous Bantu people, numbering 10,000, form an inadequate labor supply for the plantations so that there are twice as many immigrants, especially Ibos from Nigeria. As usual in such cases, men outnumber women by three to one.

São Tomé and Príncipe

These Portuguese islands lie between Annobón and Fernando Po and form part of the same line of volcanic peaks. They constitute a province under a governor. With an area of 372 square miles, they have over 60,000 people, including a thousand Europeans and three thousand of mixed blood. São Tomé in particular is prosperous and well developed, with roads and numerous well-equipped plantations. Exports include cocoa, coffee, copra, palm oil and cinchona. Here again, with favorable physical conditions, is proof that the Portuguese are not backward in fostering the economic development of their colonies. The soil is extremely fertile. Settlement and development on a permanent basis by the Portuguese date from 1493. The earlier prosperity was based on sugar. Labor shortage, as in Fernando Po, led to the introduction of contract labor from Angola and elsewhere, now forming the bulk of the population.

There are interesting historical survivals in many parts of Africa. A good example is the fortress of São João Batiste of Ajuda on the coast of Dahomey still claimed by Portugal, and forming part of the province of São Tomé and Príncipe.

CHAPTER
17

East Africa

The Physical Background

Each of the great regions into which the continent of Africa naturally falls has certain points of distinctive individuality. Over so much of the continent the point of individuality is the river basin—the basin of the Nile and the basin of the Congo and to a less extent the basin of the Zambezi, for example. East Africa is different in that there the emphasis is on the unity suggested by a great continuous plateau on the surface of which, occupying a shallow depression, is that enormous stretch of shallow water, Lake Victoria. To the west is the most remarkable trough to be found on the earth's surface, the main East African Rift Valley, with its chain of long, narrow, deep lakes. To the east are coastal lowlands of varying widths.

The greater part of the East African plateau lies at an elevation of more than 4000 feet above sea level. Large sections in Kenya where the plateau is crossed by the equator are at an elevation of over 6000 feet. An entire modification of climatic conditions results, in such a way that under the very equator itself are lands claimed to be ideal for the settlement and development of white men nurtured in cool mid-latitude lands. As elsewhere around the fringes of Africa the plateau descends to the coast by a series of steps, and as soon as lower land is reached physical conditions afforded by the terrain and the climate are utterly different. Hence the eastern half of Kenya with the port of Mombasa, or the islands of Zanzibar and Pemba off the coast, or farther south Portuguese East Africa, which lies almost entirely on land of lower elevations, offer marked contrasts to the regions high up on the plateau itself.

Structurally the East African plateau does not differ in any marked degree from the other parts of the African continent. There is the same complex of ancient metamorphic rocks of gneisses and schists,

Figure 1. East Africa.

of ancient sandstones, and there are huge areas occupied by granite, all making up the plateau mass. As elsewhere in Africa, the solid rocks are obscured by a varied mantle of decomposed rock and soils predominantly of a red color, a mantle sufficiently deep to hinder the discovery of those mineral riches sought by man and which occur scattered through the ancient complex. In consequence there are important mineral deposits still in course of discovery and doubtless others to be discovered so that East Africa affords examples of some spectacular mineral developments within recent decades, including the discovery of some of the richest diamond-bearing ground in the world.

We have discussed elsewhere the development in Africa of peneplain surfaces, that is, of surfaces which are almost plains and which in terms of years are very ancient. At a time when great mountain-building movements in other parts of the world were folding the weaker rocks to form the great mountain chains, the western Cordillera of North America, the Andes system of South America, the Alpine and Himalayan chains of Europe and Asia, and even the Atlas of northwest Africa itself, the bulk of the African continent was a great rigid block, resistant to any further folding movements. Its very rigidity, however, resulted in the development of great cracks, and along these cracks there was differential movement. In particular it would seem that in East Africa, to compensate for the great movements of compression in other parts of the world, a region of crustal tension developed. Parallel cracks developed, and long narrow blocks of country were let down between them, giving rise to rift valleys. It is possible that the rift valleys of East Africa link up into two great lines, an eastern and a western. This possibility is shown diagrammatically in Fig. 2.

According to this scheme, based on the early interpretation of Professor J. W. Gregory (*The Rift Valleys and Geology of East Africa*, London, 1921), there is one main or eastern trough. This is occupied today by Lake Nyasa in the south, and passes almost directly northward through the heart of Tanganyika and Kenya to include the depression occupied by Lake Rudolph near the northern border of Kenya. It then passes through the heart of Ethiopia, where it is partly filled by outpourings from volcanoes, though also marked by a chain of deep lakes. It then broadens northward to be occupied by the Red Sea; and finally it terminates in the north-south trough of western Asia occupied by the Dead Sea, the Jordan Valley and the Sea of Galilee.

From this main rift valley Gregory believed that a major branch passed off westward, forming the trough occupied successively by Lakes Tanganyika, Kivu, Edward and Albert. More detailed geo-

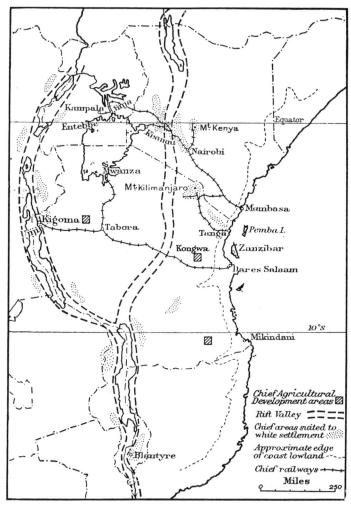

Figure 2. The Rift Valley (Generalized) and Settlement Areas of East Africa.

logical investigation over the ensuing quarter of a century confirmed the existence of the great faults and the troughs, but suggested a succession of rifts rather than the continuous lines of faulting postulated by Gregory. The later more moderate view is expressed in the map on page 48.

If one draws a section across the country of the great rifts to true scale the rift valleys appear insignificant in that the foundering of their floors to the extent of a few thousand feet is small in comparison with the horizontal distances involved. Nevertheless, when seen on the surface of the ground they are spectacular indeed. To reach the edge of the East African Rift, to see the ground falling away at one's feet and, if atmospheric conditions permit, to catch a glimpse of the mountain wall on the far side are experiences never to be forgotten.

It would be surprising indeed if such a fracturing of a large section of the earth's surface did not give rise to another of the earth's phenomena. It was associated with a great outburst of volcanic activity. Huge sheets of lava cover enormous areas in Kenya and extend southward into Tanganyika and westward into Uganda, to be continued northward by still larger areas amid the mountains of Ethiopia. These stretches of lava have in many areas broken down to form some excellent soils. More conspicuous than the sheets of lava are the gigantic individual extinct volcanoes which tower to great heights above the plateau surface. Among the outstanding giants are Mount Kenya itself, almost on the equator, and rising to heights (17,040 feet) which ensure a permanent snow capping. Southward, within Tanganyika territory, Kilimanjaro rises to 19,320 feet. On the Kenya-Uganda border the notable Mt. Elgon is 14,176 feet, while along the line of the western rift the trough is bordered by a whole succession of giant peaks, the most famous of which is Mt. Ruwenzori, reaching 16,794 feet.

Between the two great branches of the rift it would seem that the old plateau surface sagged, hence the reason for Lake Victoria, so different from the other lakes of East Africa. It is a shallow, island-fringed lake with gently shelving coastlands. Similar, though much smaller, is Lake Kyoga to the north, through which the waters from Lake Victoria drain on their way to make the White Nile. Thus the heart of the plateau forms part of the great Nile basin, that part which we have discussed in Chapter 10 as the upper or plateau course.

East Africa as a whole, however, is not dominated by river basins as are most parts of Africa. Instead an irregular network of streams join up to form rivers important locally, though ones whose names are little known outside the country, whose waters may yet be used for those smaller storage and irrigation works advocated by writers like Professor Debenham (see page 89) for the improvement of agricultural conditions over large parts of the continent.

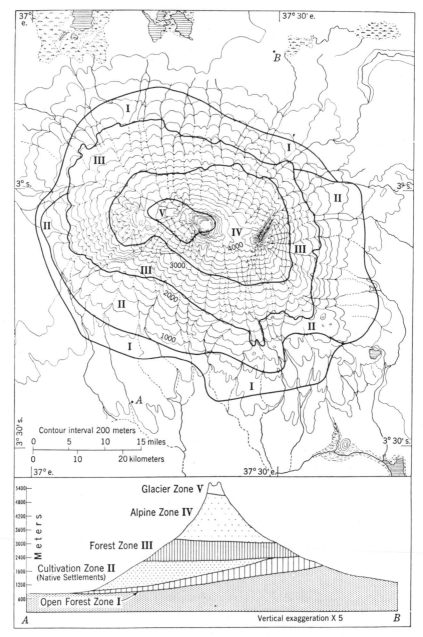

Figure 3.   Vegetation Zones around Mount Kilimanjaro.   (After *Geog. Univ.* [Figure 28].   Topography from 1/50,000 map by F. Klute [1912] and 1/300,000 map by Sprigade and Moisel [1914].)

If we turn to a consideration of climatic conditions, the coastlands, roughly from Mombasa southward, enjoy the hot, wet climate which we associate with equatorial latitudes. Mombasa, it should be noted, lies some 4° south of the equator, but the hot, wet conditions extend virtually through the whole of Portuguese East Africa. Northward from Mombasa there is a remarkable and very rapid change to the arid conditions characteristic of the northeastern deserts, so that from the 40 inches a year of Mombasa the total drops to 20 inches on the border with Italian Somaliland and, before the equator is reached, far less.

Away from the coastal strip as the plateau is ascended, the first feature of outstanding importance is the lowering of average temperatures. The most favored regions are those of central Kenya and Uganda lying under the equator; for here violent fluctuations in temperature are absent. The rainfall tends to be well distributed throughout the year, and, though periods of drought do occur, Kenya escapes the worst of those violent seasonal differences associated with the destructive storms which become more and more significant as one goes southward across the plateau through Tanganyika, and which prove such a serious deterrent to agricultural development (see page 422). As one reaches the interior lower ground around the lakes, the climate becomes again more truly equatorial. According to Maurette, the rest of the country is subject to the influences of the seasonal or permanent winds from the Indian Ocean and receives from them more or less rain according to the altitude and the exposure of each region. Local variations are often sharp. Certain regions are very wet, others much less so. In some parts great heat and evaporation combine to lower the efficiency of a precipitation which is already small. On the high plateau there may be seasons of relative cold. Nights may be chilly as a result of rapid radiation through the rarefied air.

Such are the essential features of the climate of eastern Africa which distinguish it so clearly from that of equatorial Africa. They exercise a marked influence on the river regime, on the vegetation, on the life of the indigenous peoples and on the possibilities of white colonization.

Historical Background

The pioneer journeys of exploration by David Livingstone quickly inspired others to follow him. The early missionaries and traders into east and central Africa found the vast lands of East Africa sparsely populated by primitive peoples menaced by famine and disease, the prey of intertribal warfare and under the perpetual shadow of the slave trade. At that time the slavers were Arabs based primarily on the island of Zanzibar whose Sultan—himself of Arab descent—claimed a loose sovereignty over a great part of East Africa. Reference has already been made (Chapter 2) to the efforts of the British consul to persuade the Sultan to take strong action against the slave trade and to the way his authority was undermined when Karl Peters concluded treaties with local chiefs leading to the establishment of German East Africa. In 1886 the Sultan's authority was limited to a coastal strip. The mainland was divided between German and British interests defined by treaty in 1890, in which year Zanzibar became a British protectorate.

The British East Africa Company began trading in 1887, but incurred such losses that by 1893 it had to withdraw from Uganda. The British Government was persuaded by F. J. D. Lugard, afterwards Lord Lugard, not to break faith with the Africans with whom the Company had made agreements but to take over responsibility. This led to a protectorate over Buganda in 1894 and East Africa (later Kenya) in 1895. It was in the latter year that the railway from Mombasa inland to Uganda was begun, a vital line of communication if Uganda was to be freed of the slave traffic and opened up economically. Labor was short and had to be brought from India, but the supply was hindered by plague. Disease killed off the transport animals as well as many of the workmen themselves, while the failure of the rains in 1898 led to famine over all of Kenya. The railway did not reach Kisumu on Lake Victoria until 1901, and Kisumu remained the port of entry to Uganda for the next 25 years.

Farther south, slave trading had a strong hold, but missions were successfully established at Blantyre in 1874 and Livingstonia in 1875, followed by trading companies. In 1891 Portugal recognized British rights to the country around Lake Nyasa, and to the west lay the country where the British South Africa Company had been accorded rights in 1889. In 1891 Lewanika, paramount chief of Barotseland, asked for and received British Government protection. Arab slave traders who had been encroaching from north and west were defeated in a pitched battle by Sir Harry Johnston in 1894, and the last slave train, intercepted on its way to the coast in 1898, was set free at Fort Jameson. King Lewanika was a great ruler who foresaw coming changes. He granted trading and mineral rights to the British South Africa Company and later land rights. The Company in return extended railway and telegraph lines northward from South Africa. In 1924 the British Government took over administration of the country, which had then come to be known as Northern Rhodesia.

The Peoples of East Africa

Apart from a few pockets in remote areas occupied by the primitive pygmies the vast majority of Africans in East and Central Africa

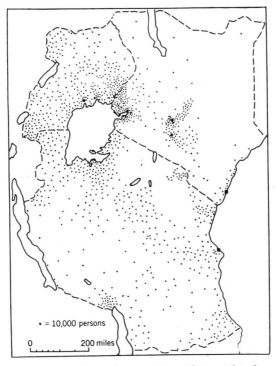

Figure 4. The Distribution of Population in East Africa. This shows the irregular concentrations of population.

are Bantu Negroes. For centuries they had been subjected to constant pressure from the war-like nomadic Hamites from the north, brown-skinned peoples with aquiline features. The conquering Hamites intermarried with the conquered Negroes and adopted their mode of life. Some tribes, such as the Masai of Kenya and Tanganyika, are clearly half Hamites; elsewhere the Hamitic element gives rise to an aristocratic class amongst predominantly Bantu.

In the absence of a written language the various tribes of East Africa have gradually evolved forms of spoken speech mutually unintelligible. This, in turn, has resulted, with improved communications following European entry, in the need for a *lingua franca* and the use of Kiswahili (Swahili) for this purpose.

For many centuries the Arabs had been active traders along the East African coast, and it was they who drove the Portuguese from their last stronghold at Mombasa toward the end of the seventeenth century. In 1832 the Iman of Muscat transferred his capital to Zanzibar, and in 1861 his son established Zanzibar as a separate Sultanate, with wide claims in East Africa. The administrative and legislative authority of the Sultan and his government is now limited to the islands of Zanzibar and Pemba.

European settlement was one of the objectives of the British South African Company from the start, but in East Africa it came later as the attractiveness of the climate of the Kenya highlands was increasingly appreciated and the first true settlers took up land in 1902. The land which was granted to them was largely uninhabited except when, every few years, the war-like Masai drove their cattle into the pasture from which they had long before frightened away potentially permanent agriculturalists.

It was the British who brought for the building of the Mombasa-Uganda railway large numbers of indentured laborers from India. Some 6000 elected to remain, and they have been joined by many who handle much of the import and export trade, retail distribution, as well as providing artisans, craftsmen and clerical workers. Only gradually is the African interesting himself in these spheres: as a trader he has lacked the sustained interest needed to build up a good business.

The First World War of 1914 to 1918 resulted in the voluntary mobilization of every British settler and the abandonment of most of the farms and the conquest of German East Africa. That territory, renamed Tanganyika, became a mandated territory entrusted to Britain, but the uncertainty of its political future did not encourage either settlement or economic investment. However, the discovery of gold and diamonds in Kenya and Tanganyika and the development of the great copper zone in Northern Rhodesia gave new incentives, white settlements in the Kenya Highlands grew and Nairobi developed into a modern city.

References are made below to the careful work of the late Clement Gillman who showed so clearly the remarkable contrasts in population distribution which are such a feature of East Africa. There are fertile coastlands round Lake Victoria where 400 persons are crowded on each square mile; the islands of Zanzibar and Pemba support more than 250 per square mile. On the other hand, vast areas in the heart of Tanganyika are virtually uninhabited; yet they are far from being desert lands.

Figure 5. A White Farmer's Home on the Kenya Highlands. The farmhouse is not unlike a traditional English home, but local materials have been used: mud brick walls and grass thatch. (Courtesy East African Office.)

The peoples of East Africa too show striking contrasts. The well-organized Kingdom of Buganda, the Arab Sultanate of Zanzibar, the war-like Masai of almost legendary valor and the pockets of primitive peoples are but some of the indications of the range of human adaptation to the environment. Superficially there are huge monotonous stretches of rolling plateau country, yet the work of the physiographer, the soil scientist and the ecologist suggests rather a complicated pattern though one repeated again and again.

When the World Land Use Survey initiated pilot surveys of existing land use in East Africa in 1951, the great surprise when air photographs were examined was the complexity of the pattern, too detailed to show fully even on the scale of 1:50,000. This work, carried out by Mr. John Callow under my direction, emphasized the outstanding need for factual surveys—the mapping of what exists, the attempt to interpret the pattern before any future planning can be contemplated.

The question of European settlement assumes a special significance in Kenya. On the high plateau almost under the equator are about 30,000 whites. Many are town dwellers, and 10,000 live in Nairobi alone, but there are 2000 registered landholders representing, with their families, some 8000 people. Reserved for European farmers are 17,000 square miles, though much of this will probably be kept under forest. This area cannot be extended; it is hemmed in by the African reserves.[1]

Portuguese East Africa

Portuguese East Africa, occupying a large part of the East African coastal plain, together with the adjoining plateau here relatively low and much dissected, occupies some 300,000 square miles, with a total population probably of the order of 15 million. The country is almost bisected by the Lower Zambezi, and it forms part of the great tract discussed in Chapter 18, or the Zambezi Basin. South of the Zambezi the port of Beira serves as the modern outlet of Southern Rhodesia, while still farther south the narrow tongue of Portuguese territory which is interposed between the Transvaal and the Indian Ocean includes the port of Lourenço Marques, the natural outlet—geographically speaking—of the Witwatersrand gold field.

It is only therefore the northern half of Portuguese East Africa which begins to have affinities with the British sphere in East Africa, the main tract discussed in this chapter.

Portuguese interest in the East African coast dates from the days of the early Portuguese ascendancy in the Indian trade, but for some 300 years little was done by the Portuguese to develop the African territories they claimed. In the latter part of the nineteenth century, when the boundaries with Nyasaland and the newly established Rhodesia were fixed, the Portuguese gave a 50-year concession to the Mozambique Company which did not expire until 1941. Thus about one-sixth of the whole area, the part lying between the Zambezi and about latitude 22° South, was administered until that date by this Portuguese chartered company, and included the very important port of Beira.

[1] R. R. Rawson, "Emigration to British East and Central Africa," *Econ. Geog.,* XXVII, 1951, 65–71.

The remainder of the territory, administered by the Government, was known as the Mozambique Colony. The whole has now passed under unified state control, but the major part of the development of the country in the present century has been the result of foreign investment, notably in the two great ports and in the railway communications, including the great Zambezi Bridge, linking Beira with Nyasaland.

A large part of Portuguese East Africa south of the Zambezi lies less than 500 feet above sea level and consequently is covered by rich vegetation of the low veld which extends also into the eastern Transvaal. Portuguese territory extends far inland up the Lower Zambezi to the small frontier port of Zumbo. Zumbo is well below the great Kariba Gorge discussed in the next chapter, but obviously any development of power and control of Zambezi waters at the Kariba Gorge would affect the whole course of the lower river through Portuguese territory. There is a navigable stretch below Zumbo through a somewhat narrow gorge to the Kebrabassa Falls. Here the river descends by a series of cataracts over a distance of some 50 miles to the coastal lowland, where there is a broad navigable channel from Tete, past the junction with the Shiré, to the delta.

North of the Zambezi hilly country projects much closer to the coast. Here Portuguese territory occupies the whole width between Lake Nyasa and the Indian Ocean and, overlooking Lake Nyasa, includes the Namuli Highlands, rising in places to over 6000 feet and giving Portuguese East Africa a range of climatic conditions not yet fully exploited.

Most of Portuguese East Africa is occupied by younger sedimentary rocks fringing the crystalline plateau. Mineral wealth as far as metallic minerals are concerned is thus restricted to the interior zone of crystalline rocks with which communications at present scarcely exist.

The territory has compensation in the occurrence of some useful coal deposits in the Zambezi valley near Tete.

Climatically the coastlines of Portuguese East Africa offer some interesting points. There is the southward-flowing ocean current of warm water derived from equatorial latitudes, known as the Mozambique Current. As a result the waters in the port of Mozambique are several degrees warmer than those of Mombasa 800 miles nearer the equator. Though the regime of rainfall is that of a normal Trade Wind type, with a rainy season (December to May) and a dry season, the coastal lands suffer from constant high humidity as well as a small temperature range not more than 10 degrees in the year. The latter part of the hot season is not infrequently characterized by destructive cyclonic storms (see page 71). As elsewhere in East Africa the rainfall decreases inland from the coast, followed by an increase as higher ground is reached and orographical rainfall results.

Broadly speaking African subsistence agriculture is the rule throughout the country, with the exception of the regions more immediately around the major ports where food is grown for consumption in the towns and there is a small development of commercial agriculture. Thus sugar cane, supplying raw sugar to Portugal, is cultivated behind Lourenço Marques and Inhambane, in the Limpopo valley, as well as in the Zambezi valley around the great bridge at Sena and in the hinterland of Quelimane. Among other comparatively recent developments which point the way to future progress is cotton growing and fruit growing (bananas, pineapples, citrus fruits, especially in the Lourenço Marques district). The uplands and the drier areas have parts suitable for sisal, peanuts and other oil seeds. The ubiquitous Indian corn is the mainstay of African diet. Livestock is unimportant, owing to the low-lying nature of much of the territory and the prevalence of disease.

It is clear that just as the development of Portuguese East Africa to date has depended upon the happy collaboration of the interested powers, in this case Britain and Portugal, so does the position of the country make development in isolation unthinkable. The international implications are well seen in the story of the port of Beira. It is an example of a port whose hinterland is distant and not immediate. More than 80 per cent of its total trade, exports and imports, come from or go to the Rhodesias, Nyasaland and especially the far-off Katanga region of the Belgian Congo. The Rhodesian railways operate the line between Beira and the Rhodesian frontier at Umtali; similarly the great main line northward crossing the Zambezi by the bridge at Sena has been constructed with British capital and is operated by British interests. Somewhat similar is the position of Lourenço Marques, only 55 miles by railway from the Transvaal frontier, which handles nine-tenths of the trade of Portuguese East Africa as well as a large volume of trade with the industrial area of the Rand. British capitalists have spent over 5 million dollars on the improvement of the port, and the expansion of the port has enormously stimulated the development of the surrounding agricultural lands, which have unusually rich soils and a climate favoring bananas and sugar.

By comparison the purely Portuguese East African ports, though situated where there are rich agricultural hinterlands, like Mozambique, Quelimane and Inhambane, remain small and undeveloped. The changing fortunes consequent upon development of modern communications are well illustrated in the case of the port of Chinde, just north of the Zambezi mouth and the river port of Chindio, both of which have been eclipsed by Beira since the construction of the railway bridge.

British East Africa

For certain purposes the British East African territories comprising the Uganda Protectorate, the Kenya Colony and Protectorate, the Tanganyika Trusteeship territory, formerly German East Africa, later held under mandate from the League of Nations, and the Zanzibar Protectorate operate as one unit. There is an East African High Commission consisting of the governors of the first three named, which came into existence on January 1, 1948, to provide for the administration of services common to the three territories. The High Commission is assisted by the East African Central Legislative Assembly of twenty-three members, seven from the staff of the High Commission, five from each of the territories and one Arab, which is empowered to legislate for such specific common services as railways, taxation assessment, telegraph, civil, education and research services. The governments of the separate territories remain responsible for other basic public services.

An important step in the unification of East Africa was also made in 1948 when the East African Railways and Harbors Administration took over on a unified basis the control of the varied railways together with the ports of Mombasa (including the modern Kilindini harbor), Dar-es-Salaam, Lindi, and a number of smaller Kenya ports. The same board operates steamer services on Lakes Victoria, Kyoga and Albert, as well as on the River Nile, and also some important road services.

The former isolation of the individual East African territories is being automatically broken down. As facilities for transportation and communication have steadily improved, lengths of railway formerly isolated have become woven into a general network and East Africa's contacts as a whole with the outside world have become more important. This is clear when one looks at the position of Uganda, entirely landlocked and dependent for its contacts with the outside world on facilities offered by its neighbors.

The Uganda Protectorate

The territories now comprised within this Protectorate came under British influence around about the period of 1890, and for a time some parts were administered by the British East Africa Company. It was in 1894 that the British Protectorate was declared over the Kingdom of Buganda and some of the adjoining territories. Today the Province of Buganda is recognized as an African Kingdom ruled by His Highness the Kabaka, who is assisted by three African ministers and a Lukiko, or assembly. Similar Lukikos advise the chiefs or kings of neighboring territories.

Uganda affords a very interesting example of the British system in Africa of indirect administration. The principal British representative is the Governor, who is assisted by a Legislative Council, eight of whose members are Africans. The Governor resides at Entebbe, pleasantly situated on the shores of Lake Victoria and within a short distance of the capital of Buganda, Kampala,[1] railhead of the main line through Kenya to Mombasa, the commercial center, and now through the establishment of the University College (with a strong medical school) at Makerere near by, a center for higher education in East Africa.

Makerere, with its counterparts, University Colleges in West Africa at Ibadan and Achimota like the former Gordon Memorial College at Khartoum in the Sudan, are all University Colleges established as such since the Second World War for the development of education at a university level and for the fostering of research in British African Colonial territories. In their early stages these colleges are guided in their development by a loose association with the University of London, which offers advice on matters of curricula and provides external examiners to help in the maintenance of good standards of scholarship. Appointments to the academic staffs are made by or on the advice of a Council for Higher Education, with its headquarters in London. Periodic visits are paid by members of this Council and by senior members of the University of London to African Colleges, and the whole arrangement is typical of mod-

[1] Dr. E. S. Munger has made a detailed study of *Relational Patterns of Kampala, Uganda* (University of Chicago Department of Geography Research Paper 21, 1951). Among many subjects of great interest the influence of Makerere is discussed.

ern British efforts to guide African development towards self-government in educational as in political affairs. Naturally the system has its critics. There are some who feel that it results in systems of education and associated curricula being imposed by those who have inadequate knowledge of local conditions and needs, certainly a serious fault of British educators in the past. But it is recognized by most as an essential and a wise step in a progressive evolution.

That the University College to serve East Africa has been established in the heart of Uganda may be regarded as indirectly, though not inaptly, associated with the dominant position which Uganda has held in East African affairs for a long time. When the country first became known to Europeans Buganda was already a well-organized and efficiently run African Kingdom.

Although the total area of the Protectorate is only 80,000 square miles, if one excludes the tracts of inland water which lie within its boundaries, the first full census taken in August 1948 revealed a population of just under 5 million (4,993,965). This represents a very high density for Africa, of no less than 60 per square mile. On the slopes of Mount Elgon and on the shorelands of Lake Victoria the density exceeds 200. Europeans at that time numbered between 3000 and 4000, being administrators, missionaries, educators and those engaged in commerce. But already 37,500 Asiatics, mainly Indians, had settled in the country, having been employed originally mainly on railway construction. Of the African population nearly one-third were members of the Baganda tribe from which the Protectorate takes its name. In the remoter areas there are still forest tribes at a very different level of development from those in the remainder of the country.

The bulk of Uganda lies on the lake plateau at an elevation of 3500 to 4000 feet, draining from Lake Victoria through Lake Kyoga into Lake Albert and so into the Nile. Thus Uganda must continue to have close association with the Sudan and Egypt in that it covers the gathering grounds of the headquarters of the White Nile. The great works at Owen Falls have been referred to elsewhere (page 227). Already Jinja has factories; with cheap electric power it seems destined to become a great industrial center.

The eastern boundary of the country is roughly the line of highlands which separates the Nile drainage from the Lake Rudolph basin. In the west Uganda includes part of the western Rift Valley, and here the Bunyoro Plateau overlooks with great scarps the deep trough occupied by Lake Albert. As a result of its elevation the plateau has a modified equatorial climate. Thus Entebbe at 3900 feet has a characteristically small annual range of 70° to 73°F., and over most of the plateau the rainfall, averaging between 40 and 60 inches, shows two maxima. The first is about April to May, and the second about October to December, but the intervening "dry" periods are dry in the relative sense only. Though there is considerable variability in annual fall of rain associated with variations in the strength of the air masses which converge on this part of Africa, there are not the periods of drought which are such a curse over much of Africa. And, although the rain—largely convectional— may fall during thunderstorms, sometimes with great violence, it does not do the damage that heavy falls may do on land left dry by months of drought, as happens farther south in Tanganyika.

The absence of marked seasonal rhythm makes possible cultivation throughout the year, but this is the type of climate not appreciated by Europeans. They find it enervating, and Uganda has been subject from time to time to very serious epidemics of sleeping sickness and other insect-borne diseases. Uganda thus enjoys a climate which is conducive to great agricultural development but drives the few Europeans to seek the mountain slopes of Elgon and the Ruwenzori Range, also called the Mountains of the Moon. On the whole the natural vegetation is that of moderately open forest or a dry savanna with abundance of trees. There are large stretches of swamp forest on the lower ground around the lakes. With decreasing rainfall toward the northeast, the savanna becomes poorer. Other local variations include stretches of grassy downland, and as elsewhere in Africa the existing vegetation pattern is doubtless in major part due to human interference and shifting cultivation.

In contrast, however, to the shifting cultivation so universal in Africa the Baganda in the populous areas have developed an intensive system of permanent garden cultivation. A large proportion of the Baganda are Christians, and the church is often a central feature of a group of homes. A modern home would probably have a corrugated iron roof, plastered walls, doors and windows and a cement floor. The thatched kitchen is a separate building at the back, and the house is surrounded by a carefully swept yard with a shade tree or two and a few flowers. The surrounding garden consists of several parts. First there is the banana garden tended by the wife, then plots with sweet potatoes, cassava, maize and beans. Then there is the cotton patch tended by the husband, who weeds the crop. The family does the harvesting about January, and the cultivator takes his sacks of cotton tied to his bicycle to the Indian-owned ginnery.

Such is the life of the people within reach of modern roads, but throughout the country the large population naturally practices subsistence agriculture, with cereals, particularly millets, cassava, and bananas occupying pride of place. The great cash crop, cultivated commonly by the Africans mainly in small plots from one-fourth acre upward, is thus cotton. The local varieties formerly grown for current use have been largely replaced since the introduction of American and Egyptian seed in 1903 so that most of the crop is now American Upland. Grown all over the country, the acreage reached a peak of 1⅓ million acres with an output of over 70,000 tons, but increasing competition of essential foodstuffs for land caused a subsequent drop. The bulk of the crop is grown for export, and it is interesting that the local ginneries are largely owned by the immigrant Indians.

Tobacco, like cotton, is an introduced crop, grown by the Africans but not primarily for their own use. Some is sold to the factories at Jinja and Kampala, the remainder is exported. There is, however, a constantly increasing demand for cigarettes due to the high prices of the imported article and the fact that they formerly came from dollar areas.

The western highland zone in the Tororo and Ankole districts has attracted attention because of the possibilities of growing tea with good yields and coffee, both of *arabica* and *robusta* varieties. There has been a rapid growth in the development of coffee, mainly produced on African small holdings though some on European-owned plantations. Indian settlers have become interested in the development of sugar cane, and sugar factories near Lake Victoria have satisfied local demands and produced a surplus for export.

Turning to livestock, Uganda faces the difficulty of large tsetse fly areas. The bulk of the cattle are of low-grade type, becoming better on the higher grasslands of Ankole, where large herds of humped big-horned cattle are the pride of the Banyankole. The country supports some millions of sheep and goats, and there is a trade in hides and skins.

The emphasis in Uganda has been upon agriculture rather than upon minerals, the exploitation of which has been hindered by the high cost of transportation to the coast. There has been a small output of tin ore, but the extension of the railway from Kampala has made possible the development of important copper deposits at Kilembe.

Uganda may be cited as an object lesson for other parts of Africa. It has natural advantages of soil and climate, but not without the disadvantages inherent in African conditions, such as infestation with tsetse fly. The relatively favorable natural environment is reflected in the number and the standard of living of its African population. In so far as trade with the outside world is concerned such advantages are of no use without modern means of transportation. Thus the modern development of Uganda began in fact with the completion of the railway through Kenya to Mombasa, though actually the first railway in Uganda ran from Jinja to Namasagali, the head of navigation on the Victoria Nile. As elsewhere in Africa, development of roads has played and is playing an enormously important part in opening up the country. With the prosperity resulting from the export trade in cotton and coffee Uganda has now thousands of miles suitable for motor traffic throughout the year; and the truck is to be found everywhere transporting agricultural produce. The airplane has brought the country within hours instead of days or weeks of its neighbors and, via Khartoum and Cairo, with Europe.

Kenya

Kenya, the British East African Protectorate, was proclaimed a Crown Colony in 1920 when it took the new title of Kenya Colony from the famous volcanic peak almost exactly on the equator, which is its highest point. Along the coastlands are territories rented from the Sultan of Zanzibar, which became the Kenya Protectorate. A treaty signed in 1924 with Italy ceded to Italy (Italian Somaliland) the whole of the Juba River and a neighboring tract of arid country, formerly in Kenya. In 1926 the area around Lake Rudolph in the northwest was transferred from Uganda Protectorate to Kenya.

The whole of Kenya Colony and Protectorate now covers an area of 219,730 square miles. As in Uganda the census taken for the first time in 1948 revealed a larger actual population than that which had previously been calculated, a total of 5,379,966. The Kenya coastlands have long been under the influence of Arab traders arriving by sea, so that the population included more than 24,000 Arabs. Indians, together with Goanese, to a large extent descendants of those who were brought to work on the railways and other construction, totaled at the time of that census nearly 100,000. They constitute an important and very active minority in the Kenya population. The 1948 census revealed the presence of 29,666 Europeans. In contrast to the other British territories in tropical Africa, a large proportion of these Europeans are British settlers. They live on the pleasant heights of the Kenya plateau and are engaged in farming, about which more will be said later. The Africans in Kenya are mostly peoples speaking Swahili and further inland numerous tribes speaking Bantu languages.

A simple physical division of Kenya is into: (1) the coastal plains; (2) the broad plateau of the Nyika—a step up to the plateau; (3) the eastern rift valley with its bordering mountains; and (4) the lake plateau, extending to Lake Victoria and the Uganda border in the west. If one looks at the rainfall map it is clear that only the southern margin of the coastal plain receives an adequate rainfall, and this is the fertile stretch around Mombasa. Northward a very large proportion of Kenya with less than 20 inches of rainfall is arid, and much of it incapable of supporting permanent settlements. Indeed it is not generally realized that about three-quarters of all the people in Kenya live where the rainfall is more than 30 inches a year, and that three-quarters of the whole country is very sparsely populated indeed. Most of the one-quarter of Kenya which can be considered as fully productive, either actually or potentially, is on the better-watered highlands and is divided between the 11,000 square miles of European estates and the 47,000 square miles of native reserves.

On the surface of the Kenya highlands there are large stretches of volcanic rock. The varied elevation, well seen on the slopes of Mt. Kenya, gives rise to a zonation, basically climatic, reflected in the natural vegetation. The eastern rift valley as it passes through Kenya is not a simple, straight, even-floored trough, but consists rather of several distinct basins. Those in the center, like the basin of Lake Naivasha, 6100 feet above sea level, are themselves at considerable elevations. The land drops in steps to the north to Lake Rudolph, and also to the south, where Lake Magadi—a valuable source of soda salts—is at 2500 feet above sea level. Part of the irregular character of the floor of the rift is due to the occurrence of subsidiary volcanic cones.

On both sides of the rift highland masses rise to over 10,000 feet, but the associated marginal plains, such as the Kikuyu Plateau, afford some of the most valuable land in the country. On the Kenya Highlands it is the cooling effect of altitude which is such an important factor, and at these high elevations there is a very considerable daily range of temperature. Especially in the drier parts of the year, cool and bracing evenings and nights are the result; the thermometer may drop as low as 35°F. at Nairobi at night, whereas daytime temperatures may reach more than 80°F. It is this absence of monotony in the daily regime which renders the climate on the Kenya Highlands, accompanied as it is with abundant sunshine, so attractive to the European settlers.

The very wide range of physical and climatic conditions in Kenya is reflected both in natural vegetation and in agriculture. The mangrove swamps of the southern coastal fringe pass northward into the semi-desert vegetation of Somaliland. The greater part of the huge coastal plain is a dried scrub with scattered acacia trees and baobabs. Narrow belts of bushes of a rather dry character follow up the main river valleys. The plains of the high land are largely grass with scattered acacias, or low bush, as on the Kikuyu Plateau, on the arid red volcanic soils. The highlands where they rise in the Aberdares and Mau Plateau, and particularly the slopes of the great volcanic piles of Kenya and Elgon, show a remarkable and very interesting vertical zonation of vegetation and are classic examples which have been extensively studied. Good savanna occupies the Lake Plateau draining toward Lake Victoria.

The grasslands of Kenya were long occupied by aggressive pastoral tribes, notably the Kikuyu and Masai, who had tended to force the peaceful agricultural peoples off the better lands on to the poorer. It is these grassy uplands which naturally offer the greatest attraction to Europeans, and, as in Southern Rhodesia, the European lands are strung out in a belt along the main line of the railway, with the native reserves occupying the less accessible though by no means less fertile fringing lands. The construction of the railway from Mombasa to Uganda, as we have already seen, was part of Britain's great campaign to suppress the slave trade. It made possible both the development of the Kenya Highlands and of Uganda as a whole. The whole system is meter gauge, and gradually the main line has been extended and branch lines constructed to tap such important areas as Lake Magadi and the Mt. Kenya slopes.

The main agricultural production for export comes from the lands of the European farmers. Among the chief plantation crops are coffee, sisal and tea, but the extensive farms are devoted to cereals, especially corn and wheat, with a little barley and oats. Kenya produces the major part of the world's pyrethrum, still important despite the development of D.D.T. The successful growing of coffee is almost entirely confined to areas east of the rift, but it has proved rather an uncertain crop even on the good red volcanic soils in the Nairobi area. Very little is grown by Africans, despite encouragement. The sisal industry is particularly suited to large-scale pro-

Figure 6. Eastleigh Airport, Nairobi, Kenya. One of the crossways of the African continent, halfway between Cairo and Durban. The later and well-equipped airport at Entebbe in Uganda is a strong rival. (Courtesy British Overseas Airways Corporation.)

duction because there is a considerable period before it yields, and expensive machinery is needed for its preparation for the market. There is, however, a considerable production by Africans. Maize remains the great foodstuff for Kenya Africans, and the smaller quantities on European farms are grown as cattle food. Wheat has increased, but is grown almost entirely by Europeans. Hybrid seed evolved in the experimental stations has proved very suitable for special local conditions, and an export has been developed.

Tea is a crop of the wetter parts of the Colony at about 7000 feet in the Kericho area and the Limuru area about 17 miles west of

Figure 7.   Contrasts in Nairobi.   A modern block of apartments over a gas station and a Moslem mosque.   (Courtesy British Overseas Airways Corporation.)

Figure 8.   A Modern Block of Apartments in Nairobi.   (Courtesy British Overseas Airways Corporation.)

Nairobi. Fruit is another recent development. Wattle bark and wattle extract form a large export of African-grown produce, though small in comparison with Natal's. Perhaps the most intensive African cultivation is in the Nyanza district, which though higher than the coastal plain is not attractive to European settlement.

How far can the white farmers of Kenya be regarded as true settlers in the sense that they make or intend to make the country

Figure 9. Plucking Tea on an Estate near Kericho, Kenya. (British Official Photograph.)

their permanent home, to bring up their children there and cut off ties with the mother country? Though the British population has been seen to show a marked increase and one not infrequently meets white Kenya folk of the second and third generations, census statistics do not show how far the white settlers form a permanent population. There is rather the tendency to buy a farm, farm it for a number of years, then sell to new settlers before returning "home." It is perhaps not always realized that European farming depends to a very large extent, as do the domestic arrangements in the home, on African labor and African servants.

Kenya now has in the more settled areas a good network of all-weather roads. Considerable development was made possible by

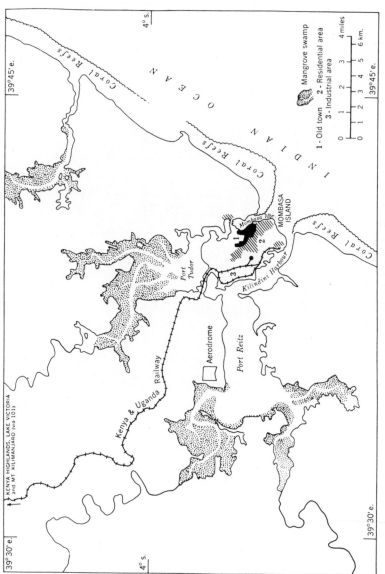

Figure 10.   The Site of Mombasa.

the use of Italian prisoners during the Second World War, and a feature of the country is the long-distance luxury coach services operating between all the main towns. There are, however, two towns in Kenya which overshadow all the others. Mombasa is situated on the eastern side of the small island on a coastal inlet, and with its medieval fort is the old Arab settlement. Thirteen thousand Arabs still remain in Mombasa, but they are now less numerous than the 24,000 Indians, together making one-third of the total population. The island itself is intensively cultivated, and on its western or landward side is the magnificent deep-water harbor of Kilindini, probably the finest harbor on the east coast of Africa and the starting point of the railway to Nairobi and the interior.

Nairobi, the capital, owes its existence to European settlement. It was originally a small railway headquarters, but has surpassed even Mombasa in population. It has become the focus of road and air communications as well as the largest European settlement in East Africa and the headquarters of the East African High Commission. By charter it has been constituted a City.

Kisumu, the terminus of the old main line to Lake Victoria, is the third town. Two others serve as foci for European settlers and their activities, namely, Nakuru in the Rift Valley and Eldoret on a fertile part of the plateau.

Tanganyika Territory

Tanganyika Territory occupies a larger area than Kenya and Uganda combined, covering 362,000 square miles, or 342,000 excluding inland water. The coastal plain in Tanganyika is comparatively narrow, and nearly the whole of this vast tract lies on the plateau stretching from Lake Tanganyika across to the edge overlooking the Indian Ocean, a width of 600 miles. It might be thought that Tanganyika therefore enjoyed the advantages of the higher parts of the plateau in Kenya. It stretches from 1° to 12° south of the equator and might therefore be supposed to have an excellent climate where tropical heat would be tempered by elevation. Such, however, is not the case. And although Tanganyikan development has been hindered by its uncertain political position, the natural environment is far less favorable than in Kenya to settlement and development. The plateau is less varied, there are vast gently rolling areas, the climate is modified tropical, not equatorial—that is to say, there is a strongly marked dry season. The relief is less varied than in Kenya, and so over the greater part the rainfall verges on the inadequate, and there are not the pockets of really good land found in Kenya. It is perhaps possible to distinguish four zones within the country.

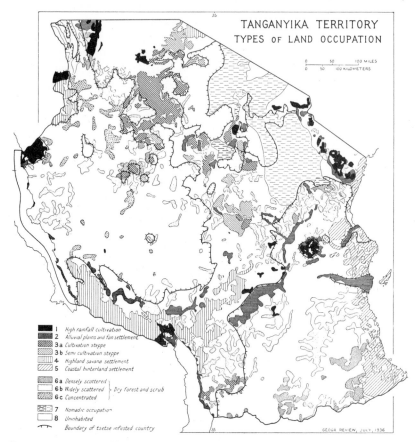

Figure 11.   Types of Land Occupation in Tanganyika.   This map illustrates the huge areas uninhabited or occupied by a widely scattered population.   These are largely areas without permanent surface water, or infested by tsetse fly.   (From C. Gillman, *Geog. Rev.* 1936 and 1949.   Courtesy of the *Geographical Review*, American Geographical Society.)

The Coastal Lowlands.   These are hot throughout the year, enjoying a total rainfall between 40 and 50 inches.   They may be described as pleasant in the dry season, but somewhat unhealthy during the rains.   Mangrove swamps fringe much of the coast, especially around the estuaries.   Behind them are groves of coconut palms, giving place inland to thorn forests.

THE SUBCOASTAL BELT. This lies between the coastal belt proper and the highlands and is comparable to the hot, rather dry, Nyika belt of Kenya. Here thorn woodland with drought-resisting trees and spiny shrubs are dominant.

THE MAIN CENTRAL AND WESTERN PLATEAU. Here the rainfall, though it averages 30 inches, is markedly irregular from year to year and in its incidence in the wet season. The atmosphere in the dry season is particularly dry, and a large daily range of temperature is the result. The vegetation may best be described as an open savanna or dry forest, but often forms a great matted tangle of vegetation. These are the extensive lands which promised much under large-scale mechanized clearing and cultivation and gave rise to the ill-fated groundnut or peanut scheme of the British Government, described in detail below. The failure of that scheme suggests that the proper use of these vast sparsely peopled plateau areas remains an unsolved problem.

THE HIGHLAND ZONES. These have a heavier relief rainfall of over 50 inches a year, a bracing atmosphere, considerable range of temperature and the land is clothed with luxuriant tropical forests, changing at higher levels into mountain grassland. Such lands are found in the Usumbura in the extreme northeast on the slopes of Kilimanjaro and other mountains, and afford environments attractive to white settlement.

We owe much of our scientific knowledge of Tanganyika geography to the careful studies of the late Mr. Clement Gillman, who contributed successively articles on population, vegetation and white settlement to the *Geographical Review.*[1] His very careful population map, published as a folding plate, reveals a very remarkable state of affairs. There are areas of fairly dense population along the coastlands but especially from the neighborhood of the Kenya border and along the northern railway inland. Settlement had even in 1934, to which Gillman's map refers, been attracted by the construction of the Central Railway, and there were important clusters along the road towards the southwestern border. But the main population concentrations were actually along the borders of Lake Victoria in the north, where in places his dot system of representation breaks down and where the density actually exceeded some 400 per square mile.

[1] "A Population Map of Tanganyike Territory," *Geog. Rev.*, XXVI, 1936; "A Vegetation Map of Tanganyika Territory," *Geog. Rev.*, 353–375; "White Colonization in East Africa," *Geog. Rev.*, XXXII, 1942, 585–597.

Vast areas of the heart of the country are shown as virtually or entirely unpopulated.

The comparatively backward development of Tanganyika may be connected to some extent with its varying political fortunes, but what are the main reasons behind this extraordinarily irregular distribution of its people? Is it the infertility of the soil, which has

Figure 12. Kibo, the Main Peak of Kilimanjaro, and the Highest Point in Africa. In the foreground is Mawenzi, also part of the Kilimanjaro mass. (Copyright Aerofilms Limited.)

remained so long unattractive to agricultural settlers, is it the depredations of war-like tribes engaged in perpetual feuds in the past? Is it the result of animal pests, or human disease? It may be suggested that the answers to these questions are not yet available. Considering the possibilities for white settlement, Gillman came to the conclusion that East Africa, more particularly Tanganyika Territory, was not a white man's country, although there were no climatic, economic or sociological reasons why a limited number of small owner settlers, who were prepared for a hard life, should not establish homes. He said, however: "Their problems will always be those of the precarious pioneer fringe along the margin of the world's spaces suitable for permanent settlement." And he doubted whether they would be able to survive without subsidies. He considered that settlers in large enough numbers to relieve pressure in their European homelands were quite out of the question. He expressed favor towards a system of co-operation with Africans along the line of the experience which had proved so successful in the Sudan (see page 348).

What has, in fact, been accomplished in Tanganyika? In the agricultural region of the coastal plain the products include sisal, coconuts, rice and sugar cane. Around Lake Victoria rice and sugar are again cultivated, and African-grown cotton has become very important. In the scattered highland areas coffee is the most important economic crop, being produced by both African and European peoples on the Usumbura Highlands and the slopes of Kilimanjaro, and increasing quantities of African-grown coffee come from the highlands west of Lake Victoria. The sisal plantations—sisal being notably a crop possible on poor lands of low rainfall—are situated mainly in the Tanga Province, and sisal in the years following the Second World War represented over half the total value of exports from the Territory. The industry was also the largest employer of African labor and also the most important dollar earner in the Territory's economy. Tea and tobacco have also been cultivated to some extent by European planters and by African cultivators.

If agricultural development has suffered serious setbacks, the mineral industry in Tanganyika has made staggering progress. An amazing find of diamonds in the Shinyanga District brought diamonds into the limelight as the leading mineral product. Gold has become significant, tin and mica are being worked and some of the indications of coal, more especially south of the central railway, may prove of importance. The lead deposits, such as Mpanda southwest of Tabora, necessitated a railway spur from the central line.

Tanganyika has not yet either a railway or a road network in any way adequate for the opening up of the country, though Dar-es-Salaam is now linked by the Central Railway through Tabora with both Lake Tanganyika and Lake Victoria. Dar-es-Salaam, the country's main port, lies along the north and northwest shores of an almost land-locked harbor, affording perfect protection.

Mikindani was the new port first proposed in the south to serve groundnut developments, but Mtwara proved a better site. The future of both is uncertain. Prior to that, Tanga on the Northern Railway was the second port, serving particularly the sisal and coffee estates but with indifferent port facilities.

Figure 13. Sisal Industry in East Africa. Above the bundles of cut leaf are being loaded on to open wagons. Below women are spreading drying fibers, and removing blemished strands at the same time. (British Official Photographs.)

In sum, Tanganyika still issues a challenge to the world of today to investigate scientifically its problems and to produce the right answers.

Zanzibar

The dominions of the Sultan of Zanzibar, a British Protectorate, comprise Zanzibar Island (640 square miles) and Pemba Island to the northeast (380 square miles), together with a small portion of the coastland of Kenya.

The port of Zanzibar lies on the sheltered western side of the island and for centuries held a dominating position in the trade of East Africa. It was a great Arab trading center, and the Arab city of the tall white-washed houses, so familiar in Arab lands farther north, still occupies the sea front. This Arab city still offers a remarkable contrast to the small European quarter, or to the large sprawling African city, with its wattle and daub huts. Of the total population of the islands, over a quarter of a million—20 per cent —are still Arabs, and some 5 or 6 per cent are formed by recently immigrated Indians into whose hands much of the trade has passed.

Before the building of the railways and the concentration of the trade of Tanganyika in the well-equipped terminal ports, the produce was brought across by small boats and transferred to larger ocean-going vessels at the port of Zanzibar. This entrepôt trade has largely disappeared, and, though Zanzibar is still an important port of call for liners, its economic interests have shifted. However, it still retains a great local coastwise trade. The climate of the islands, as so often happens, is a pleasant edition of that on the neighboring mainland, with a total rainfall of some 60 inches in Zanzibar and some 80 or 90 inches in Pemba. Though there are two rainfall maxima in March, April and May, and the second in November, it is rare for a whole month to be rainless. The temperature range is small, and as a result the vegetation is the luxuriant vegetation of equatorial latitudes. In the course of centuries of long association with Indian Ocean trade, plants have been introduced into the islands from distant lands. Intensive cultivation of many crops is carried out by the inhabitants of Zanzibar, and almost every available piece of ground is made to produce something of value.

Coconut palms are numerous, large quantities of copra are exported and the preparation of coconut oil and the manufacture of rope and matting from coir are important. But the great specialty of Zanzibar is in the production of cloves. These are actually the unopened buds of a small tree. There are some three million clove trees in large plantations, owned especially by Arabs but also found in African

Figure 14.   A Healthy Clove Tree, Zanzibar, in Full Leaf.   (Courtesy East African Office.)

small holdings. It is difficult to find an adequate reason why there should have been this specialization, but it remains a fact. A serious disease that threatens the industry in Zanzibar has resulted in a concentration on Pemba.

If any emphasis were needed, Zanzibar offers an illuminating example of contrasts which still exist within even the area which we have here described as East Africa. A unique and fascinating small domain, with a population density of over 250 to the square mile, it offers a remarkable contrast to the vast, almost uninhabited, tracts of the neighboring mainland.

Figure 15. A Stricken Clove Plantation, Zanzibar, Taken at the Same Date as the Last Picture. (Copyright Central Office of Information, London.)

The East African Groundnut Scheme

No example illustrates better the difficulties which still beset any attempts to develop tropical Africa than Britain's ill-fated attempt to grow peanuts on a large scale in East Africa.

Britain emerged from the Second World War with many acute shortages, not the least being margarine and cooking fats. It was Frank Samuel, Managing Director of the United Africa Company, itself a subsidiary of the vast Unilever concern with assets of over 500 million dollars, who visualized during a tour in 1946 the possibilities of the empty spaces of East Africa for growing peanuts, an annual crop and so with a quick return. Britain's harassed Minister of Food seized on the idea, sent out a mission of three experts—John Wakefield, former Director of Agriculture of Tanganyika, David Martin, plantations manager of the United Africa Company, and John Rosa, banker. After nine weeks on the ground, the Wakefield Report [1] was written, soon to be accepted by the British Government as a major contribution to the African population and development problem and the home food problem. This decision was reached after careful scrutiny of the report in which two strong voices, W. M. Crowther and Dunstan Skilbeck, were raised in favor of making haste slowly by pilot experiments, but the Socialist Government through Minister of Food Strachey decided on full speed ahead. The United Africa Company acted as Managing Agents until a Government Corporation, the Overseas Food Corporation, could be organized and take over, which it did in March–April 1948. Meantime second-hand, heavy bush-clearing machinery was collected, especially bulldozers from American Army surplus in the Philippines. Massey-Harris had already agreed to supply Canadian tractors.

The scheme was to clear 3,210,000 acres by 1953 of scrub—dreary, useless, closely matted tangle of vegetation, through which only a rhineroceros could force a way with difficulty—in "units" or farms of 30,000 acres and to secure at the end of the five years an output of 600,000 tons of peanuts. The areas chosen were:

Tanganyika Central Province (Kongwa)	450,000 acres	
Western Province (Urambo)	300,000	
Southern Province	1,650,000	
Kenya	300,000	
Northern Rhodesia	510,000	

The Central and Western Provinces are reached via the Tanganyika Central Railway from Dar-es-Salaam; the Southern Province is reached by railway to be constructed from the new deep-water port of Mtwara near Mikindani. Advance guards of European personnel arrived at Dar-es-Salaam early in 1947; the first "cut" in the bush was

[1] Alan Wood, *The Groundnut Affair*, London, The Bodley Head, 1950. *A Plan for the Mechanical Production of Groundnuts in East and Central Africa*, H.M.S.O., Cmd. 7030, 1947 (The Wakefield Report). *The Future of the Overseas Food Corporation*, H.M.S.O., Cmd. 8125, 1951.

actually made on April 30, 1947. Alan Wood has well described the effect on native life under the title "From Tribe to Trade Union." The chiefs co-operated in many ways, notably in securing labor, but soon their authority faded away. In the haste to get labor a large daily ration of food (totaling 3500 calories a day, basically corn [maize], beans, meat, sugar and oil) was issued, supplemented by

Figure 16. Land in Southern Tanganyika Cleared in Preparation for Ground-nuts. Although scrub piled in lines to form windrows has been left, should the land have been cleared in this way? (Copyright Aircraft Operating Company of Africa.)

cash wages ranging from 15 shillings (2 dollars) a month upwards. Even that was too much! Prices soared, and local economies were completely upset. Although medical skill became available and was beneficial, the workers in crowded quarters missed their womenfolk and sought satisfaction elsewhere. The Dar-es-Salaam dockers or-ganized the first trade union. There were ugly strikes. Those Afri-cans who had served in the Army seemed to have lost their me-chanical skill, and, although the African quickly picked up the han-dling of heavy machines and could maneuver them with the best, running repairs were another matter. Soon three-quarters of all the machines were out of action.

There are many reasons which may be given for the failure of a scheme conceived in the grand manner which might have been an African T.V.A. Too much bureaucratic control was one. In January 1951 there were 1283 Europeans on the Corporation staff compared with 384 on Earthmoving and Construction Limited, the company actually doing the work. The organization did not work smoothly, but primarily failure was due to lack of knowledge of the conditions. The machinery failed in its task partly perhaps because it was "secondhand," but mainly because the immensely long roots of the brush provided a tougher proposition than bush clearing in middle latitudes; the micro-structure of the soil (described on page 96) defeated the disc plows; the sandy soil was "packed" by the machinery and rendered unfit for peanuts; the vagaries of the rainfall were not sufficiently appreciated. Consequently the first crops are said to have been less than the seed put in the ground.

By September 1949 it was clear the objectives could not be reached, and a revised plan for a total of 600,000 acres by 1954 was introduced, concentrating on a rotation of crops rather than peanuts. Then in January 1951 the British Government was forced to abandon, in its original form, the whole project. Against an original total estimated cost of 23 million pounds, in January 1951, 36 million were written off as lost, roughly 2 dollars for every man, woman and child in Great Britain. Land already cleared was to be used for experimental purposes: four farms with about 10,000 acres under crop in Kongwa; 60,000 acres in Urambo with 13 farms. The Southern Region seems to have proved that "fully mechanized land clearing is far too costly and could be reduced by substituting hand labour," and experience suggested that cropping with peanuts, corn (maize) and millet (sorghum) should be combined with cattle grazed on grasses.

The proposals for Kenya and Northern Rhodesia were early abandoned, but permanent works of lasting value include the southern port of Mtwara and the railway planned for extension westward to Lake Nyasa. The branch railway from Moagali on the Central Line to Kongwa is likewise a permanent asset.

The groundnut scheme reinforces Julian Huxley's words that "the most important lesson of history for Africa is to go slowly." It is an expensive lesson, but the day will come when with increased knowledge development will go ahead in these areas.

The Overseas Food Corporation as part of its work in East Africa set up a Scientific Department under the direction of Dr. A. H.

Bunting as Chief Scientific Officer in charge of a staff of 30 or 40 scientists. His summary [1] of the work undertaken during the life of the department, 1947–1951, is a good example of the range of studies needed in tropical Africa. The soil scientists found top dressings of phosphate and nitrogen were required on all soils, but how to retain nitrogen (possibly by use of grass courses) remained unsolved. There was some evidence that a common weed played a major part in the mobilization of soil phosphate, and the retention of the weed was therefore vital. Unless there is an exact balance of nitrogen and potash, plants seem to develop abnormally; tobacco notably has a "tang" which renders it commercially of little value. It seemed that continuous cropping allowed no accumulation of moisture in the soil whereas fallowing did. Thus following the African's system of bare fallowing, an increase of nearly 50 per cent in peanut yield resulted. Among the plants it was found that successful American types of soybean were not adapted to the equatorial equal day and night temperatures throughout the year. Sorghum needed a horny peripheral layer at maturity of the grain as a protection against storage pests; sunflowers failed to pollinate because the bees or other pollinators were too few; destructive stem borers were not affected by insecticides successful elsewhere. The *Aphis*, which carries rosette disease of peanuts, needed to have its life cycle traced before it could be controlled. Thus the scientists indicated dozens of problems to be solved before success in development could be achieved.

BIBLIOGRAPHY

Apart from the references in the text and the work of Milne and others quoted in Chapter 5, reference should be made to the various official publications of the British Government, especially:

The British Territories in East and Central Africa, 1945–1950, His Majesty's Stationery Office, Cmd. 7987, 1950.
Overseas Economic Survey: British East Africa, 1948, His Majesty's Stationery Office, 1948.
Annual Reports on Kenya, Uganda and Zanzibar, His Majesty's Stationery Office.

The volume edited by J. D. Tothill, *Agriculture in Uganda* (New York, 1940), is a veritable encyclopedia on that country.

Much useful information will be found in the *East Africa Year Book and Guide,* issued by the Union Castle Steamship Company.

[1] *Nature,* CLXVIII, No. 4280, Nov. 10, 1951, 804–806.

CHAPTER
18

Central Africa and
the Southern Savanna Lands

There are several reasons why separate considerations should be given to that belt of southern Africa stretching from the Atlantic shores of Portuguese Angola to the Indian Ocean along the southern part of Portuguese East Africa, or Mozambique. It is a belt of Africa which lies between the equatorial forests of the Congo and the lofty plateaus of East Africa on the north and the extra-tropical white man's land of the Union of South Africa to the south. It has been pointed out repeatedly in this book that perhaps the most natural division of the continent of Africa is into river basins, but that rarely do river basins coincide with existing political divisions. In very broad general terms the area to be considered now is the basin of the great Zambezi, with the addition of various peripheral tracts. In terms of political units we shall consider the great territory of Angola on the west and that huge area of central Africa occupied by Northern Rhodesia, Southern Rhodesia and the Nyasaland Protectorate, the sphere of British influence. To round off the picture, the land below the plateau which forms the southern part of Portuguese Africa and through which the Zambezi passes on its way to the sea is considered here rather than entirely with East Africa, where the plateau element predominates.

In the great French *Géographie universelle*, Dr. Maurette considers the whole of southern Africa together, and it is perhaps natural that the British territories of the Rhodesias and Nyasaland should be linked for purposes of study with the British Dominion, the Union of South Africa. There are in fact some very interesting contrasts between the two, contrasts which have their roots partly in physical geography—the transition from a temperate environment to a tropical —and partly in historical geography.

426

Historical Geography

The story of the exploration and subsequent organization of this part of Africa has been briefly considered in Chapter 2. The Portuguese established settlements at an early date on both the Atlantic and the Pacific shores. The discovery of Angola was claimed by the Portuguese Diogo Cão in 1482, and points on the coast have been occupied continuously by the Portuguese since 1505, with the exception of the years 1641–1648, when the Portuguese were temporarily ousted by the Dutch. Comparatively little, however, was done to develop the vast area. The great drain of population from Portugal to Brazil in the sixteenth, seventeenth and eighteenth centuries drew Portuguese attention away from Africa. As a result the boundaries of the Portuguese sphere in Angola remained loosely defined, and along the south the long-disputed frontier was not finally settled until 1926, when it was agreed that the Kunene River with the Rua Cana Falls, 406 feet high, were to be shared as far as the water was concerned equally between the Governments of Angola and the Union of South Africa. On the Indian Ocean side the great Portuguese trading company, the Mozambique Company, administered the area long settled and claimed by the Portuguese until as late as 1942.

It will be recalled that the Portuguese claim to the whole of the hinterland stretching right into the heart of Central Africa and an attempt to exclude other nationals led directly to the activities of that British Rockefeller, Cecil John Rhodes. The heart of Africa in this latitude may almost be called Livingstone's land. We have noted how Dr. Livingstone, arriving in Africa as a medical missionary in 1841, proceeded at once to the mission station at Kuruman in Bechuanaland. He early discovered Lake Ngami, now in northern Bechuanaland, and the neighboring Okovango, and in 1850 reached the Upper Zambezi. His determination despite illness to follow this great river to its mouth led to his next journey, his discovery of the Victoria Falls in 1855, and his tracing the Zambezi to its mouth by the following May.

Thus directly it was Livingstone who brought the knowledge of this heart of Africa to the English-speaking peoples. It was Rhodes who brought the territories into the British sphere of commercial and political influence. Rhodes worked with amazing speed. In 1887 the Portuguese attempted to close the Zambezi basin; in 1888 Rhodes secured from the King of the Matabele exclusive rights to work minerals. Matabeleland is the core of Southern Rhodesia. In 1889 the great British South Africa Company, formed by Rhodes for the purpose of exercising these rights, set to work and by 1891 the limits of Portuguese and British spheres of influence had been settled. Nyasaland became a British Protectorate, and the huge territories, now Northern and Southern Rhodesia, were handed over to Rhodes's company.

It must not be thought that the advent of the British South Africa Company meant the advent of a period of exploitation. There is a twofold contrast continuing to this day between the Union of South Africa on the one hand and the Rhodesias with Nyasaland on the other. In the Union of South Africa the dominant white element is still the Afrikaans-speaking Boers; and, as we shall see in the next chapter, the effort to maintain the Union of South Africa as a white man's country involves a varying degree of racial discrimination. The British elements in South Africa have never been completely in accord with the dominant Boer view on these matters, and in the Rhodesias the development has been entirely in the hands of the British. Until the recent movement northwest of Boer farmers, after the Second World War, there was only a small Afrikaans-speaking element in British central Africa. Consequently the development of the Rhodesias, although carried out to secure both agricultural and mineral products needed by European peoples, has been carried out in conjunction with a liberal policy towards the African inhabitants, and the importance of improving their standard of living, if not always stressed as fully as it might have been, has always been present.

British Central Africa

There are ancient ruins and mines in Southern Rhodesia's territory which have intrigued and still intrigue anthropologists and archeologists. The earliest inhabitants of the country may have been Bushmen who have left behind rock carvings and colored paintings of hunting scenes on the walls of caves and rocks. Scattered through the country there are large numbers of workings from which former inhabitants gained gold, silver, copper and iron. Though extensive, the deposits were not worked below water level, and it would seem that the workers at that time had no knowledge of how to remove water by pumping. There are several hundred elaborate stone buildings which may or may not be the work of the same mining people. Most famous of these are the ruins of Zimbabwe. Who were the

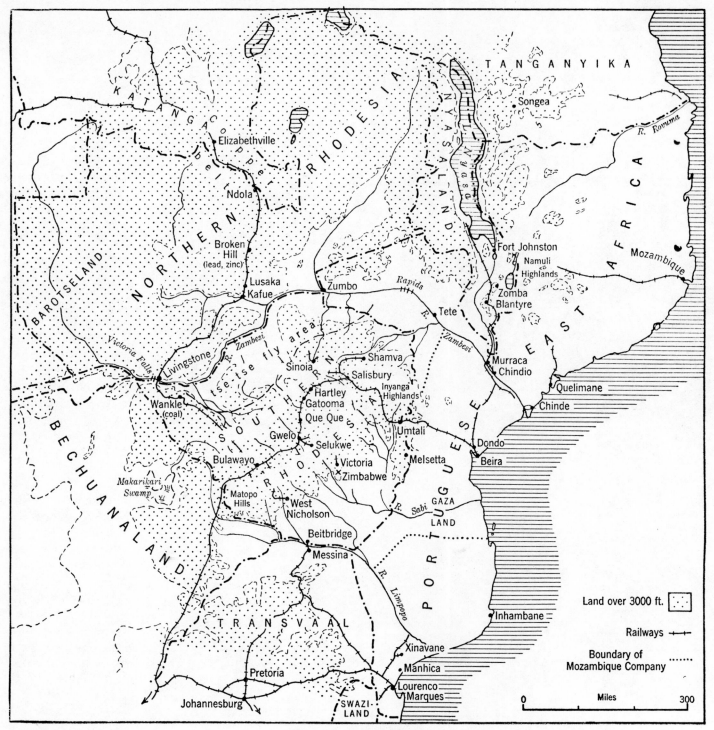

Figure 1. Central Africa.

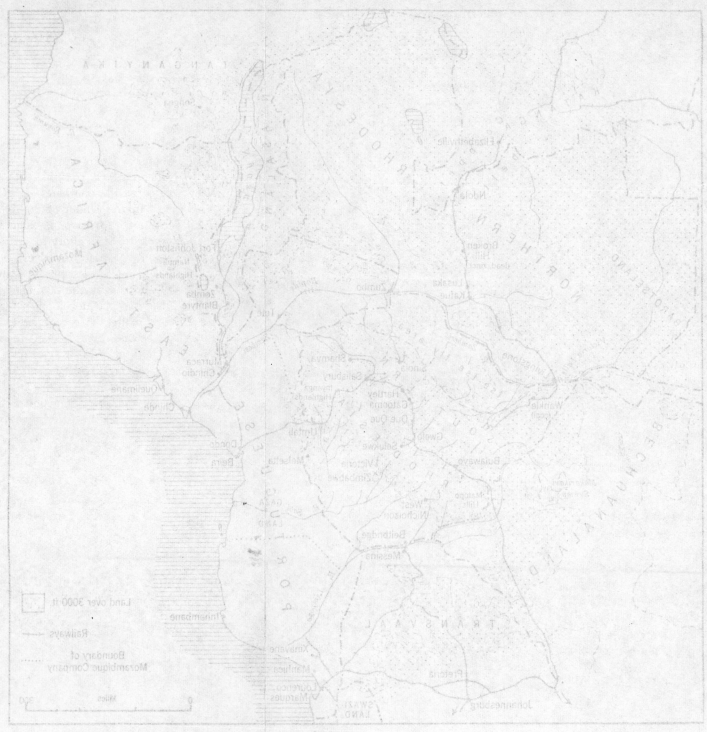

Figure 1. Central Africa.

builders of these great erections? Were they medieval Bantu? Were they members of peoples who have since disappeared? There are those who urge that some of the obscure references in the Old Testament are to the rulers of this great southern land. Who was the first European to reach Zimbabwe is not precisely known. It was probably the Portuguese Franciscan monk, Francis Silveira, who is believed to have reached there in 1561 and suffered martyrdom. In the three centuries which followed, before the journeys of Livingstone, the country must have been visited from time to time by missionaries and traders, but otherwise remained forgotten. Although gold was discovered in the area in 1865, the discovery did not give rise to any immediate movement, so that it was the concession granted by King Lobengula to Rhodes and his associates which really started the development of the area.

It is interesting that when the territory was proclaimed a British sphere of influence on July 20, 1888, it was known as Zambezia, thus emphasizing the association of what are now Northern and Southern Rhodesia with the Zambezi River. The pioneer column of settlers, consisting of 187 Europeans and 150 Africans, left Cecil Rhodes's farm near Kimberley on May 6, 1890. They were joined by police and guides, reached the site of the present town of Salisbury on September 12, 1890, and commenced the building of a fort. The British Protectorate over Bechuanaland was declared on May 9, 1891, thus protecting the route to the new settlements.

South African farmers soon evinced an interest in the new lands, and there was never any prohibition to Boer farmers. They were dissuaded from occupying part of the country by force and were invited to take up farms, which some of them later did. The arrival of the settlers and various restrictions necessary for the preservation of peace led to some resentment by the Matabele. In 1893 they attacked a post of the British South Africa Company, and war followed. It was brought to an end by the occupation of Lobengula's kraal near the present site of Bulawayo, which was founded on its present position in the following year, 1894.

In 1895 Northern and Southern Zambezia officially became Northern and Southern Rhodesia. The subsequent history of Southern Rhodesia includes the revolt of the Mashonas, but is closely bound up with the improvement of means of access by the coming of the railway. That from Kimberley reached Bulawayo in 1897, that from the Portuguese port of Beira reached Salisbury in 1899. The Zambezi gorge was bridged below the Falls in 1904, and one enters upon the modern phase.

The question whether or not Southern Rhodesia, which then had a European population between 30,000 and 40,000, should join the Union of South Africa or have a resident governor was decided by referendum in 1923. The result was for a resident governor, and on October 21, 1923, Southern Rhodesia became a self-governing colony of the British Commonwealth. Gradually the new state acquired mineral and other rights from the old South Africa Company, and Southern Rhodesia developed along modern lines.

Referring briefly to the history of Northern Rhodesia, we see that it was not until 1911 that the separate territories of Barotseland, or Northwestern Rhodesia, and Northeastern Rhodesia joined, and it was not until 1924 that a first governor was appointed in Northern Rhodesia, taking over the administration of the country from the South Africa Company. Thus the development of Northern Rhodesia came later than Southern.

Though geographically the Nyasaland Protectorate falls within the Zambezi basin, being drained by the Shiré—that important tributary of the Zambezi—the history of Nyasaland has been somewhat different. Modern roads now make it possible to travel between Northern Rhodesia and Nyasaland, but the natural outlet of the country is along the general line of the Shiré River to the Zambezi at Chindio, and from thence down the navigable stream to the port of Chinde near its mouth. Not till the bridging of the Zambezi in 1935 did Nyasaland become part of the commercial hinterland of the port of Beira. Formerly known as the British Central Africa Protectorate, the area was renamed Nyasaland in 1907, having been transferred to the control of the British Colonial Office in 1904.

The three British territories in the heart of Africa clearly have certain common interests. An advisory and consultative body to deal with non-political subjects, such as communication, health, education, and statistics, known as the Central African Council, was in due course set up. The question of the closer association of Northern and Southern Rhodesia and Nyasaland came to the fore in 1951, when active consideration was given to the possibility of forming a British Central Africa with dominion status, or its equivalent. By this time the three territories had developed along rather different lines. By virtue of its southern situation, the elevation of the great central tract of the country above 3000 feet, its well distributed and adequate rainfall, Southern Rhodesia has become a land of white settlers predominantly of British origin, though white settlers relying to a large extent on African labor. Its chief towns, Bulawayo, Gwelo and Salisbury, are European in concept and execution. European agricultural production maintains a dominant note, despite the existence of the important coal field at Wankie, and despite the development of the iron ore deposits for the works at Que Que.

The larger territory of Northern Rhodesia, with savanna or bush cover, nearer the equator, generally lower in elevation, has not been recognized to the same extent as a white settlers' country. But its richness in minerals, not only in the part of the country which lies along the Belgian Katanga border and is part of the great copper belt of central Africa, but also in the mineral deposits still being explored and developed in other parts of the territory, has given Northern Rhodesia an importance in world economy of a different character from that of Southern Rhodesia. In some respects Northern Rhodesia has overtaken in importance its older settled neighbor to the south.

Nyasaland, an African Protectorate, has but a handful of white settlers, though there are very important possibilities in the development of plantation agriculture.

Can these three territories, with their different backgrounds, form a satisfactory union? The Federation of the Rhodesias and Nyasaland was set up in 1953 and the first federal parliament met at Salisbury in 1954.

Southern Rhodesia

Southern Rhodesia consists of a broad belt of highland more than 4000 feet above sea level running from southwest to northeast. The northern side drains to the Zambezi, the southern to the Limpopo. The plateau is generally of rolling relief, and the 3000-foot contour may be taken as separating the healthy high veld from the low veld, where malaria is one of the disadvantages associated with climatic conditions. The natural vegetation is a savanna grassland, passing into open forests, and in the Zambezi lowlands to denser forests where Rhodesian teak and Rhodesian mahogany are obtained.

Along the eastern border between Umtali and Melsetter the elevation increases and the country is more dissected so as to become mountainous in character. This is a well-watered area, and the average rainfall between 20 and 35 inches over the bulk of the plateau renders it excellent agricultural country. It is in the south and west that irrigation becomes necessary as a precaution against drought. Soil erosion is a problem, especially owing to the heavy character of rainstorms.

On the European farms which occupy the upland belt, corn is the main crop and cattle rearing is of great importance. Rinderpest, which seems to have broken out first in 1895, has played great havoc,

Figure 2: The Rail and Road Bridge over the Zambezi Gorge below the Victoria Falls. This bridge, completed as a rail bridge in 1903, was for long the only bridge across the Zambezi linking Northern and Southern Rhodesia. (Copyright Aircraft Operating Company of Africa.)

but strenuous efforts have succeeded so well in curbing the disease that there are huge ranches for beef cattle, and near the main railway through Bulawayo, Gwelo and Salisbury dairying is firmly established, with creameries at each of the large towns. With the development of cold-storage facilities there is a growing export in chilled beef, while pig and poultry rearing flourish, dependent largely on the corn crop, with associated bacon factories. The Witwatersrand and the mining districts of the Katanga offer markets which are not very far distant.

There is a general correlation between the more infertile soils and lower rainfall in Matabeleland with cattle ranching. Where better soils and more reliable rainfall permit, arable cultivation on the European farms becomes dominant. Tobacco, introduced as a commercial crop in 1910, has become of paramount importance on areas of light sandy soil overlying granite. Citrus fruits grow well, and there is an export of oranges as far as Europe. Other crops include cotton, peanuts, sunflowers for seeds, beans, fiber plants and vegetables for local use. In the African belts subsistence agriculture is the general rule, with corn occupying four-fifths of the cultivated land.

The fact that the lower lands draining to the Zambezi remain seriously infested with tsetse fly deters development there.

Turning to minerals, we see that the coal field at Wankie with its output of 2 million tons a year is insufficient to meet all demands. Some goes northwards to the Katanga, much is consumed by the railways and the towns of Southern Rhodesia and coke is made and supplied to the iron and steel works at Que Que, which began production in 1948, using local ores. Gold, worked from time immemorial in small scattered mines, remains an important mineral product, but the small scattered copper mines do not compare in significance with those of Northern Rhodesia. Chrome ore, now extensively worked large reserves of asbestos, mica and others may be taken as indications that the mineral resources of Southern Rhodesia are far from being fully exploited.

The railways both in Northern and Southern Rhodesia were constructed in part to permit the development of minerals. In order to avoid expensive bridging over streams they followed where possible main watersheds. They do not thus necessarily tap the richest agricultural districts, but the development of roads, marked in Southern Rhodesia as elsewhere in Africa, has to a considerable extent obviated the necessity for further railway construction.

Southern Rhodesia has attracted well over 100,000 white settlers. They are settlers in the sense that they make their permanent homes in the country. A large number are town dwellers. Roughly one-third of the population of both Salisbury and Bulawayo is white, and the larger towns have more than half the total white population of the country. It is recorded that in 1948 28 per cent of all new arrivals went to manufacturing industries in the towns, only 7 per cent to the farms, leaving a large proportion for administrative, distributional and other occupations not directly productive. At first sight it might appear that this urban growth is undesirable in a country where so much remains to be done in the open lands. Actually it enables a balanced urban-rural economy to be developed; there is not the pressure of the white farmer tending to encroach on African farmlands that there is in Kenya. Whereas in Kenya Euro-

Figure 3.   The Wankie Colliery of Southern Rhodesia.   This photograph shows the modern by-product coke ovens making coke for Southern Rhodesia's iron and steel industry.   (Courtesy Southern Rhodesia Government.)

Figure 4. One of the Largest Asbestos Mines of Southern Rhodesia at Shabanie. Asbestos ranks as the third export of Southern Rhodesia, and the country is third among the world's producers, after Canada and Russia. (Courtesy Southern Rhodesia Government.)

pean settlement may be limited to a few thousands before all available land is absorbed, Southern Rhodesia can absorb its intake of 10,000 to 20,000 a year, who go largely with their families to the towns. In this heartland of Southern Rhodesia are the basic requirements of modern industry—coal, iron, metals, water power and a good climate. Secondary industries such as the Gatooma textile

Figure 5. A Crop of Tobacco in Southern Rhodesia. Tobacco accounts for two-fifths of the value of the country's exports and is the leading cash crop of the white farmer settlers. (Courtesy Southern Rhodesia Government.)

mills and the machine-tool industry of Salisbury illustrate the current trend.

About half of the African population lives in the reserves. The remainder is employed directly or indirectly by Europeans.

Southern Rhodesia entered the iron and steel business in a substantial way when the Rhodesian Iron and Steel Commission established a plant located at Que Que near good deposits of iron ore and supplies of limestone and in direct main rail communication with the coking coals of Wankie (500 miles) and supplied with electric power from Umniati. The plant consisted of a blast furnace, an open hearth furnace and Bessemer converters, with a capacity of 33,000 tons of finished steel in 1950. Coal is also available nearer at Subungwe (needing only a railway), and a new town, Redcliffe, near Que Que, was planned for 12,000 inhabitants by 1953.

Northern Rhodesia

The emphasis in Northern Rhodesia is on minerals. Along the Belgian Congo frontier at least 400 million tons of copper ore with a metallic content averaging 4 to 5 per cent have been proved, and this is only one of the mineral ores. The older mining settlement of Broken Hill with its large output of lead and silver was one of the reasons for the early extension of the railway line northward from Livingstone.

Much has been written about the suitability of Northern Rhodesia for white colonization, that is, for the permanent settlement of white peoples. There seems to be even on the highlands a persistent form, mild yet recurrent, of malaria. It may be that white settlers would gain the immunity from it in time which seems to be enjoyed by African inhabitants.

At present it may be said that modern forms of development in Northern Rhodesia are scattered, and that as far as development under European influence is concerned it is restricted to the known mineral areas and to one or two other specialized pockets of land.

The extreme south of the country in the Zambezi valley west of Livingstone is an area yielding good hardwoods—Rhodesian teak and Rhodesian mahogany. In this area Livingstone, which until 1935 was the administrative capital of Northern Rhodesia, has saw-milling establishments. The heart of Africa is still in the stage of trial and error. It was agreed that the original site of Livingstone was proving itself to be unhealthy, with the result that shortly after it ceased to be the capital the whole town was bodily moved to higher and supposedly healthier ground some miles away. The capital was shifted to Lusaka, farther north along the railway.

There are two interesting pockets of white settlements, both far removed from the railway. One is at Abercorn in the highlands south of Tanganyika, where there are government plantations, and here the outlet is via the lake and the Central Tanganyikan railway. The second is around Fort Jameson on the Nyasaland border where tobacco planting has become important. This area is linked by motor road to Blantyre in Nyasaland and thence by rail to the port of Beira.

Nyasaland

The long narrow strip of Nyasaland lies mainly to the west of Lake Nyasa, and this too is a country where development in the modern sense is still in isolated pockets. At the southern end of the country the healthy Shiré highlands have become the focus of the tea and tobacco production. The growing export trade centers on the principal town of Blantyre, though the administrative capital is at Zomba. Power development on the Shiré River would make possible great changes.

Figure 6. The Conforzi Tea Estates, Nyasaland. Tea accounts for a quarter of the exports of Nyasaland and is an example of a large-scale plantation industry controlled by Europeans, unusual in tropical Africa. (Copyright Aircraft Operating Company of Africa.)

Angola

Portuguese West Africa, otherwise known as Angola, is the largest of the Portuguese colonies and stretches from the Kunene River in the south to the Congo estuary in the north. Along the coastline north of the Congo mouth is a small enclave lying between Belgian and French territory, known as the Cabinda enclave, which is administered as a detached portion of Angola.

The total area of Angola is a little short of half a million square miles, but the total population does not reach 4 million, so that the average density is low. The heart of the country is a great plateau now crossed by the railway from Benguela and Lobito Bay to the

Katanga. This is savanna country, where cattle rearing is a natural occupation and where the opening up by the railway at the same time makes possible developments quite impossible in the less accessible parts of the country.

From this central plateau the land slopes in the southeast into the arid country of the Upper Zambezi Basin. To the southwest lies the coastal desert of the Namib. Northward from the plateau the country drains in the northeastern sector to the Congo; to the northwest lie equatorial coastal lowlands. Thus the vast territory of Angola is in large measure a transitional area with many and varied possibilities.

Dr. Derwent Whittlesey [1] distinguished three western regions—those of Luanda, Benguela and Mossamedes, based on those principal coastal centers of population, a northern and northeastern one (Congo Border), a southeastern (Upper Zambezia) and a narrow southern Kalahari Desert border. These bear a broad relationship to natural vegetation. Much of the surface is monotonous, and most is covered by a poor type of savanna; the trees lose their leaves in the dry season. The vegetation, which has been carefully described, affords a basis for a study of development possibilities.[2]

The Problems of the Zambezi Basin

More and more attention is being given to the need to consider the Zambezi Basin as a whole.

In Chapter 3 the Zambezi was referred to as a typical African river. In the 1700 miles of its course it flows through three distinct regions. The first is its plateau course, lying partly in Angola, partly in Northern Rhodesia, but receiving also intermittent streams from the great Okovango swamplands of northern Bechuanaland. The second part of its course is the Middle Zambezi, or Rhodesian trough, essentially the part lying below Victoria Falls where the river passes through a succession of relatively narrow valleys over waterfalls and rapids. The key to its development lies at the lower end of this course in the Kariba Gorge, where the Zambezi narrows to less than 100 yards as it cuts through a rocky barrier. Shortly below, it reaches its third course through the Mozambique plain.

Reference has been made elsewhere to the possibility of small irrigation works, using the upper headstreams of the Zambezi (page

[1] "Geographic Provinces of Angola," *Geog. Rev.*, XIV, 1924, 113–126.
[2] H. K. A. Shaw, "The Vegetation of Angola," *Jour. Ecology*, XXXV, 1947, 23–48.

90), but the Kariba Gorge offers an ideal site for the construction of a large-scale dam. According to calculations, if a dam 250 feet high were built in this gorge, it would give a storage reservoir with sufficient head for the generation of 750,000 kilowatts. There are smaller though comparable possibilities for using the waters of the Kafue River where it passes through a similar gorge. The use of the waters

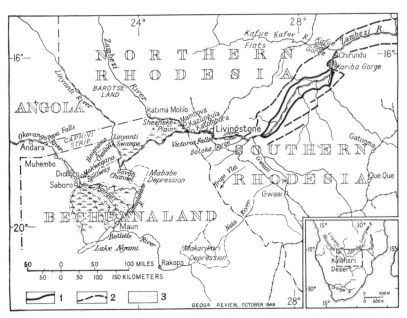

Figure 7. The Zambezi-Okovango Relationships and the Kariba-Kafue Projects. (1) Approximate limits of the Kariba reservoir. (2) Faults bounding the Middle Zambezi. (3) Border of present and former swamps of the Okovango Delta. (From F. Debenham, *Geog. Rev.* 1949. Courtesy of the *Geographical Review,* American Geographical Society.)

of this river, entirely a Northern Rhodesian stream, would not have the international complications that any great development of the Zambezi would.

In a survey of the whole basin and various projects, Professor J. H. Wellington [1] draws the conclusion about the northern Kalahari: "There seems to be no other place in Africa where so much agricultural development is possible at so little cost, and the success of the French in the swamps of the upper Niger shows what planning, en-

[1] "Zambezi-Okovango Development Project," *Geog. Rev.,* XXXIX, 1949, 552–567.

gineering skill and sound irrigational practice can accomplish in terrain of this character. One looks forward to the time when the trans-Kalahari railway will not only connect Southern Rhodesia with the west coast but will also serve a great food-producing area of

Figure 8. The Kariba Gorge of the Zambezi River. This is the proposed site of a power dam to exceed Boulder Dam in size and able to generate 750,000 kilowatts. (Copyright Aircraft Operating Company of Africa.)

two million acres, now only the playground of crocodiles, hippos, and fish hawks."

The Bangweulu Swamps of Central Africa

Although lying in the part of Northern Rhodesia outside the Zambezi Basin these great swamps recently investigated by Professor Debenham [1] draw attention to problems common to other parts of Africa.

In the first place we have here another of the great inland deltas, a natural consequence of the plateau character of the surface of the heart of Africa. Here there have been periodic rises and falls in the

[1] *Geog. Rev.*, XXXVII, 1947, 351–368.

level of water, and because of the accumulation of vegetation the swamp water is not level but has a pronounced gradient from northeast to southwest of some 3 inches in a mile. The swamps not only cover 3000 square miles, but also are the home of some thousands of people engaged in fishing and the growing of cassava.

Should such an area if possible be drained with the idea of adding to Africa's productive capacity and vast area of fertile alluvial soil, or would this simply destroy the important fishing industry and upset the African cultivators' careful adjustment to existing conditions? That adjustment can be only partial. Changes in water level are at once evident in drowned villages and gardens, and the now submerged Lunga Bank was once densely populated. Surely there could be no clearer proof that Africa still holds many problems for which we have no ready solution.

BIBLIOGRAPHY

In addition to references in the text, the following works will be found useful. A convenient short summary has been issued by the British Government entitled *Central African Territories: Geographical, Historical and Economic Survey,* His Majesty's Stationery Office, Cmd. 8234, 1951. There is an *Official Year Book of the Southern Rhodesian Government* published at Salisbury, but it does not appear annually. There is a *Northern Rhodesia Official Handbook* issued at Lusaka (1950). A full survey on *The Soils, Vegetation and Agricultural Systems of Northwestern Rhodesia,* by C. G. Trapnell and J. N. Clothier, was published at Lusaka in 1937. On Nyasaland an *Annual Report* is issued in London (His Majesty's Stationery Office). A *Handbook of Nyasaland* by S. S. Murray was published in London (1932) by the Crown Agents for the Colonies.

CHAPTER
19

South Africa[1]

Historical Introduction

Mastery of the Cape of Good Hope meant the control of the commerce between Europe and India. That was the reason for the early Portuguese interest in the Cape; that was the reason why the Dutch East India Company sent Jan van Riebeeck in 1652 to establish a settlement on the shores of Table Bay under the shadow of Table Mountain; that was the reason why the British dispossessed the Dutch temporarily in 1795 and permanently in 1806. It is van Riebeeck's ship which has long been pictured on the penny stamps of the Union of South Africa, and the Afrikaans-speaking South Africans regard this as their "Mayflower." Little remained of former Portuguese interests, and it was not the intention of the Dutch to establish a colony —simply a rewatering and revictualing halt on the way to India. But, as we have already indicated in Chapter 2, when the settlement became firmly established, expansion was inevitable. The hinterland was occupied by Hottentots, who, their tribal organization broken down and decimated by plague, became the white man's servants while nominally remaining free. From the first the settlement and later the colony depended upon these Hottentot servants and on imported Malay and African slaves. Unlike the Hottentots, the Bushmen farther in the hinterland showed an incapability of benefiting from contact with the white man and sought only to preserve their isolation by bows and poisoned arrows. They became practically extinct.

By 1795 the Dutch colony had expanded to some 15,000—free "burghers" who had retired from the Company and remained, together with a few pioneer settlers on the one hand and the servants

[1] I am greatly indebted to Dr. Monica Cole for valuable comments on this chapter.

of the Dutch East India Company on the other. The whole colony resented the harsh restrictions imposed by the Company, and they were ripe for revolt when in August 1795 the Dutch capitulated to the British, whose occupation of the Cape was a strategic move against the French. Actually the British held the Cape from 1795 to 1803 in the name of the Prince of Orange, then a refugee from the French, living in England. Although the British removed all restrictions on trading, things did not go smoothly for long. The flow of European goods was cut off; the Dutch, although willing to work hard for themselves, had the tradition that to work for others was for blacks and slaves. The British objected to the harsh Boer attitude toward the Africans, though it differed but little from the attitude of white people in European North America at the time. It has already been indicated how eventually the Great Trek started in 1836. The establishment of the Orange Free State and the Transvaal Republic followed. By way of contrast, Natal was proclaimed British in 1843 and made a province of the Cape Colony the next year. With the recognition of the independence of the Transvaal in 1852 and of the Orange Free State in 1854, the four provinces of the future Union of South Africa—two British (Cape of Good Hope and Natal) and two Boer—were broadly defined.

In 1877 the impoverished Transvaal was being harassed by several war-like African tribes. The British stepped in, annexed the country and restored order. But the old problem remained. The Boers needed military assistance but hated interference by the British Government; the British felt the need to protect whites against blacks but regarded the Boer treatment of Africans as the root of the trouble. The result was the First Boer War (1880–1881), with a British defeat and the Transvaal again independent.

Then came the discovery of the richest gold field in the world, the Rand Goldfields. The Boers had no capital to work the deposits; British capital and Western industrialization poured into the country. The patriarchal Boers, headed by President Paul Kruger, hated these "outlanders" (uitlanders); they tried to tap their wealth by taxation while denying them rights of citizenship. The coup d'état, known as the Jameson Raid, failed, and the British found themselves involved in the costly Boer War of 1899–1902 against a wily foe, thoroughly used to the terrain. The British were several times besieged, notably at Ladysmith and Mafeking. The relief of the latter on May 17, 1900, resulted in such wild rejoicing by crowds in London that

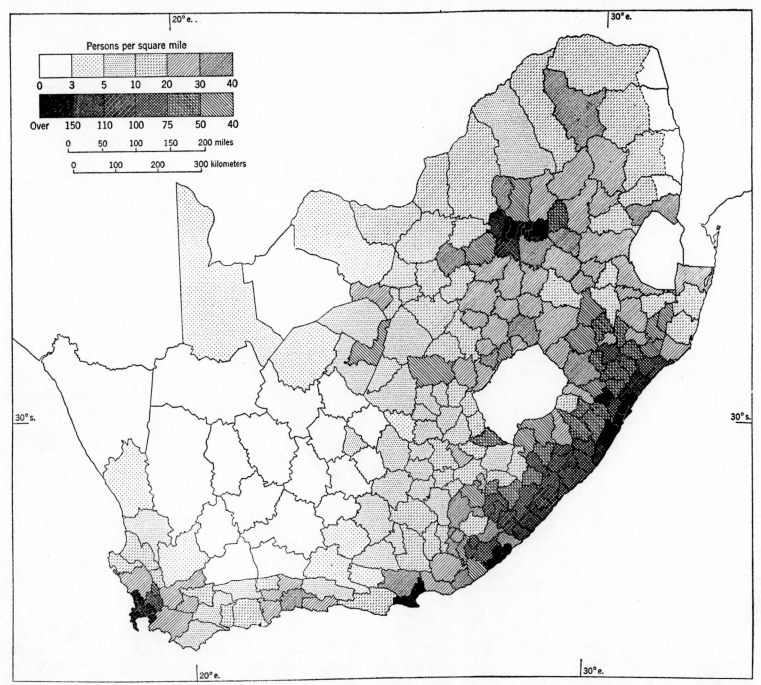

Persons per square mile

| 0 | 3 | 5 | 10 | 20 | 30 | 40 |

| Over | 150 | 110 | 100 | 75 | 50 | 40 |

0   50   100   150   200 miles

0   100   200   300 kilometers

Figure 1. The Density of Population in the Union of South Africa by Magisterial Districts. Census of 1946. (Specially drawn by John Callow.)

the word "mafficking" was long used to denote extravagant crowd behavior.

By the Treaty of Vereeniging (1902) the Boers surrendered. Fortunately great men on the British side like Lord Milner were matched by great men amongst the Boers—General Botha and General Smuts. The Boers were granted British citizenship, given 15 million dollars with which to restock their farms and other measures were immediately put in hand to restore the devastated areas. Within three years the Transvaal and Orange Free State were granted responsible government; a little later, after two years of discussion, the four colonies joined to form the Union of South Africa with dominion status (1910). In the World Wars of 1914–1918 and 1939–1945 South Africans, Boer and British alike, fought side by side with Britain.

The Population of South Africa

In order to maintain the domestic life of the settlement the Dutch East India Company, especially between 1685 and 1688, sent out numbers of orphan girls as well as about 150 French Huguenot refugees. There was little to tie either the Dutch orphans or the French refugees to their mother countries, and the growth of illiteracy is not surprising. With little contact or fresh immigration from Holland after 1688, they even abandoned their own language of Holland for a limited patois, the *Taal*—the origin of Afrikaans, which includes many African, especially Kaffir, words. For twenty years after the British occupation in 1795 the colony remained essentially Dutch, but the British supplied troops as protection against Kaffir and Bantu inroads. It was largely to secure a new frontier that 4000 selected (out of 90,000 applicants) British immigrants were settled on the west side of the Fish River in 1820 (the Albany settlement). By that time the European population, mainly of Dutch descent, numbered 42,000. The Albany settlers founded Port Elizabeth and Grahamstown and drifted to Cape Town. The more influential worked for freedom of speech and forced not only a more liberal government policy but a substitution of English institutions for Dutch. With the abolition of slavery and the Great Trek, the stage was set for the Cape to become predominantly English speaking.

The other English-speaking stronghold was Natal. The original settlers of 1824 whose presence deterred the Boer trekkers formed a small group so that Natal was annexed to Cape Colony in 1844, placed under a separate government in 1845 but in 1856 was established as a separate colony. Zululand was added to Natal in 1897 and some districts of Transvaal transferred in 1903.

In the white colonization of South Africa there are certain interesting points of comparison with North America. South Africa is outside the Tropics and climatically a "white man's country," just as North America is. Colonization was with the object of cultivating the land, and permanent settlement in both cases took place from the seventeenth century onward. In South Africa there were two language streams—Dutch-speaking and English-speaking—which may be compared with the French-speaking and English-speaking in North America. Afrikaans has moved farther from the original Dutch than has French-Canadian from French mainly because of the incorporation of African words. At the time when the South African settlers spread out over what became the Cape Province the Bantu had not yet reached the area, so that apart from the Hottentots and Bushmen the whites did not have to dispossess the Africans of their lands as the Indians were gradually dispossessed in North America. The clash occurred in the southeast Cape Province in the area still designated as the Border.

The need for labor led to importation of slaves from other parts of Africa and Malaya and later of indentured labor from India and elsewhere. The immigrant labor has remained to constitute a race problem—in which East Indians in South Africa may be compared with Negroes in the United States. We are familiar with the old frontiersman's adage, "The only good Indian is a dead one." This bears comparison with the older white South African's view of the blacks; not that they were better dead, but must be regarded only as inferior beings to be used as servants and could not be treated as equals. To some the old slavery was the right answer.

Just as the United States revolted from rigid and stupid control so the Dutch in South Africa were ripe for revolt in 1795. What in the ordinary course of human affairs might have become a separate Afrikaans-speaking United States of South Africa and an English-speaking Dominion of South Africa became, by supreme statesmanship on both sides after the Boer War, the present Union of South Africa.

To the United States and Canada the Indian problem has become essentially a moral one—responsibility for the remnants of erstwhile fine people. To the United States the Negro problem is one of a difficult minority. Here the Union of South Africa is in a very different and vastly more difficult position. The whites are in a minority of about 1 to 4; there is a bottomless reservoir of Negro Africans in the whole continent to the north. A democracy of equal citizenship for white and black and equal voting rights would immediately give the Negro African control of the Union; hence the present dilemma. The Representation of Natives Act of 1936 provided for the direct representation of native Africans in the Senate—four additional to the twenty-eight elected Senators and eight nominated (four with special knowledge of native affairs), but all Senators must be of European descent. The House of Assembly has 153 elected members, of whom three are native members. Thus the African point of view is directly represented but obviously in no sense in proportion to numbers. A very comprehensive study of the whole racial position is contained in Professor J. M. Tinley's book, *The Native Labor Problem of South Africa.*[1]

The conclusions that Professor Tinley draws are depressing. He points out that to all intents and purposes the Union of South Africa is an independent republic, and hence its policies such as those towards the Africans can and do contrast sharply with those of the British Government in London administering the British African colonies and protectorates.[2] Although successive South African Governments vary in their liberality toward the Africans, and the Nationalists under Dr. D. F. Malan (elected to power June 4, 1948) became much less tolerant than the previous United Africa party under General Smuts, all are bent on maintaining the supremacy of the whites and regarding South Africa as a White Man's country. The Malan Government declared its policy to be one of "apartheid" —the segregation of the Africans into specific areas.

SOUTH AFRICA: AREA AND POPULATIONS OF THE FOUR PROVINCES

Year	Area in Square Miles	Europeans	Non-Europeans	Total	Density
1904	472,550	1,116,806	4,059,018	5,175,824	11
1911		1,276,242	4,697,152	5,973,394	13
1921		1,519,488	5,409,092	6,928,580	15
1936		2,003,857	7,586,041	9,589,898	20
1946	472,494	2,335,460	8,923,398	11,258,858	24

Increase of Europeans over 42 years: 2.6 per cent per annum.
Increase of non-Europeans over 42 years: 2.9 per cent per annum.

[1] University of North Carolina Press, 1942. See also G. W. Broomfield, *Colour Conflict,* London (Edinburgh House Press), 1943.

[2] See *Labour Supervision in the Colonial Empire, 1937–1943,* London, His Majesty's Stationery Office, 1945.

This table illustrates the very rapid population growth since the establishment of the Union of South Africa. Both European and non-European populations have been growing at a rate roughly three times that of the world average.

Officially the Union of South Africa is bilingual; government servants are required to know both Afrikaans and English. The adherents of the Dutch Churches in 1946 numbered 1,285,195, but this is scarcely a clue to the number of Afrikaans-speaking whites because of African adherents. The Afrikaans-speaking whites—Boer descendants—definitely outnumber the English-speaking. This is predominantly the case in the Orange Free State and in rural Transvaal but not in the other two provinces or in the urbanized Witwatersrand. Of the non-Europeans the majority are Bantu, but 3 per cent (over 285,000 in 1946) are Asiatic and over 10 per cent (nearly a million) are "other races."

The Africans

In the Union of South Africa the Africans are described officially as "natives," and their affairs are in the hands of the Department of Native Affairs. Practically all the Africans in the Union are Bantus; the majority belong to the two major groups, the Nguni and the Sotho. Originally they were all tribally organized and lived in kraals or small villages. Whether or not the dwellers in an individual kraal were actually related or not, the kraal was regarded as a family unit and there was no marriage permitted between dwellers in the same kraal. The kraals were controlled according to tribal law by a Headman, who was usually a member of the traditional Bantu aristocracy, and nominally all allocation of tribal land was carried out autocratically by the Chief. In actual fact, though grazing was common, cultivated fields tended to remain in the hands of the same families for many decades. Under the old organization the men provided food by hunting and took care of the stock, whereas the gathering of fruits and roots and the cultivation of fields were women's work.

Broadly speaking, the Africans in the Union can now be divided into three classes. There are the tribal natives, living in the reserves, where to a varied extent the old tribal organization is still maintained. There are the "squatters" on the farms belonging to the white Africans, who in many cases continue to recognize more or less directly their tribal obligations. And, third, there are the town dwellers, who do not recognize any such obligation. In addition to these three groups are the African workers recruited for work in the mines, especially the gold mines of Witwatersrand. They come mainly from Portuguese East Africa, Basutoland, Bechuanaland, Swaziland and from various parts of tropical Africa. The recruitment of these workers in the mines is carried out systematically by the Native Recruiting Corporation Limited for the three High Commission territories, and under various agreements and regulations where other countries are concerned. For example, in Portuguese East Africa there is a convention between the Union Government and Portugal dating from 1928 and revised at intervals since then whereby a maximum number is permitted (it was fixed at 100,000 in 1940) and whereby conditions of work such as a period of acclimatization of 28 days of service are laid down. On leaving the mines the workers are not allowed to remain in the Union.

The steady breakdown of tribal organization among the Bantus may be attributed to several causes. There is a pole tax, standardized at 20 shillings ($2.80) for every adult male, and there is also a local hut tax of 10 shillings ($1.40) per hut imposed upon the occupier of every dwelling in a native location. These taxes must be paid in cash, and thus there is an immediate incentive for the earning of money. It is still the rule for young men to pay in kind or cash to the parents of their brides, and the increasing tendency is to pay in cash rather than in cattle. Thus the desire on the part of the young men to obtain the necessary cash is probably the strongest inducement for them to leave their kraals and to obtain work in the mines, on farms or as laborers in the towns. There is a constant demand for domestic servants in all the larger towns, and the number of Bantu female servants has been increasing rapidly. It is urged by some that missionary enterprise is also largely responsible for the process of detribalization. Approximately half the total native population in the Union is recorded as belonging to various Christian denominations. With missionary enterprise has come the spread of education, and as we have pointed out elsewhere modern ideas of democracy are in conflict with autocratic tribal organization.

The squatters on the farms provide the greater part of such farm labor as is available. Arrangements differ in different parts of the country. A common arrangement in the Free State is for the head of a family to contract to serve the farmer throughout the year in return for which he receives a small cash remuneration plus the right to graze an agreed number of stock and to cultivate an agreed area of ground free of charge. In the Transvaal the agreement is to work for the farmer without wages for 90 days, with complete liberty for the remainder of the year, either to hire himself out to the best bidder or to work land provided by the farmer.

It is illegal for the farmer to sell land to the African squatters. It is generally agreed that the system is unsatisfactory and the labor indifferent.

The general trend in South Africa—a trend much accentuated by the accession to power of the Malan Government in 1948—is toward residential segregation of the three racial groups, white, colored and native, with Asiatics included in the colored group. Under the Group Areas Act passed in July 1950 persons of one group are not permitted to own or occupy property in the controlled area of another group, except under permit. This involves registration, together with details of race, of all persons resident in the Union; and under the Immorality Amendment Act, also passed in July 1950, sex relations were entirely prohibited between Europeans and non-Europeans, that is, both colored and native groups. Previously the prohibition had applied only to marriages between Europeans and natives.

It will be seen that this trend in legislation is diametrically opposed to the general trend in other parts of the African continent. It is based essentially on the concept that the Union of South Africa is and should remain a white man's country. The initial step was really taken as long ago as 1913 with the passing of the Natives' Land Act, in which native reservations were demarcated. This of course was as much for the protection of the natives as anyone, and they have since obtained some increases in their land.

The Cape Coloured

The community known as the "Cape Coloured" is a critical element in the complex population structure of the Union. It owes its origin to three centuries of miscegenation between the immigrant Europeans—especially of Portuguese, Dutch and British stock—with the original Bantu, Hottentot and other African peoples and also with slaves of West African, Malayan, East Indian and other origins. It is reported on contemporary evidence that in the early years of European settlement in the Cape three-quarters of the children born to slave mothers had European fathers. Officially the term covers the relatively pure-blooded original non-Negro peoples, such as the Bushmen, Hottentots and Griquas, about 25 per cent of a total of about a million. The remaining three-quarters are the mixed peoples properly speaking, whose cultural affinities are with the mass of Europeans. Nearly 90 per cent live in the Cape Province where they are concentrated in the western parts, constituting there over half the total population. Except for the small English-speaking groups in Natal the majority of Cape Coloured speak Afrikaans. Large num-

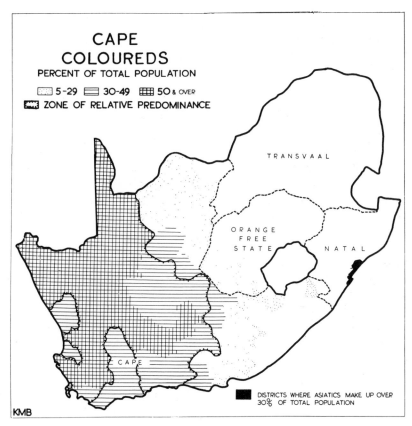

Figure 4. Distribution of Cape Coloured. (From K. M. Buchanan and N. Hurwitz, *Geog. Rev.* 1950. Courtesy of the *Geographical Review,* American Geographical Society.)

bers are employed on Afrikaans farms, especially in the more intensively farmed districts. In the towns they provide unskilled labor, domestic servants and industrial workers. Only a small "upper class," tending to remain aloof from the majority, includes teachers, skilled workers and professional men. The worst elements drift to the underworlds of the larger towns, especially Cape Town. Nearly all the Cape Coloured are nominally Christians but adhere to English denominations even more than to the Dutch Reformed church. Among the Coloured the birth rate is 50 per cent above that of the Europeans, but poverty, deplorable housing and malnutrition result in high mortality. On the whole the position of these people has steadily deteriorated. Employers prefer Europeans wherever possible, and the tendency under the racial discrimination policy of the Nationalist Government which came into power in 1948 was to squeeze them out of the slightly advantageous position which they had held over the African.[1]

The Asiatics

Ninety-seven per cent of the Asiatic immigrants [2] living in the Union of South Africa speak Indian languages so that the designation in the census return "Asiatic" may be read "Indian." It was in 1859–1860 that the sugar planters and other colonists in Natal secured legal permission to bring "indentured" coolie labor from India. After completing five years the Indians were free to choose their own job; after ten years they were entitled to a free return passage. Many came, few returned. They became traders and market gardeners, and with their low standard of living were able to undercut the European settlers in many fields. The reaction was inevitable. Natal, where seven-eighths of the total are found, prohibited free entry in 1896; the Union Government in 1913 prohibited further immigration entirely. By that time the numbers had come to exceed numbers of Europeans in Natal, but with cessation of Indian immigration numbers of Europeans drew slightly ahead after about 1925. In 1946 there were 285,000 Asiatics in the Union.

The Indians came from many parts of India—Muslim Gujaratis from Bombay and Tamil-speaking Indians professing Hinduism from the Madras coasts are most numerous, but there are many Hindi speakers from North India and Telegus from the south. Muslims constitute nearly a fifth of the total.

Among the Indians men heavily outnumber women (a legacy from the old days), but the birth ratio is high and the total is rapidly increasing. In the British Commonwealth as a whole Indians enjoy a citizenship status of equality with Europeans. In the Union of South

[1] An excellent study of these people by K. M. Buchanan and N. Hurwitz appears in the *Geog. Rev.*, XL, July 1950, 397–414. ("The 'Coloured' Community in the Union of South Africa.")

[2] K. M. Buchanan and N. Hurwitz, "The Asiatic Immigrant Community in the Union of South Africa," *Geog. Rev.*, XXXIX, July 1949, 440–449.

Africa their official status is different and closer to that of the Africans, hence the source of friction between India and Pakistan and the Union of South Africa. In 1927 inducements in the form of a free passage and a bonus were offered to Indians to return to India, and in the following twenty years about 100,000 took advantage of the scheme. But the majority have no wish to leave. They are much better off than they would be in India. They make good livings as traders, market gardeners and in some of the professions. Some have become very wealthy.

The Physical Background

What are the essential characteristics of the land into which Briton and Boer penetrated, and which is today the Union of South Africa?

In common with other parts of the African continent there is in the south a great central plateau separated from the shores of the Indian and Atlantic oceans by a varied width of lower country.

In southern Africa the plateau reaches remarkably high elevations, especially over the eastern half. Nearly all this eastern half has an elevation of more than 4000 feet, and considerable stretches exceed 6000 feet above sea level. The eastern and southeastern edge of the plateau forms a remarkable feature known as the Drakensberg or the Quathlamba mountains, and the gigantic rocky wall viewed from the east is one of the world's spectacular features. Although the edge of the plateau is somewhat less marked along the south where it receives various names, it is nevertheless a distinctive feature. In the dry country of the west the edge is less distinct and the elevation reached, though almost everywhere over 3000 feet, is less, and only a few points reach the level of 6000 feet. The plateau itself is over large stretches almost flat. At other times it is rolling, and sometimes low flat-topped hills rise from its surface. The latter feature is associated particularly with the presence of the almost horizontal sheets of sandstone associated with igneous rocks, belonging to the Karroo beds (see above, page 51). A marked change of scenery is associated with a change from the Karroo beds to the underlying ancient rocks.

In southern Africa the surface of the plateau sinks greatly towards the center, and over the heart of the dry land of Bechuanaland the average elevation drops below 3000 feet. In the Union of South Africa the greater part of the plateau lies in the basin of the Orange

River, together with its main tributary the Vaal. Only the northern half of the Transvaal comes within the drainage of the Limpopo.

Climatically the elevation of the plateau lowers the general temperature 10° to 20°F. throughout the year, and the frost danger is of considerable importance. Since the plateau is a region of summer rain and falls in the winter are infrequent, snow is rare except on

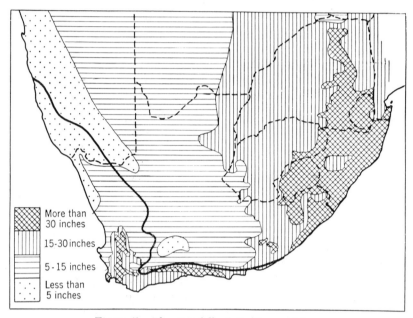

More than
30 inches

15-30 inches

5-15 inches

Less than
5 inches

Figure 5.   The Rainfall of Southern Africa.

the mountains of the edge. By a curious coincidence on my first visit to the Witwatersrand in the month of July I awoke in the early morning when my train was approaching Johannesburg to find the whole veld as far as the eye could see thickly mantled in 4 or 5 inches of snow. It proved to be the first time that snow had fallen for some five years, and most of the small children were seeing it for the first time.

The plateau lies in the so-called Trade Wind Belt. The rain-bearing air masses of summer are from the Indian Ocean, and the heaviest fall is consequently in the east; but only on the higher eastern parts of the plateau does the average exceed 30 inches a year. It is possible to consider the high plateau as divided into eastern and western halves by the isohyet of 15 inches a year. With less than this amount

cultivation except by irrigation becomes impossible. Even where
the fall is between 15 and 20 inches a year crop production is precarious, and perhaps it is better to say that normal arable farming
is limited to those eastern regions of the plateau which have more
than 20 inches a year. Furthermore, the rain tends to fall in sudden storms, and the quantity from year to year is subject to serious
variation. The sudden falls are conducive to serious soil erosion

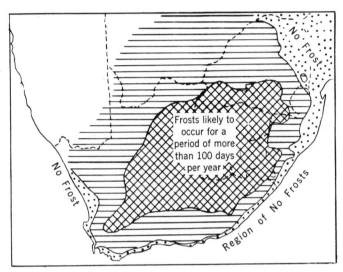

Figure 6.   Frost Map of South Africa.

and the rapid formation of deep *dongas*, or gulleys. In addition to
direct soil erosion the rain falling suddenly on the hard parched surface of the land does not readily soak in but runs off instead of
enriching the soil. It follows that most of the South African rivers,
the tributaries of the Orange, are liable to sudden floods, whereas
for a large proportion of the year the water courses are mainly dry.

The country between the high plateau and the sea is not in southern Africa a coastal plain. In the east throughout Natal under the
great scarp of the Drakensberg Mountains there is a belt of very
varied hilly land, and visitors to Pietermaritzburg who pass through
the Valley of a Thousand Hills will recognize in that name the essentially broken-up nature of this tract. Here the underlying rocks
are the same Karroo Beds that underlie neighboring parts of the
plateau. But they are here gently folded, and the process of subaerial weathering has cut through the horizontal or gently inclined

layers to carve out a varied relief which because it is still actively in course of being sculptured geologists would describe as a "young relief." Only along the coasts of Natal is there a strip which can be described as a coastal plain, fringed along the ocean itself by lines of sand dunes against which pound the ever-lasting breakers from the Indian Ocean.

In the south, that is, in Cape Province, the land between the plateau edge and the sea is much more varied. Here in contrast with the whole of the heart of Africa but in common with the north-west of the continent, the rocks have been considerably folded, and one gets the familiar features of folded mountain ranges. Though these ranges differ in detail in direction, elevation, degree of dissec-tion, on the whole they tend to be parallel to the edge of the plateau. Between them are broad or narrow valleys, sometimes wide enough to form extensive plains. And it may be said, therefore, that the descent from the plateau to the sea is by a series of gigantic steps, each separated from the next by a range of mountains. In the most typical development the lowest step is a narrow coastal plain, or coastal plateau, then a range of mountains—the Langeberg and Outeniquas—followed by the second step, a dry plateau known as the Little Karroo. The Great Black Mountains (Groote Zwarte Ber-gen) are followed by the third step, the plateau of the Great Karroo. The Great Karroo itself is overshadowed by the scarp here known as the Nieuwveld, which forms the edge of the plateau.

This southern tract is the one where the summer rains from the Trades alternate with the winter rains from the westerlies and so receives a rainfall well distributed throughout the year. The rain-fall is largely relief rainfall, with the consequent sharp differences be-tween an exposed hill ridge and a sheltered valley. But there are numerous small rivers, rising among these favored mountains of the Cape Province. They naturally tend to flow as far as possible along the valleys, but at intervals they cut through the intervening moun-tain ridges by great gaps known in South Africa as *poorts*. Several of the rivers are naturally of considerable importance in providing water for irrigation of the flat valley plains.

Best known of South African mountains are those which lie in the southwest. Table Mountain, under which nestles the town and port of Cape Town, is in fact a prototype of flat-topped mountains found throughout Africa wherever beds of resistant rock are approxi-mately horizontal. Near by, overlooking Gordon's Bay, are those more varied mountain forms associated with irregularly folded rocks.

This southwest region of course is the region of winter rain, South Africa's belt of Mediterranean climate, with the consequent reproduction of so many physical features reminiscent of southern California or southern Portugal.

Farther north and in Southwest Africa the land between the plateau edge and the sea is the desert stretch known as the Namib, of varied but not very distinctive relief. Throughout the vast stretch from 30° South to the border of Angola in 17° South only one permanent stream, the Orange River, reaches the coast.

Gold

For many decades South Africa has led the countries of the world as a producer of gold. The African continent is responsible for about three-fifths of the world's output, and of this total some 80 per cent comes from the Union of South Africa. Although recent discoveries suggest that an important part will be played in the future by gold fields in the Orange Free State, from 1887 to 1949, inclusive, nearly all the gold came from the single gold field of the Witwatersrand with a total yield approaching 500,000,000 ounces. This field alone in 1948 was furnishing 97 per cent of South Africa's output, nearly 48 per cent of the estimated world's output and its value represented two-fifths of all the commercial exports of the whole continent of Africa, excluding Egypt. Geological experts are satisfied that South Africa's output can be maintained at comparable levels for at least another quarter century even if no further reserves are discovered.

The Witwatersrand Gold Field has been described from the geographical point of view by Peter Scott.[1] He points out that the field, commonly known as the Rand, extends for 50 miles from Randfontein eastward to Springs and for 20 miles southward from Springs to Heidelberg. Structurally it comprises the areas where gold-bearing conglomerates called "reefs" of pre-Cambrian age either outcrop at the surface or dip steeply southward under a cover of younger rocks. Twelve-thousand feet is regarded as the possible limit to economic mining. At a depth of 9000 feet in the Crown mines the rock temperature is 109°F., and in order to protect the miners from phthisis and silicosis the air has to be kept saturated with moisture; and deeper mining is possible only if dry methods with dry air can be adopted.

[1] *Geog. Rev.*, XLI, October 1951, 561–589.

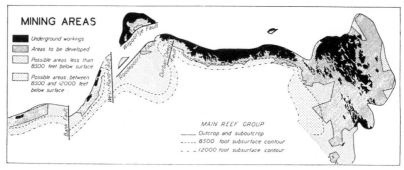

Figure 7

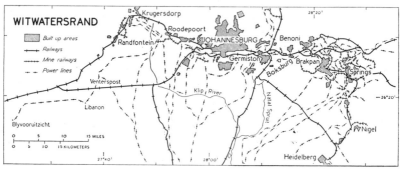

Figure 8

Figures 7–10. Four Maps of the Witwatersrand Gold Field. In the 1948 map (Figure 10) the largest circles represent companie$ producing between 500,000 and 1,000,000 fine ounces a year, the smaller circles 100,000 to 500,000 and

Structurally the gold field may be divided into four main regions: the Central Rand, the Far East Rand, the West Rand and the Far West Rand. As shown in Figures 7 and 9, these areas are separated by structural features.

The gold was discovered in 1884, the field proclaimed in 1886 and production became important in the following year; and by 1888 the whole length of the outcrop of the Central Rand was being mined by numerous companies. Gradually as surface working gave place to mines and the mines had to go ever deeper, the work passed into the hands of large units. The Central Rand dominated production until 1897, and it was during this period that the cyanide process made possible the recovery of gold from pyritic ores which had previously been regarded as valueless. The process was introduced in 1890 and generally adopted from 1892 onward.

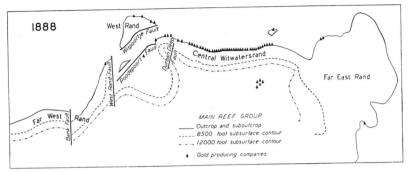

Figure 9

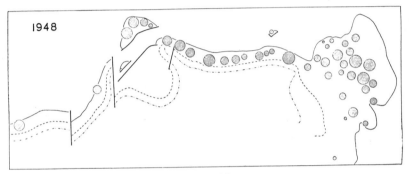

Figure 10

under 100,000. (From Peter Scott, *Geog. Rev.* 1951. Courtesy of the *Geographical Review,* American Geographical Society.)

There followed the great development of the West Rand from 1898 to 1911 and then the Far East Rand (1912 to 1923), which became dominant in the years 1924 to 1938 when the Far West Rand, previously insignificant, began to be important. Up to and including 1950 the all-time record of output was in 1941 with over 14 million ounces. It dropped to 11½ million ounces in 1948, but the devaluation of sterling in 1949 rendered economic the working of deposits at a time when the abandonment of some mines was in contemplation. In 1898 for every ton of reef which was milled, 9.78 pennyweights (0.489 ounce) of gold was obtained. By 1948 this had fallen to 4.01 pennyweights (0.2005 ounce), but vast additional areas had been proved.

It should be noted that the development of the gold field was made possible by the near-by existence of coal, first in the neighborhood of the Far East Rand itself, latterly from the Witbank field where the seams are almost undisturbed, the coal of excellent quality and the reserves very great. An electric power supply, vital to deep mining operations, was built up after 1907 on the basis of unlimited coal resources.

The great problem of the Rand has always been labor. There was an early attempt to use demobilized European soldiers as unskilled labor. There was also an attempt to recruit Africans in Central and East Africa. In 1904 Chinese laborers, on a three-year indenture system, were introduced, and at one time as many as 53,000 Chinese were employed in the mines; but repatriation was decided upon and was completed in 1910. Since then Africans have been recruited under the regular systems mentioned elsewhere, and increased technical efficiency has steadily lowered the average number of employees per 1000 tons of ore milled—now under 6. The mines employ over 300,000.

The development of the Rand has given rise, naturally, to many other problems. One of the most serious is adequacy of water supply, which may prove to be a limiting factor in the future. The spread of the gigantic conurbation based on Johannesburg has been rendered difficult by the huge areas occupied by mining dumps of white crushed quartzose conglomerate. Naturally, apart from the important iron and steel industries, the development has given rise to a wide range of industries designed to supply local needs.

Diamonds

Gold is far from being the only mineral of importance in South Africa. Until the discovery in 1908 of diamonds in Southwest Africa and later discoveries in Tanganyika and elsewhere, South Africa was almost the only source of diamonds in the world. A pebble from the banks of the Orange River was identified as a diamond in 1867; but the most famous diamond field is at Kimberley in Cape Province, where diamonds were first found in 1871. They were found in a decomposed rock known as *yellow ground* outcropping at the surface in oval or circular patches corresponding to depressions, or pans. It was found that underneath the decomposed yellow rock was a hard igneous rock, known as *blue ground,* and the momentous discovery of the diamond industry was the realization that this blue ground was the parent rock of the diamonds. The geologist knows blue ground as kimberlite, an igneous rock occupying pipes going down into the earth's crust which probably represent old volcanic necks. There are large numbers of these pipes though only a few are diamond-bearing. At first they were excavated in great pits from the surface to depths of 400 feet or more. Then it became necessary to follow the blue ground by underground mines, which took the diamond-mining industry out of the hands of individuals or small companies and made it a monopoly of large combines, such as De Beers, able to command the necessary capital, human skill and technical equipment. In due course the great diamond combines were able to control and restrict the output in order to maintain prices. Their principal mines were near Kimberley, at Jagersfontein, Koffiefontein and finally, the largest single mine of all, the Premier diamond mine near Pretoria, from which the world's largest diamond, the Cullinan, was obtained in 1905. In the years 1925–1927 when discoveries of rich diamond-bearing alluvial deposits were made elsewhere, especially in Southwest Africa, diamond mining was temporarily shut down to counteract the output of alluvial stones.

Other Minerals

The fortunate possessor of the only extensive fields of bituminous coal in Africa, South Africa has in the Orange Free State, in the southern Transvaal, in Natal and to a smaller extent in Cape Province vast reserves of valuable fuel. The coal occurs in the lower part of the Great Karroo system. Principal workings are at Witbank and Middelburg in the Transvaal which supply Johannesburg and around Newcastle in Natal.

Among other minerals of the Union of South Africa there are copper ores in Namaqualand and at the mines of Messina in the northern Transvaal, as well as in Southwest Africa. Tin ore occurs in the Transvaal Bush Veld, and South Africa has such other minerals as asbestos, chromite, platinum ore, mica, manganese and chrome ores as well as limestone for local use. Uranium is now extracted in the Rand.

Thus the Union of South Africa is far from being dependent upon a single mineral commodity, however important.

The Iron and Steel Industry

The development of the South African iron and steel industry affords a very interesting example of progress towards economic self-sufficiency which marks the growth of so many of the "newer" countries of the world. The start dates only from 1910 to 1916, when three plants using scrap were established in the Witwatersrand mainly to supply some of the needs of the gold-mining industry and another also using scrap was located on the Vaal River at

Vereeniging and received government support. The curtailment of overseas supplies during the First World War (1914–1918) helped the industry, but it was hurt by the post-war depression. Nevertheless, the Union Steel Corporation (USCO) of Vereeniging established

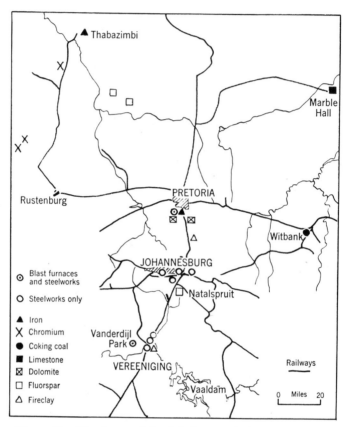

Figure 11.   The Iron and Steel Industry.   (After Peter Scott.)

a blast furnace at Newcastle in Natal in 1926 and an additional steel works on the Klip River at Vereeniging in the same year.   The South African Iron and Steel Corporation (ISCOR) was established at Pretoria in 1934 to use the local medium-grade quartzitic bedded ore deposits, and by 1949 it was producing three-quarters of South Africa's output of about 650,000 tons of steel.   The discovery of rich hematite deposits at Thabazimbi, 156 miles from Pretoria by a railway which was pushed there in 1934, soon made that the chief source of ore.   Though only some of the seams are suitable for making metallurgical coke, the Witbank coal workings are only 70 miles from the ISCOR works. But Vereeniging has proved to have an even better location; it is actually on a coal field and other suitable coal from northern Natal is near, water supply is good and the location is central for South Africa's railway system. In 1944 a site at Vanderbijl Park 10 miles west of the old works and on the bare veld was chosen. Five years later this South African Gary had blast furnaces, steel and engineering works and was a fast-growing town of 20,000 people. Despite expanding demand South Africa in 1950 was on the verge of being completely independent of imports of iron and steel. The old works on the gold field had expanded into a considerable industry but were completely overshadowed by Pretoria and Vereeniging. The geographical aspects of the industry have been considered by Peter Scott,[1] who has kindly permitted me to reproduce the accompanying map (Figure 11).

The Regional Divisions of South Africa

Some years ago when I was working in South Africa in collaboration with the late Mr. J. N. Jamieson, we agreed that, from the geographical point of view, southern Africa falls naturally into a number of regions, each with a distinctive character, whether regarded from the point of view of natural endowments or from the point of view of human reactions as illustrated by land use and types of farming. We used this scheme of regional divisions in a number of geographical textbooks which have been widely used in South African schools.[2] At a later date Professor J. H. Wellington of the University of Witwatersrand, in a paper entitled "Land Utilization in South Africa,"[3] independently drew up a series of regions based on land use, which agree so closely that it is possible to combine the two concepts. The account which follows is based essentially on modifications of my original scheme suggested by Professor Wellington's work.

As he very rightly says: "Two facts stand out in any consideration of land development in South Africa. The physical environment is inexorable and the geographical advantages can be realized to the full only when the country realizes its true economic relationships

[1] "The Iron and Steel Industry of South Africa," *Geography*, XXXVI, 1951, 137–149.
[2] *The World: A General Geography for South African Schools*, 1st Edition, London, 1927.
[3] *Geog. Rev.*, XXII, 1932, 205–224.

with the rest of the world.   Of the inexorable physical circumstances rainfall is of foremost importance."

On the basis of rainfall Wellington recognizes three main divi-

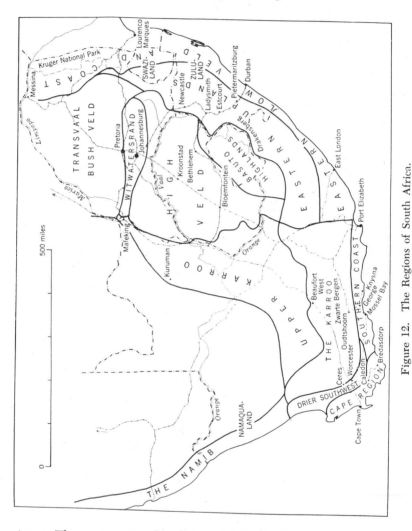

Figure 12.   The Regions of South Africa.

sions.   The eastern is where the rainfall is adequate and land may be utilized in the production of crops requiring a summer fall.   The southwestern is where crop production is also possible on account of sufficient rainfall either coming this time in the winter or distributed throughout the year, or where there are perennial streams

which permit continuous irrigation.   The third, which he calls the
middle area, perhaps more appropriately the western, is where rainfall of less than 15 or 20 inches a year is insufficient for crop production.

The three main divisions and subdivisions proposed and named by
Professor Wellington are indicated on Fig. 12.   We may consider each
in turn.

Figure 18.   General View of Cape Town and Docks, Sheltered by Devil's Peak
and Table Mountain.   The original site afforded some shelter, but the modern
port is entirely artificial.   In the foreground is the older dock; beyond it is the
larger and newer dock, with reclaimed foreshore.   (Courtesy South African
Railways.)

THE CAPE REGION.   This is essentially the area of winter rainfall
where the rainfall is sufficient for crop production.   It is an area of
mountain ridges and intervening valleys or plains.   There is the so-
called *swart* land in the west, and the *ruens* or ridge lands of the
Caledon and Bredasdorp districts to the southeast.   This is the birth-
place of European agriculture in South Africa, and it is the region
which bears the closest comparison to other parts of the world enjoying a Mediterranean climate, but notably to southern California.

The farmlands are used mainly for wheat production, with about
half the land under crops and the other half lying fallow.   But there
is a natural infertility of the soils, and the yields are lower than in
other countries relying chiefly on wheat production.   Farms are large.
Wellington quotes an average size of 1600 acres, but this includes
land within farm boundaries which cannot be actually farmed.   In
certain areas there is a specialized development of viticulture, and

the holdings are naturally smaller. On the scanty natural pasture of shrubby Mediterranean type, sheep farming is a profitable secondary industry, and the animals graze also on the stubble and fallow lands. There is little cattle farming, the summer is too dry. But this suggests that more land should be devoted to fodder crops, to enable the pastoral industry to be expanded.

Figure 14. The Docks at Cape Town. In the background is Table Mountain, covered with its "table cloth" of cloud. South Africa makes great use of long-distance luxury buses, one of which is shown. On the right a Union Castle liner from Britain. (Courtesy South African Railways.)

The production of wheat has tended to rely to a considerable extent on the protection afforded by duty on imported wheat. This is not a region, however, which need necessarily rely primarily on agricultural production. Its climate has the attractive features of sunny southern California. Quite apart from the early start enjoyed by Cape Town and the facilities which it has for easy communication by rail and latterly by road with the whole of the subcontinent, this Cape Region is one which naturally attracts those who have worked elsewhere and saved sufficient to retire into a part of the country climatically most attractive.

Incidentally the botanists include a large tract of Southwest Africa in the region of the "Cape flora," the richest in the whole of Africa and one characterized by a great wealth of flowering plants, especially those of shrubby habit.

THE DRIER SOUTHWESTERN REGION. This region differs from the preceding one in that the rainfall is almost everywhere too small for agriculture. It includes many of the folded mountain ranges, but interest centers on certain of the valleys which lie between them. These include the valley of the Olifants River in the north,

Figure 15. The Main Cape Town–Johannesburg Rail at Gulbagh Kloof. The South African railroads are 3 feet, 6 inches gauge, and the train shown is the express "Blue Train" about 70 miles from Cape Town. (Courtesy South African Railways.)

the Brede River and its tributaries in the south, as well as the famous Ceres valley and the Hex River valley. Both the Olifants and the Brede are perennial streams, and therefore water can be used for irrigation during the dry summer season. Fortunately the land which can be irrigated has good fertile soils, and soils which are suitable for fruit growing command very high prices per acre, fifteen or twenty times that which cannot be irrigated, and the use of which is restricted to grazing. This is the main area of production of grapes, but it also includes some of the best deciduous fruit orchards of the country, notably plums and apples. Some tobacco, especially of Turkish types, is grown, and there are winter crops of oats and barley. This fruit-producing region has the advantage that the seasons are the reverse of those of the northern hemisphere and consequently

Figure 16. The Road through Meirings Poort, Groot Zwartbergen. One of the finest of the "poorts" or gaps through the ranges which bound the Great Karroo. (Courtesy South African Railways.)

there is a large export of South African fruits to British and other European markets at a time when local supplies are non-existent.

In the valleys of this region such small towns as Paarl and Worcester are primarily concerned with fruit drying, fruit packing, and the manufacture of wines and brandies. Much progress has been made in the technique of wine production. In particular South Africa has succeeded in producing excellent wines of the sherry type, able to compete on their own merits with the long-favored products of Spain. Light table wines, though they cannot be matched directly with

German hocks or with French wines, have been proving their popularity, especially in Canada and Britain.

The expansion of quick freezing has opened up new possibilities in the marketing of fresh fruits.

This too is a country of magnificent scenery: long sinuous passes between the lofty mountain barriers, through which go river courses filled with roaring, surging cataracts and flood waters in the wet season. The wealth of spring flowers as in the Cape flora is remarkable, but the sheltered valleys with their neat fruit orchards and tidy vineyards and attractive, compact, color-washed farmhouses also offer a picture of great beauty.

Though originally introduced by the early Dutch settlers, both viticulture and fruit farming owe much of their development and success to the influence of the French Huguenots who, after the revocation of the Edict of Nantes in 1685, settled in this part of South Africa.

In contrast to other Mediterranean climatic regions, neither climate nor soil seems suitable to olives.

THE SOUTHERN COASTAL REGION. This is the region where there is a gradual merging of the winter type of rainfall into the area of summer rain. Heavy mists are frequent on the southern slopes of the boundary ranges known collectively as the Langebergen, and the more even distribution of rainfall results not only in perennial streams but in soils with a character different from those of other parts of southern Africa.

Where the soils are derived from the Table Mountain sandstone they tend to be poor and leached, but where they are formed from shales and the rainfall is moderate or low, soil acidity tends to disappear and the land is particularly productive. Unfortunately the area concerned is strictly limited in extent. Among field crops oats and potatoes are important, wheat relatively less so. The well-distributed rainfall results in a comparatively luxuriant grass growth in wetter regions. An improvement in pasture grasses would mean a definite increase in beef and dairy breeds of cattle, whereas sheep flourish on the drier hill slopes. There is obviously great variation from place to place according to local conditions, with the result that land values, type of farming as well as intensity of production show marked variation also. Some of the best land is on the alluvial soils by Gamtoss River between Port Elizabeth and Humansdorp. Irrigated land commands a high price.

George is a fruit-growing center with special interest in apples; Knysna, with a heavier rainfall, lies in a forested area where afforestation has assumed importance on the neighboring hillslopes. Mossel Bay is a port lying in a sheltered bay commanding two passes into

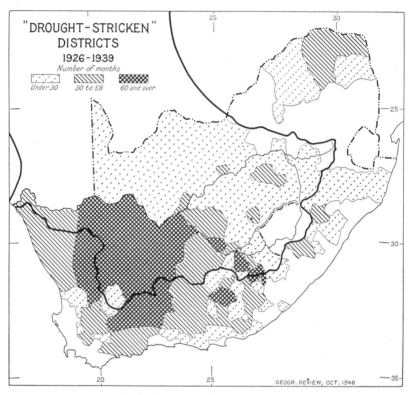

Figure 17. Districts Classified as Drought Stricken and Entitled to State Relief Measures. The heavy line shows the limits of the Orange Basin. (After J. H. Moolman, *Geog. Rev.* 1946. Courtesy of the *Geographical Review*, American Geographical Society.)

the interior so that it is an outlet for the Karroo country behind. But in this respect it does not rival Port Elizabeth on Algoa Bay, which is both the natural outlet of a large and productive hinterland, including not only the eastern part of Cape Province but also much of the Orange Free State which lies behind, and has also been provided with a good harbor.

THE KARROO. Both the Great Karroo and the Little Karroo are treeless plains hemmed in by mountains and lying below the main scarp of the great African plateau. They both suffer from a small rainfall—everywhere less than 15 inches and in the west less than 10 inches—and a rainfall which is very irregular in its incidence during the year as well as from year to year. On the whole the flora is that of the Mediterranean Cape Region, with an admixture of those plants characteristic of the dry Upper Karroo on the surface of the

Figure 18. Churchill Dam near Port Elizabeth. This is typical of the many modern dams designed primarily to provide irrigation water. (Courtesy South African Railways.)

plateau itself. Usually drab and monotonous with the gray-leafed shrubs separated by tracts of bare soil, after a shower of rain the shrubs and the succulent plants burst into flower. This is country of which it can truly be said, "The desert shall blossom as a rose." The streams are nearly all intermittent in flow, with the exception of a few which derive from the Swarte Bergen range. Here it is possible at the foot of the great escarpment and near the higher mountain ranges of the region to use the water for the cultivation of crops of wheat or lucerne, together with tobacco and grapes. Where major conservation dams have been constructed on the Dwyka, Olifants and Sundays rivers, lucerne and citrus fruits are intensively cultivated. The Sundays River valley is a leading area.

Oudtshoorn was long famous as a center of the ostrich-farming industry which flourished in those days when women of fashion in many parts of the world took pride in their ostrich feather fans, or wore the huge plumes as a decoration to their headgear. Despite repeated efforts to resuscitate a comparable demand, ostrich farming

Figure 19. A Citrus Farm near Grahamstown, Cape Province. In the distance is a typical treeless plateau surface. The valley sides are wooded; the orchards are on the fertile valley floor. (Courtesy South African Railways.)

must be classed as a dying, almost dead industry, but Oudtshoorn has become the center of extensive irrigated lands with an intensive form of agriculture.

Outside such specialized irrigation settlements, the Karroo is essentially a pastoral area, supporting considerable numbers of Merino sheep and goats from which mohair is obtained. The bushes typical of the Karroo vegetation appear to have a high nutritive value as well as medicinal properties which keep the animals in good condition, though the carrying capacity of the land is low. Farms are

4000 to 10,000 acres in area; their value where they cannot be irrigated is less than a dollar an acre.

Apart from Oudtshoorn in the Little Karroo, Beaufort West in the heart of the Great Karroo is the chief settlement. Since the main railway from Cape Town to Johannesburg or Rhodesia passes through the heart of the Great Karroo, the country is not isolated.

THE DRY REGIONS OF THE PLATEAU. To the north of the Great Karroo and beyond the great escarpment are the dry regions of the plateau. In general, aridity increases toward the west and north, and a dry pastoral region where cattle can find a fair pasturage fades into the Kalahari bush veld and Kalahari Desert.

The southern part of the region immediately north of the great escarpment is often known in South Africa as the Upper Karroo or the Karroid Plateau. This vast flat or very gently undulating treeless plain is broken by flat-topped hills, sure indication of the existence of horizontal beds of Karroo sandstone and Karroo dolerite. Everywhere the soil is shallow and rocky, and the vegetation consists of small scattered bushes capable only of supporting a few sheep and goats. The small population depends upon underground water which may be reached by wind-driven pumps.

Not only is the rainfall low, but it is extremely irregular, and it is not unusual for two or three years to pass without appreciable rainfall. Such small towns as Carnarvon and Victoria West are centers of the pastoral industry, but the farmers require anything from 4000 to 20,000 acres in order to maintain a flock of reasonable size. The Persian fat-tailed sheep seems to be the best adapted to the area where the Karroo shrubs occur, but northward in Namaqualand the bushman grass and other coarse grasses provide winter pasturage for a few thousand cattle. In the bush veld to the north of the Orange River cattle may find a fair pasturage in the summer, which here becomes the nominal rainy season.

Although little water reaches the Atlantic Ocean, the Orange River itself is a perennial stream, and along its banks are terraces large enough to be worth irrigating. As shown in Fig. 6 winter frosts occur over most of the area, but summers are long enough and hot enough for cotton to be possible on the alluvial soils of these terraces. In a few favored areas an interesting type of cultivation may become possible, as, for example, in the Zak River basin. When this river comes down in flood its waters are diverted into shallow basins separated by low earthen banks. After the soil has been thoroughly soaked the water is allowed to flow through sluice gates into other prepared basins. Wheat is then sown on the damp mud and matures with this single flooding. Clearly such a cash crop is precarious and possible only in certain years.

THE NAMIB. Although the greater part of the Namib Desert lies in Southwest Africa it stretches into the Cape Province and is in fact the coastal strip where is to be found the most extreme of the desert conditions known in South Africa. The irregular rainfall even on an average does not exceed 5 inches a year.

THE HIGH VELD. The regions so far considered lie within the Cape Province of the Union of South Africa. Although the surface of the high plateau as a whole may be called and often is called the High Veld, this term can be properly restricted to the eastern part of the plateau surface, covering the larger part of the Orange Free State together with the neighboring parts of the Cape Province and stretching northward into the southern Transvaal. Geologically the surface is of almost horizontal beds of the Karroo system, sandstone predominating in the south and east with some dolerites and lavas in the northwest. The whole is a great expanse of rolling grassland, treeless except where shade trees have been planted around a few of the farms. It is in this area that the rainfall, more than 15 inches, tends to average between 20 and 30 inches a year, and is of greater reliability than in the drier parts. The even surface has moderately fertile, loamy soils, but the elevation, usually between 4000 and 6000 feet, results in a great range of temperature, as well as a frost period extending certainly for more than 100 days in the year. Although there is much land in pasture, this is essentially a region of South Africa characterized by extensive arable cultivation. Although some wheat is grown in places as a winter and early summer crop, corn (maize) is the mainstay of the region. This is the so-called maize triangle of the Union where this is outstandingly the most important crop. With the development of mixed farming, however, the term has become something of a misnomer.

Some years may be affected severely by droughts, and occasionally the summer rains arrive too late for the late sown corn to ripen before the advent of winter frosts. The corn has then to be used for silage.

Although the dry climate results in a dry and compact grain, yields are low when compared with the Rhodesian maize area. Commonly the yield is not more than four bags, or 800 pounds, an acre, which can be doubled or even trebled by use of fertilizers, but is only about one-quarter or one-fifth of the average South American yield or less than one-quarter of yields which have now become common in the Corn Belt of the United States.

Corn is the staple food grain of the Africans, and a considerable proportion is used as human food. It might be thought that a better use of the corn would be for the development of cattle, pig and sheep farming. The High Veld is indeed a great sheep area, but with Merino rather than mutton sheep. It would seem that the

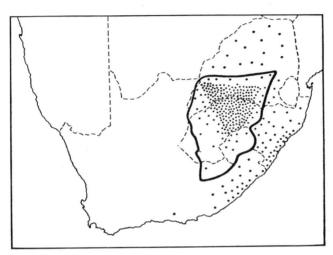

Figure 20. The Distribution of Corn (Maize). Each dot represents 1,000,000 pounds (50,000 bags) in a good average year. The heavy black line is the boundary of the High Veld within which lies the so-called maize triangle.

natural grasses of the High Veld are far from being as nutritious as they should be. It is believed that this is due to a lack of phosphorus, and that the comparatively poor quality of South African beef and mutton is in large measure due to this deficiency. It has been shown that a ration of bone meal or calcium phosphate can double the milk yield and more than double the market value of cattle or sheep intended for slaughter. In the meantime this has long been a corn-exporting region, yet the low yields combined with the relatively expensive and inefficient labor previously mentioned render the growing of corn for sale economically unproductive. Among the other difficulties faced by the farmer was the liability in the past to locust plagues. The menace still exists, but there are effective control measures. Nevertheless, the High Veld is dotted all over with its attractive little farms, each often sheltered by a plantation of pines or gum trees, or the Australian wattle, the bark of which has a value in tanning leather. Many farms too have their apple orchards, and a windmill pumping water is an almost inevitable adjunct to the whole. Edward Ackerman has expressed the view that even the relatively favored "maize triangle" is a problem area. More than three-quarters of the cultivated land of the Union is inside the triangle, which has long been a one-crop region, though changing to mixed farming. Crop failures recur because of uncertain rainfall, with heavy summer thundershowers (when much-needed moisture is lost in runoff), high evaporation and destructive hailstorms. The possibilities of crop failure do not encourage permanent investment in farm buildings, implements or fertilizers. Plentiful early rains encourage shallow root systems, a liability for the plant if dry months follow.

The administrative center of the Free State, Bloemfontein, is the natural clearing and distributing center for the agricultural products of the High Veld. It lies rather to the drier side of the state in a wheat and sheep area slightly outside or on the margins of the main maize-cattle triangle. In the maize triangle itself Kroonstad and Bethlehem are clearing centers, and most of the corn is now handled in bulk through storage elevators and not by the old system of bags.

North of the Free State the High Veld stretches into the Transvaal. Here are to be found the same scattered farms, until the great Witwatersrand industrial region is reached. This extends for 70 to 100 miles east and west through the great city of Johannesburg and follows roughly the belt of the gold-producing banket reefs.

THE RAND. Although this is not an agricultural land-use region in the same sense as those already described, the Rand, or correctly the Witwatersrand, is so distinctive that it merits separate consideration. It lies where the ancient rocks of the great complex crop out from beneath the Karroo beds which hide them farther south. It lies in fact between the High Veld properly speaking and the region of the northern Transvaal known generally as the Transvaal Bush Veld. As already described, it is the greatest gold-producing region of the world. The ore, extracted from depths of up to 9000 feet, must be crushed by powerful machinery before the gold can be extracted by chemical means.

This implies large-scale organization with adequate capital. An essential factor in the development of the region has been the supplies of cheap coal from the great field which extends from the eastern end of the Rand over the edge of the plateau into Natal. The focal point of the Rand is the great modern city of Johannesburg, second only to Cairo in population among Africa cities, and with a population approaching a million. East and west of Johannesburg are such industrial towns as Springs, Germiston, Benoni, Krugersdorp, Brakpan and Boksburg, which together form the nearest approach in Africa to a conurbation.

Figure 21. The Skyscraper City of Johannesburg. Notice the mine dumps of white quartz in the background. (Courtesy British Overseas Airways Corporation.)

Johannesburg was founded in 1886, and its progress was rapid. At first the surrounding veld was scarred by the huge dumps of waste white sand left after the gold-bearing banket was crushed and the gold extracted. But Johannesburg itself has been beautified by plantations of trees, notably Australian gum trees, which not only add character to the region but are also economically important as supplying pitprops and mining timber.

Rather naturally subsidiary industries have developed in the Rand, including chemicals, engineering works and the preparation of agricultural products for food.

THE TRANSVAAL BUSH VELD. This complex and interesting region occupies the northern two-thirds of the Transvaal between the Witwatersrand and the Limpopo River. There is thus a full range from the temperate climatic conditions characteristic of the high plateau at 6000 feet to the tropical climate of the Limpopo Valley at under 2000 feet.

The gently rolling surface of the High Veld of the south gives place to a more broken and diversified relief where the older rocks

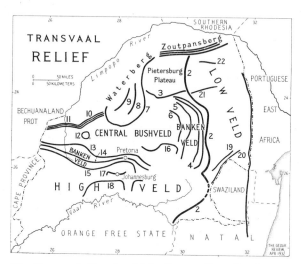

Figure 22.   The Transvaal Showing Main Ranges (Numbered) and Subregions. (From J. H. Wellington, *Geog. Rev.* 1932.   Courtesy of the *Geographical Review,* American Geographical Society.)

outcrop.   It is possible to distinguish a whole succession of low hill ranges, separated by relatively flat areas, in fact a number of distinct physiographic regions in each of which a distinctive agricultural economy is developed.

The name Bush Veld suggests that here the treeless, grassy, high veld gives place to a vegetation so characteristic of tropical Africa as a whole, here one with scattered bushes rather than trees.   As the altitude drops towards the north, average temperatures become higher and the frost period decreases until along the Limpopo itself frost is completely absent or at least rare.   In comparison with other parts of the Union of South Africa this is a region of recent development.   A simple subdivision of the whole is not easy, but South Africans frequently distinguish the following parts.

(1) *The Bankenveld,* otherwise the banken or slopes. Around Pretoria the country consists of lines of hills running from east to west with gentle northern slopes, grass covered and steeper than the southern rocky slopes with thorny bushes. Pretoria, the capital of the Union, lies in this country. Somewhat similar ridges but trending north to south lie northeast of Pretoria.

A short distance eastward from Pretoria is the famous Premier diamond mine, for many years the largest diamond field in the world, and certainly one of the largest man-made holes in the African continent.

(2) *The Central Bush Veld* lies to the north of Pretoria, and here are remarkable irrigable valley floors such as the fertile Springbok Flats. An important tract is irrigated by the Hartebeestpoort Dam on the Crocodile River around the settlement of Brits. This is a land of new and flourishing farming developments with large citrus orchards.

(3) *The Waterberg, Sandveld and Pietersburg Plateau* lie to the north of the Transvaal Bush Veld, and here the excessively sandy soils in the valleys limit productive capacity, so that the land becomes pastoral rather than agricultural.

(4) *The Limpopo Bush Veld* occupies the broad valley of the Limpopo Valley. Again soils are sandy, and dense bush covers much of the area, which resembles similar country to the north of the river lying in Southern Rhodesia. It may perhaps be regarded as cattle-ranching country, but owing to natural conditions some 80 acres are regarded as necessary for each beast.

Apart from the first modern iron smelting works in all Africa being at Pretoria, where smelting began early in 1934, there have been many other recent developments in the northern Transvaal. The completion of the railway through to the Limpopo River, which it crosses by the famous Beit Bridge, made it possible to work copper deposits at Messina. It was the intention that this railway should link up directly with the Southern Rhodesian system, but the connecting link in Southern Rhodesia has been long delayed, though the Beit Bridge is used by through road traffic.

Where communications make settlement attractive in the northern Transvaal have come the development of spacious orchards, the cultivation of cotton, tobacco and peanuts and the possibility of extensive development of other tropical or semi-tropical crops.

THE BASUTO HIGHLANDS. Returning to the southeastern margin of the High Plateau, the High Veld in the Orange Free State gives place southeastward before the crest is reached to country where the horizontal Karroo sandstones, capped by resistant basaltic beds, reach elevations of 6000 feet and over, but where the land has been deeply dissected to form a series of precipitous crags and deep narrow valleys. Most of the country of this type lies outside both the Free State and the Cape Province and for the most part within the limits of Basutoland. Because Basutoland is a territory under direct British Colonial administration and not part of the Union of South Africa it is separately considered.

THE EASTERN UPLANDS. Professor Wellington uses this name—perhaps not a very satisfactory one—for the broad stretch of foothill country below the great escarpment and lying mainly in Natal and including the middle veld.

The great scarp of the Drakensberg needs to be seen to be appreciated. Its highest point—incidentally the highest point in South Africa—is Giant's Castle, reaching over 11,000 feet. There are forests in some parts, but many slopes are covered with grass, so that this area has been called the Mountain Grass Veld or Sourveld.

Basaltic rocks of the plateau cap the great scarp and below are the almost horizontal Karroo beds with their seams of coal. It is, therefore, in this belt that the Natal coal field has been developed, the focal point being the town of Newcastle. There is an obvious advantage that the export of coal to the Port of Durban is essentially downhill, and gravity does much of the work of haulage.

Towards the coast the Mountain Grass Veld stretches into what is sometimes called the Grass Veld and Thorn Bush Belt, where much more cultivation is possible and where there is a very extensive population of Africans.

The Sourveld (where the word "sour" indicates the occurrence of grasses lacking in food value) gives place to a grass veld where the *rooi* grass is much more nutritious and where others have been introduced to provide even better grazing. To some extent this has become a dairying and even a beef-producing region. It includes the old land of the Zulus, Zululand, and the staple food grain over much of the tract is Kaffir corn, but Indian corn, or maize, is very extensively cultivated.

South Africa has almost a world monopoly in production of wattle bark for tanning, and 70 per cent of the acreage of plantations is in the intermediate belt of Natal between 2000 and 4500 feet above sea level. There are large and small plantations on farms concerned primarily with other crops or stock and also larger plantations controlled by companies producing the extract. It was an English trader between Australia and Natal, John Vanderplank, who brought seeds of the Black wattle (*Acacia mollissimma*) from Australia to attempt to grow a thicket to shelter his home in Natal. Boer farmers soon observed the rapid growth of the wattle in wind-swept localities and quickly adopted it; not until 1884 was the value as a source of tanning material appreciated. Commercial planting began, and by 1950 nearly 100,000 tons of extract were being exported in addition to large quantities of bark.[1]

THE EASTERN LOW VELD AND COASTAL REGION. This is the coastal strip itself, and broadly can be taken to include the land below the 2000-foot contour. Here frost becomes rare and near the coast completely absent. Although rainfall averages well over 40 inches, there is both seasonal and local variation, but everywhere rainfall is adequate for agriculture. Temperature variations on either side of a 70° annual average are low when compared with the plateau. At Durban, for example, the range is from 64°F. to 76°F. Both temperature and rainfall conditions are naturally most reliable near the coast itself. Though there are good alluvial soils in the valleys, elsewhere the ancient rocks with their granite intrusions which here outcrop give rise to some sandy and poor tracts. The whole region carries a heavy population, whether in the European areas of Natal or in Zululand and other areas occupied mainly by Africans. The development of commercial crops has laid emphasis on tropical products. Sugar cane comes first, and with its development South Africa became self-supporting in sugar and later there was a small surplus for export. Cotton is of some importance, but in the years between the World Wars cotton growers were greatly discouraged in Zululand by the unexpectedly violent rainfall fluctuations as well as low prices. Tropical fruits, citrus fruits, bananas, pineapples and pawpaws are widely cultivated and sent to the interior parts of the Union. Market gardening, the production of vegetables for consumption in the towns, has also extended greatly, and it is here that one sees the conflict between European and Indian. With a standard of living to maintain, the European market gardener can easily be undercut in the markets of Durban and the other towns by the Indian squatter, content to live in a hut made of old gasoline cans.

Climatic conditions, British settlers, the introduction of fodder grasses and the local urban demand have combined to encourage a

[1] M. D. Birkby, "The Wattle Industry in Natal," *Geography*, XXXVI, 1951, 150–164.

flourishing dairying industry so that a section of Natal has become the premier dairying belt of South Africa.

Northward from Natal, the coastal belt passes into Portuguese East Africa, and Swaziland, which is separately described, lies inland. The low veld along the eastern margin of the Transvaal remained until the First World War but little developed, and it is here

Figure 23.   A Model of Port Natal (the Site of Durban) as It Was in 1852.
(Copyright Aerofilms Limited.)

that the enormous nature reserve, the Kruger National Park, is to be found. Then came a rapid and important development.

The administrative center of Natal is Pietermaritzburg, founded as early as 1839. In size it is eclipsed by Durban (the port of Natal). The harbor of Durban is a natural bay of very considerable size with a narrow entrance which was formerly obstructed by a sand bar. This has in large part been removed by constant dredging, and the largest vessels using the Indian Ocean are able to dock alongside the quays adequately protected from the stormy seas of the South Indian Ocean. Durban has naturally become the principal coal-exporting center of the Union. It is the third town in order of size, and the population is roughly one-third African, one-third Indian and one-third European.

The sandy coasts in the neighborhood form attractive holiday resorts, and surf bathing under adequate safeguards is as popular in South Africa as anywhere in the world. Resorts like Warner Beach, with their crowds of sun- and surf-bathing Europeans, add a final touch, if such were needed, to South African contrasts. Although geographically Natal and the coastal regions have here been treated as a whole, it might have been more logical to describe separately the European areas and the native reserves.

Figure 24. An Air View of Port Natal with Durban in 1952, Showing a Hundred Years of Change. (Copyright Aerofilms Limited.)

Mining versus Agriculture in South Africa

It is often urged that the economy of the Union of South Africa is insecurely based because of its marked dependence upon the production of one commodity, which is gold. If for some reason or other world demand for gold should cease, it is argued that the whole Union of South Africa would find itself in a very precarious position.

During and after the Second World War figures for the production and value of gold for export were not published, but the state of affairs in the years between the World Wars is a sufficient indication of the general trend. On an average for 1921–1925 gold represented more than half by value of the total exports of the Union of South Africa. Another 10 per cent was represented by diamonds, so that gold and diamonds together made up over 60 per cent of all exports. The only others of significance then were wool and mohair and corn (maize), with limited quantities of coal. As years went by the position in 1933–1935 was that gold had come to represent nearly two-thirds of the total value of exports. Although nominally diamonds had decreased in relative importance, this position was essentially the result of deliberate restriction. Before the outbreak of the Second World War fruits and sugar had come to exceed corn in value among exports.

It has been said with considerable truth that a tremendous part of South Africa's effort is directed towards digging gold out of the deep mines in the Witwatersrand for it to be buried, not quite so deeply, in vaults at Fort Knox in the heart of the United States. How long is this process likely to continue?

In the meantime agricultural development proceeds steadily and against considerable difficulties. To a large extent South African agriculture is primarily the concern of the Afrikaans-speaking population (with the exception of the tropical products in Natal) whereas mining has become rather more the concern of the English-speaking section. This is admittedly only a very broad half truth. Those who look to the future development of South Africa as bound up with agricultural production, though pointing to such factors as good sunshine records, are forced to recognize the numerous natural disadvantages—the inadequacy and irregularity of rainfall, the poverty of soils and liability to soil erosion, all of which combine to result in low and irregular yields. There is also the unsatisfactory labor position which many regard as being made worse rather than better by the restrictive racial legislation. If, however, South Africa is forced to rely more than in the past on agricultural production, this account should have made it clear that there are considerable possibilities, especially in parts of the country still largely underdeveloped. Thus the lines of future development in the Union of South Africa would seem to rest especially with (1) the development of irrigation, (2) the control of soil erosion, (3) the introduction of fodder crops and nutritious grasses which have proved so successful in New Zealand, and the consequent development of more intensive mixed farming with high yields of crops, meat, milk and other products.

Nothing has been said in the foregoing account of the important fisheries round the coasts of South Africa, which will be found described in detail in a paper by Peter Scott.[1] The author concludes: "Unlike other areas of the world's fisheries, South African coastal waters could be far more intensively fished than at present without

[1] "The Otter Trawl Fisheries of South Africa," *Geog. Rev.*, XXXIX, 1949, 529–551.

depleting resources." He commends a long-term program of survey and research, since fishing has previously been restricted to certain areas only. The home consumption of fish in the Union is only 7 pounds per head per annum, and existing taboos against the eating of fish held by many Bantu tribes are doubtless destined to disappear. There is little doubt that the health of these people, who suffer seriously from protein deficiency, would be improved by the addition of fish to their diet. It is recorded that in 1948 trawlers from Cape Town landed 86 per cent of the total catch, which had been steadily rising, until it began to approach 100 million pounds per year. The three other ports concerned are Port Elizabeth, East London and Mossel Bay. The bulk of the fish caught is known as "stock fish," otherwise Cape hake, which is a cold-water species, closely allied to the European hake. It is obtained by trawling in the cold waters off the southwest coast. The other principal fish is the Agulhas sole, representing 5 per cent by weight, but 16 per cent by value.

Communications in South Africa

South Africa is well served by an excellent railway system, despite the fact that the gauge is only 3 feet, 6 inches. The first railway from Cape Town to Wellington was begun in 1859, and by 1950 over 13,000 miles of railway had been constructed in the Union. The railways and harbors are owned and controlled by the Union Government, being administered by a special Department. South Africa may be quoted as a good example of the excellent results which may be achieved with a narrow gauge and unified control.

At first the construction of lines from Cape Town was based partly on strategic considerations, then dictated by the discovery of the gold of the Rand and the diamonds at Kimberley and latterly by the need to develop productive or potentially productive agricultural regions and to provide a comprehensive network to all habitable parts of the Union. The later functions are clear from the special arrangements made by the railways for the handling of coal direct from the collieries to the wharves in the main harbors. The construction of a series of maize elevators in the corn-growing districts and at the ports has been undertaken to secure ease and economy in handling one of the principal agricultural exports of the country. In comparison with the rest of Africa the Union is fortunate in its adequate and accessible reserves of coal. This has not prevented the extensive use of electrification, and Natal was able to boast one of the earliest and longest stretches of electrified main line in the world.

The railway map now shows how the lines serve the four main ports of the Union—Cape Town, Port Elizabeth, East London and Durban—and also the eastern Transvaal with its natural outlet at the Portuguese port of Lourenço Marques. These lines leading to the main ports have now been joined up in such a way as to give a reasonable network, but it is still a torturous journey, for example, from Cape Town to Port Elizabeth by rail. The concentration of development on the four main ports has meant that for many years the trade passing through the minor ports, such as Mossel Bay, Port Nolloth, Simonstown and Knysna, is less than 1 per cent of the whole.

In the years between the World Wars and subsequently there has been a great expansion in the development of motor roads and the use of motor transport. South Africans claim that they make a greater use of automobiles than any country in the world outside the United States and Canada. Whether this claim is true or not, the old ox wagon, with its span of 16 oxen, has become almost a rare sight. Although South Africans still use the expression "to outspan" when they intend to call a halt, the majority have forgotten what it really means and certainly would be as puzzled as to how to do it if they were asked as any European or American town dweller.

As in other dry countries, vast stretches of the land can be covered by automobile without special preparation of roads. The difficulty is in the wetter regions, with the sudden rise of streams and the unfortunate habit which the floods have of cutting deep gulleys across roads. This is obviated, for example in Natal, by the construction of concrete stretches so that the flood waters can find their way across the road with the minimum of damage. Traveling salesmen who have to tour extensively in South Africa were (at least until the Second World War) granted a special allowance to enable them to hire cattle to pull their cars out of unsuspected bogs or *spruits* unexpectedly deep.

Side by side with the development of motor transport has come the very extensive use in South Africa of the airplane.

Southwest Africa (Suidwes Afrika or Zuid-Wes Afrika)

This vast territory, totaling nearly one-third of a million square miles, occupies the drier side of the continent from the arid scrublands of the Bechuanaland border to the absolute desert or Namib which parallels the Atlantic Ocean from the mouth of the Orange River northward to the lower course of the Kunene River, which forms the frontier with Angola. Throughout the whole of this stretch no permanent water course reaches the ocean. The southern tropic runs through the heart of the country in such a way that a larger area lies to the north within the tropics than south outside the tropics. Only locally, as near Windhoek, does the African plateau rise to sufficient heights to cause marked amelioration of the hot dry climate. The combined white and "colored" population does not exceed 100,000. The African population is only a little over one-fourth million, so that the average of all human inhabitants over the whole territory is a little over one per square mile.

It is believed that this territory was inhabited at an early date by wandering Bushmen, who some six or seven centuries ago were replaced along the coastal regions by Hottentots. They were followed in due course by the Ovambos, and early in the eighteenth century by the Hereros. The last were checked in their southern movement by the Hottentots under a leader known generally as Jonker Afrikaner, who has since become a legendary figure. Living near the banks of the Orange River, he organized the Hottentots, equipped them with firearms and became their leader and champion until his death in 1860, when the Hereros succeeded in forcing the Hottentots southward.

As early as 1486 Bartolomeu Dias landed at Angra Pequena, now known as Lüderitz, and erected a cross to record his landing. Later travelers recorded that the Hereros in the area had great herds of cattle, and it was in 1792 that the Dutch took possession of the chief natural harbor of the coast, Walvis Bay.

In 1805 missionaries of German nationality, though in the service of the London Missionary Society, established missions in Namaqualand. It was an American shipmaster, Captain B. Morrell, who in 1828–1830 explored the coast, made journeys into the interior and drew attention to the deposits of guano on the islands off the coast. This led to the exploitation of these guano islands in 1843–1845, and to their annexation by Britain between 1861 and 1867. It was in the following year, 1868, that the great German leader, Bismarck, became interested in the area and asked whether the British Government was prepared to safeguard the lives and properties of German missionaries. The British reply was non-committal, though a few years later the Cape Government sent a special Commissioner who fixed limits for the territories of the two chief tribes, the Namaquas and Damaras.

A couple of years later, in 1878, Walvis Bay was annexed by Britain. In the eighteen-eighties when Germans were active in so many parts of Africa a German merchant, Lüderitz by name, acquired land south of Walvis Bay and soon after purchased the harbor of Angra Pequena, where with the approval of Bismarck the German flag was hoisted. This led naturally to the annexation by Germany of the whole territory north of the Orange River, excepting only Walvis Bay and the guano islands. The German Government took over responsibility for the administration of the territory from the German company, the Deutsche Kolonial Gesellschaft. Jonker Afrikaner's old headquarters were made the seat of administration and renamed Windhoek.

The Germans were subsequently concerned with long and costly wars with the Hereros and Hottentots, but it was the discovery of diamonds on the Lüderitz Bay coast in 1908 which showed the whole potential importance of this arid area.

When the First World War broke out the Germans advanced into Union territory but were quickly countered by Union forces under General Botha; on July 9, 1915, the German Army surrendered. In 1919, at the end of the First World War, the League of Nations granted a mandate to the Union of South Africa to administer the area, which became known as the Territory of Southwest Africa. Germans, including all officials, were repatriated. This was a Class 3 mandate, under which the territory was to be administered as an integral part of the territory of the Mandatory Power. But a curious situation lasted for many years. The people of Southwest Africa in due course expressed their wish to be incorporated in the Union of South Africa, but this was prevented by the United Nations Assembly in 1946.

The country as a whole is essentially a stock-raising country, scarcity of water and poor rainfall rendering agriculture virtually impossible. Between 3 and 4 million sheep and goats and more than $1\frac{1}{2}$ million cattle exist in the area, and considerable attention has been paid to the improvement of the quality of cattle and to the production of butter for home consumption and export. An important product is Karakul pelts, a valued fur in temperate lands. The area producing diamonds has been steadily expanded, and their recovery from alluvial sands and gravels takes place over a 300-mile stretch of the coastline from the Orange River northward. In the north of the country ores of vanadium, tin, lithium, lead, copper and zinc are worked, the last three especially from the Tsumeb mine. Walvis Bay, the chief port, is linked by railway with the main South African system at De Aar Junction. Within the territory of Southwest Africa are over 1000 miles of railway of the South African 3 feet, 6 inches gauge. The railway administration also operates well-developed road-motor services, covering several thousand miles of road.

Despite aridity it is clear that Southwest Africa is far from being an unimportant area. There are some parts where subterranean water can be reached by wells, and this makes possible the extension of cattle rearing. Salt is obtained from some of the salt pans in the Kalahari, which occupies the northern and eastern parts of the country.

The High Commission Territories of South Africa

Within the area which may broadly be called South Africa are three territories which for various reasons remain distinct from the four countries which united in 1910 to form the Union of South Africa. They are under the direct protection of the British Government in London, represented by the High Commissioner for the United Kingdom resident in South Africa.

BASUTOLAND. The story of this little mountain state reads more like a romantic historical novel than a story from real life. Its foundation dates from the troubled times of 1820 when the Bantu, including the Zulus, Matabele and Korannas, were sweeping southward from central Africa, exterminating all those who stood in their path. A warrior named Moshesh welcomed refugees fleeing from the invaders and constituted himself their leader. The territory he chose was well suited for guerilla warfare; it stretches westward from the edge of the Drakensberg and is for the most part more than 6000 feet above sea level. Only the western border and the westward-draining valleys are at a lower elevation. Moshesh succeeded in building up what was almost unique in Africa, a nation as opposed to a tribe. In due course the Voortrekkers reached the country (1835–1837), and Moshesh took a hand in the troubled political relationships between the Boers and the Cape Government. The latter was anxious to avoid trouble, and when action had to be taken in 1852 Moshesh was too good for the punitive force. The British abandoned the territory. The local Boers constituted it an independent Boer republic, but their attitude towards the Basutos was such that the chief appealed to Britain for help. So Britain intervened, and in 1869 Basutoland became a British Territory under the direct protection of the British Government in London. When the Union of South Africa was formed by the South Africa Act of 1909 provision was made for the transfer of Basutoland to the Union, but forty years later the inhabitants showed no wish to come under the Union. So Basutoland is a native territory, all the land being owned by the people who form a Christian nation ruled by a woman —Ma'Ntsebo—styled the Paramount Chieftainess Regent (widow of the great-great-grandson of Moshesh), with an Advisory Council of Chiefs advised by a handful of British officials. At the head of the British officials is a Resident Commissioner under the direction of the High Commissioner for the United Kingdom in South Africa.

Is it possible for such an island of tribal Africa to survive in the modern world? A careful and detailed study by Hugh Ashton makes depressing reading. Not only does it seem to show that progress is impossible in a system of hereditary chieftainship but also that economic conditions resulting from isolation have led to the survival or resuscitation of some of the most undesirable features of African life, even culminating in ritual murders.[1]

SWAZILAND. Swaziland[2] was settled in the early part of the nineteenth century by the Swazis, who had retreated northward in the face of Boer settlement, only to find themselves menaced by the warlike Zulu raiders. It was at a time when British prestige was high; Mswazi, the Swazi chief, sent a deputation to Theophilus Shepstone seeking protection. Shepstone used his influence with Mpande, the Zulu chief, to such good effect that the Swazis and the Zulus have remained ever since on friendly terms. Mswazi died in 1868. Both he and his successor Mbandeni made numerous "concessions" to individual prospectors with the result that the country was overrun by undesirable characters, often in conflict. Again came an appeal to the British in 1887, but this time it was in vain. So the chief simply appointed the son of old Theophilus Shepstone as his Resident Adviser! There followed a short period of self-government by European residents with Swazi consent, then administration by the South African Republic, then by the Transvaal until 1907. Since that year Swaziland like Basutoland and Bechuanaland has been administered by its own Paramount Chief with a Resident British Commissioner.

[1] Hugh Ashton, *The Basuto*, New York, 1952.
[2] D. M. Doveton, *The Human Geography of Swaziland*, Institute of British Geographers, Publication 8.

In 1924 the Swazis objected strongly to the suggestion that their territory should be incorporated in the Union of South Africa, and that has remained their attitude.

The country has an area of 6704 square miles and in 1946 had a census population of 185,215, including 3201 Europeans, 739 colored and the remainder nearly all Swazis. The few Zulus in the south acknowledge allegiance to the Paramount Swazi Chief.

BECHUANALAND PROTECTORATE. This is as large as the whole of France and thus much more extensive than the other two territories.

Unlike Basutoland, which is entirely surrounded by Union territory, and Swaziland, which is essentially an enclave of the eastern Transvaal, the third of the British High Commission territories in southern Africa, the Bechuanaland Protectorate, stretches away northward from the Cape Province and the Transvaal to occupy a huge area in the heart of the continent only separated from the Zambezi itself by a narrow tongue, the so-called Caprivi Strip, which was ceded to Southwest Africa. The southern boundary of the present Bechuanaland Protectorate is the Molopo River, a non-permanent stream which drains or should drain to the Orange. The southern half of the country is essentially the Kalahari Desert without any surface streams; the northern half is in the basin of Lake Ngami and the Okovango swamp from which the water overflows in favorable seasons to the Zambezi. We may, therefore, regard northern Bechuanaland as lying in the Zambezi basin.

Few political divisions in Africa coincide either with natural features or frontiers between tribes, and the present Bechuanaland Protectorate is no exception. The southern part of the land of the Bechuanas lies in the Cape Province of the Union of South Africa. The country south of the Molopo was first declared a British Crown Colony under the title of British Bechuanaland, and a Protectorate was established over the northern area by agreement with the leading chiefs. In 1895 the British area was incorporated in Cape Colony and today forms part of Cape Province. The Protectorate was administered for a short time by the South Africa Company, but the chiefs protested and in 1896 the Protectorate came permanently under the direct administration of London. In 1896–1897 the Bechuanaland Railway Company constructed the line linking South Africa with Rhodesia. It runs through the entire length of eastern Bechuanaland and makes the country an essential link in African communications.

Eight different Bantu tribes, each with an elaborate tribal organization, inhabit Bechuanaland together with a few nomadic Bushmen and some Damaras who fled from the Germans in Southwest Africa before the 1914–1918 war.

Bechuanaland may well be called "Livingstone's Africa" since it was here that he spent his early days in Africa and from which he went on to explore Zambezi land.

Over that greater part of the Protectorate which coincides with the Kalahari, perhaps misnamed a desert, the fine yellow Kalahari sand is an almost universal covering of the surface. The African population is collected in large reserves mainly in the eastern half of the country, leaving 60,000 square miles in two large areas of Crown lands. These have practically no population because there is no surface water but might be made suitable for large-scale ranching. The first need would be deep wells to provide water as watering points for cattle. There is need of fencing for control of grazing because overstocking for even a short time could begin a dust bowl and serious erosion. The natural grasses are said to be excellent in some places and at least edible in others, but droughts occur about one year in every three so that other fodder, best provided by hay in good years, must be available. All this clearly means large-scale operation; there is real danger of land damage in small-scale ranching or private ownership. Just as most of the Protectorate suffers from lack of water, so the northwest corner, the tsetse-fly-infested Okovango swamps, suffers from too much. There development is possible only with improved communications as well as control of water and the provision of incentives to the Africans—here the Batawana tribe.[1] The Okovango River rises in the Angola plateau where there is a good summer rainfall and after a course of some 800 miles enters the Ngami depression by the Popa Falls. There its waters spread out into a great swamp towards Lake Ngami which lies at the southern end of this inland delta. Lake Ngami is being steadily invaded by thorn bush and is a mere fragment of the lake Livingstone discovered. At times waters from the swamps and lake escape southeastward to the Makarikari depression (which has water only after floods), the lowest part of the northern Kalahari. At other times it seems that the waters of the Okovango escape into the Linyanti swamps and so into the Zambezi. Apparently the Zambezi is capturing the waters of the Okovango. Whatever may be the

[1] The views expressed here are those of Frank Debenham; see *Geography*, XXXVI, 1951, 107–109.

exact hydrological relationships, these swamplands are potential rich farmlands if the same methods can be applied as used by the French in the inland Niger delta.

The Bamangwato Reserve in eastern Bechuanaland with its capital at Serowe came into world limelight in 1950 because of the marriage of the chief-designate Seretse Khama to a white girl in England and of the conflict of loyalties which resulted. This has already been discussed in Chapter 8.

BIBLIOGRAPHY

Apart from the references quoted in the text, the following should be noted:

Official Year Book of the Union of South Africa (published annually). Often with articles of general interest and results of research.

A. Gordon-Brown, *Year Book and Guide to Southern Africa*, published by the Union Castle Mail Steamship Company, London.

Cambridge History of the British Empire, Vol. VIII, London, 1936.

A. L. du Toit, *The Geology of South Africa*, 2nd Ed., London, 1939.

L. C. A. and C. M. Knowles, *South Africa*, London, 1936.

W. J. Talbot, *Land Utilization in the Cape*, Cape Town, 1950.

The South African Geographical Journal. Includes many articles of importance.

J. H. Wellington, *Southern Africa*, Vol. II, London, 1955.

CHAPTER
20

African Seas
and Islands

Continental and Oceanic Islands

Emphasis has already been laid upon the uninterrupted character of so much of the coast of Africa. The absence of deep bays and gulfs is a marked feature, and associated with this smoothness of so much of the African coastline is the absence of islands, which are to be found in such numbers bordering the coasts of other continents. Geographers commonly distinguish between continental islands and oceanic islands. Those belonging to the first group rise from the continental shelf at no great distance from the mainland. They are associated structurally with the neighboring parts of the mainland, and consequently the environmental conditions which they offer to human inhabitants differ but little from those of the neighboring shores. Oceanic islands, on the other hand, frequently rising from great ocean depths and cut off from the continental masses by stretches of water which are commonly both deep and wide, may bear no close relationship with the continental masses, and are not infrequently the summits of submarine volcanoes or the higher peaks of otherwise submerged mountain ranges.

Africa has but few continental islands or groups of islands and but few oceanic islands in the neighboring seas. But members of both groups have in Africa assumed a rather special significance.

Continental Islands

The coastlands of Africa have been described earlier in this book as inhospitable. Their inhospitality in the physical sense is particularly marked where large stretches of desert shore are fringed by sandy coastlands, against which pound the oceanic rollers in everlasting lines of surf. Through these breakers boats propelled by

hand—for the larger modern vessels cannot approach within miles—
make their way in constant danger of damage or destruction.

Other stretches of the coastline are backed by mangrove swamps,
in turn giving place to thick forests affording constant cover to enemies. It is not surprising that those who sought to explore or establish trading relationships with the peoples of Africa, approaching
the continent by sea, placed particular value on any natural inlet
which might serve as a haven. Later, when they sought to establish
bases from which to carry on their trading, whether the nefarious
slave trade, or more legitimate efforts at commerce, it is obvious
that they would choose easily defensible sites. Some such sites are
afforded by rocky promontories, sheltering some bay to serve as a harbor, with land approaches which could be defended with relative
ease. Considerations of this sort entered into the choice of sites
for such settlements as Saint Louis, or Dakar in French West Africa,
or even Freetown in Sierra Leone. It is not surprising that maritime
peoples approaching by sea, used to life on the sea and able to use
their ships for escape purposes in case of need, favored especially
the use of continental islands close to the coasts for their trading
settlements. Examples are numerous around the coasts of Africa.

With the development in modern times of peaceful trading relationships these island sites have often proved inconvenient for establishing lines of communication with the interior as with Gorée. In
some cases the best has been made of a bad job. In other cases, new
settlements have been chosen and developed. Some interesting examples of island sites are afforded by Bathurst, the capital of the
British colony of the Gambia, built on an island at the entrance to
the Gambia River and consequently developed with difficulties which
have not yet been fully overcome in an attempt to improve communications with the interior. In Portuguese Africa and Nigeria
are examples of settlements on islands, where the irregular swampy
coast still remains undeveloped. Lagos is on an island in a sheltered
lagoon, but what might have originally been a good choice has necessitated the construction of deep-water wharves and the commercial
terminus of the railways into the heart of Nigeria on the opposite
mainland at Apapa.

Elsewhere around the coasts of Africa are examples of larger
islands which have served and continue to serve as more extensive
bases for European powers. Spain remains in possession of Fernando
Po, Portugal remains in possession of the islands of São Tomé and
Príncipe. The British occupancy of the Guano Islands off the south-

west African coast had a different objective, the recovery of a sub-stance of economic importance.

But the general story is repeated along the east coast of Africa, where islands are few but of not inconsiderable importance. The large and relatively fertile island of Zanzibar and its neighbor Pemba form the base from which the Sultans of Zanzibar exercised control over very large stretches of the mainland. Though the fortunes of the mainland changed, the islands remained in the possession of the Sultan as they do today. In more recent times, in the First World War, during the campaigns against German East Africa, British troops from India landed on and used the Island of Mafia. The great Arab stronghold and port of the east coast, Mombasa, is built on an island which again has presented certain difficulties in the development of the railway system through Kenya to Uganda.

Farther north a very interesting example of the changing im-portance of islands is offered by the tiny island of Perim in the midst of the narrow entrance to the Red Sea. Like so many islands of strategic importance, its significance was appreciated by Britain in the days of imperial expansion. Perim became a naval base, a signals stations, a point for re-coaling and re-fueling. But with their increasing size, warships and merchant ships were no longer able to use its limited facilities. Its functions have been transferred to the Port of Aden, another defensible position, but one with a harbor of magnificent size and depth.

There are other groups of islands farther removed from the coasts of Africa which may still be grouped as continental islands. In the northern Atlantic Ocean, lying off the northwest African coasts, are the Canaries. These partly volcanic islands with their rich soil, fav-orable climate and moderate, well-distributed winter rainfall and abundant sunshine proved attractive to the Spaniards. The islands are administered as an integral part of Spain. The existence of natural harbors, or harbors improved without difficulty to meet the needs of modern vessels, has led to the use of Santa Cruz de Tenerife as a port of call for ocean liners from Europe bound for South Amer-ica or South Africa.

The single though important island of Madeira, farther off the con-tinental shores of the northwest, long in the hands of Portugal, provides an alternative, again with a good harbor at Funchal. Like the Canaries, Madeira is an island intensely productive and extremely attractive climatically and scenically. In the early days of exploration and of trading with merchant vessels equipped only with sail, the group of the Azores, much farther out into the Atlantic, afforded like and equally important facilities, immortalized in the lines, "At Flores in the Azores Sir Richard Grenville lay" and the story of the *Revenge*.

Nearer the coasts of desert Africa are the Cape Verde Islands, climatically much more arid and less favored for settlement, whose significance therefore has tended to wane with the passing of time. These are almost the only groups of islands in the Atlantic.

In the Indian Ocean special attention must of course be given to the great island of Madagascar. Excluding the island continent of Australia and the great island of Greenland, Madagascar can claim to be one of the largest islands in the world. Although it is structurally connected with continental Africa, it is a subcontinent which has had a long story of development of its own. Associated with Madagascar to the north are several groups of islands, but of no very great importance.

Oceanic Islands

In the midst of the Atlantic Ocean there are several truly oceanic islands, far removed from land, notably Ascension, St. Helena, and the Tristan da Cunha group. It might be thought that mention of these has no place in a book on Africa, but, in the days when exploration of the African coastlands was still actively taking place, these oceanic islands had an immense significance as ports of call, as havens of refuge in time of storm or other need, and as stepping stones on far-flung ocean routes. They took on a new significance with the development of submarine electric telegraph cables, when some of them became cable stations. For a brief period it seemed that the development of trans-oceanic air transport would bring them once more into permanent prominence. But this has been prevented by the ever-increasing speed and range of modern aircraft.

In the wide expanses of the southern ocean there are other islands which again have strategic importance and a significance in the whaling industry.

In the Indian Ocean islands are far more numerous, but certain ones, notably Réunion, Mauritius and the Seychelles, have played a part comparable with that of the oceanic islands of the Atlantic. Mauritius and Réunion are sufficiently large to have a permanent existence and life of their own.

No excuse need be offered therefore for a consideration of at least some of the features of these islands which lie in the oceans around the African continent.

The Azores

The three groups of islands making up the Azores have a total area of a little over 900 square miles and a population approximating to a quarter of a million. They lie well out in the Atlantic between latitudes 37° and 39°, which is in the extra-tropical high-pressure belt, but far enough north to receive an adequate rainfall from the winter cyclones of the westerly wind belt. They are volcanic, and the peaks of the old volcanoes reach considerable elevations, for example, 8500 feet in Picot, so that the islands attract a sufficient relief rainfall to prevent serious drought. The chief town and port of Ponta Delgada is on the largest island, São Miguel.

The islands produce foodstuffs in adequate quantities for the people in cereals, fruits, wine, cattle products and fish, and there is a small trade with Portugal, which lies almost due east. The scenery and climate are attractive to tourists, but the islands are rather off main ocean routeways.

Madeira (or the Madeiras)

This group consists of the one large island, Madeira itself, about 300 square miles in area, and four smaller ones.

Farther south than the Azores, the dry summer season is longer, the period of winter rainfall shorter. But again the volcanic rocks of Madeira rise to 6500 feet, and a considerable relief rainfall results even at Funchal, on the southern coast, where the average is 30 inches. The climate, with abundant sunshine even in the winter, and the scenery are both delightful so that very large numbers of residents have been attracted to Madeira to live their years of retirement.

The once forested hillslopes, which might easily suffer from very serious soil erosion, have been carefully terraced. Attractive little houses, each with a terraced garden resplendent throughout the year with flowers, climb up the hillsides both in the vicinity of Funchal and of other settlements.

Careful cultivation yields abundant harvests of wheat and barley, but it is for its fruits—its pineapples and bananas, and particularly its grapes—that Madeira is famous. The Madeira wine, a specialty for so long of the island, is only one of the types which is made.

Though the local handcrafts, such as lace making and the making of cane chairs, are maintained to a large extent for the benefit of the numerous passing tourists, they form a lucrative sideline for the peasant population. Clearly also Madeira has a strategic significance in its position. The old treaties of friendship which have existed between Portugal and Britain for the past two centuries form

Figure 1. Terracing on the Steep Slopes of Madeira. (Copyright Geographical Publications Limited.)

the basis on which rather special commercial relationships have been established between Madeira and Britain, and it was in full accord with this tradition of friendship that Britain obtained temporary air bases in the Azores during the Second World War, when Portugal remained neutral.

The Canaries

The Canaries form a larger group of seven main islands, again of volcanic origin, with a total area of 2800 square miles and a population of over half a million. In the island of Tenerife the dormant snow-capped volcano rises in a magnificent cone to a height of over 12,000 feet. As a result of these elevations rainfall may be considerable on higher ground, though near the coast on the eastern sides of the islands it may fall to 10 inches or less. In addition, the drying harmattan blows from the African mainland, which is nearer than in the case of Madeira.

Shrubby Mediterranean vegetation with numerous succulent plants is found on the hillslopes, though Mediterranean trees such as the holm oak (*Quercus ilex*) are found in the damper areas. Again careful cultivation, especially with irrigation, has made possible the cultivation of cereals and vegetables, notably onions for home use, together with olives, citrus fruits and tobacco. A small and very sweet variety of banana, which is much liked in European markets, has been very specially developed.

Again there is an extensive tourist trade. Santa Cruz in the island of Tenerife is rivaled as a tourist center and a port of call for steamers by Las Palmas, near the northeastern coast of the island of Gran Canaria.

The delightful smaller island of Palma is essentially the top of a single extinct volcano with a huge blown-out crater. Less frequently visited, it is an island of great beauty inhabited by a cheerful agricultural peasantry.

Just as the Canaries form an integral part of Spain, the Madeiras are administered as an integral part of Portugal.

The Cape Verde Islands

Ten islands and a few islets form the Cape Verde Islands, a Portuguese colony, covering rather over 1500 square miles, and with a population of about 200,000. Being situated in latitude 15° to 17° due west of St. Louis in Senegal, they lie in the belt of the Trade Winds throughout the year and are extremely dry. The total rainfall between 5 and 10 inches falls mainly in August, September and October, in contrast to the Mediterranean rainfall of the Canaries or Madeira.

Sisal, castor oil and oranges are among agricultural products produced in excess of local requirements.

The capital of the islands is Praia, but the chief port, a coaling station mainly used by vessels on the South American run, is São Vincente.

Ascension

Ascension is an isolated volcanic island in the South Atlantic less than 8° south of the equator, but no less than 700 miles from its neighbor to the southeast, St. Helena, and a still greater distance from the African coast.

It was occupied by the British in 1815, and its importance was as a haven or refuge in case of need by vessels of the British fleet. Consequently it was for long controlled by the British Admiralty and organized as if it were a battleship, governed by a British naval officer. In 1922 it became a part of the colony of St. Helena.

Ascension takes its name from the fact that it was discovered by the Portuguese on Ascension Day in 1501. The several volcanic cones of which it is formed have rocks colored red and brown, but the central and highest one, rising to 2817 feet, owes its name, Green Mountain, and its covering of vegetation to the mists which frequently clothe the summit and a relief rainfall exceeding 30 inches. This is in striking contrast to the arid and often bare lava surfaces occupying the lower levels of the island.

It became and still is a cable station, and the handful of people living there are all employees of the British Cable and Wireless Limited, now under government control.

In the Second World War it suddenly became again of immense strategic importance. An airstrip of the size suitable for the largest transport planes, together with the necessary buildings, was built by the American forces and became known as Wideawake Field. When the American forces left the island in 1947 trans-Atlantic air transport had already become virtually independent of such stepping stones. Radio has made cable communication out of date so that this question almost automatically arises: Is there a future for this little island of 34 square miles, other than as a breeding ground for the sooty tern, which comes to Ascension three times in every two years to lay its eggs, or the sea turtles, which use the warm sands for the same purpose between January and May?

St. Helena

St. Helena, though only slightly larger—47 square miles—than Ascension and similarly an isolated volcano with its peak rising to 2700 feet, is by comparison an important island. It too was discovered by the Portuguese, in 1502. It too is just a rocky top of a gigantic volcanic pile resting on the floor of the Atlantic Ocean, but St. Helena has been British for over 300 years, since 1571, and has a greater importance for several reasons. Its position in 16° South is right in the path of the Southeast Trade Winds so that the island was of utmost importance as a haven of refuge in the days of sailing ships. It was first occupied by the East India Company for the benefit of their ships rounding the Cape of Good Hope to India. Naturally the port and chief settlement, called Jamestown, is on the sheltered northwestern side of the island.

When vessels began to use coal it became a coaling station, especially for the ships of the British navy. It is 1200 miles from the nearest point, the Port of Mossamedes, on the African mainland, and its very isolation led to its being used as a base for whalers. It is now, however, too far from the chief whaling grounds to serve this function.

The first time that the British captured Napoleon Bonaparte of France he was imprisoned on Elba off the coast of Italy and escaped The second time, after his defeat at Waterloo in 1815, the British took no chances, and he lived a prisoner on St. Helena until his death in 1821. St. Helena is famous, therefore, as the place of exile of perhaps the most dangerous prisoner-of-war of all time. At a later stage St. Helena became a cable station, with the cable running from Cape Town on the one hand to Ascension and Europe on the other. The island still has importance in collecting messages from the feeble radios of small ships and passing them on. The pleasant climate is another factor which has led to a population approaching 5000 living happily on this island. They have as much meat as they need; they grow such excellent potatoes that some in the past have been exported. New Zealand flax has been introduced, and the industry started by the government mill in 1908 includes the preparation of rope, string and lace for export.

Again, however, the question clearly arises: What is the future of such an island? Efforts to establish an airstrip during the Second World War revealed the absence of any suitable land.

St. Helena is a British Crown Colony, with a resident Governor.

Tristan da Cunha

Even more remote and inaccessible than St. Helena is the group of islands which make up Tristan da Cunha, and which since 1938 has formed a dependency of St. Helena. Tristan da Cunha itself is another extinct volcano of which the highest point reaches 8000 feet. The islands lie in 37° South, which is south of the southernmost point of Africa, and in the belt of the westerly winds, almost in the latitude of the "roaring forties." The handful of people, between 100 and 200, who live there are descended mainly from ship-wrecked sailors. Despite the cold, stormy climate and the extreme isolation, because

Tristan da Cunha, unlike Ascension and St. Helena, is not near well-used oceanic routeways, ·they have a deep affection for their island and no desire to leave. They live on a low plateau on the northwestern side of the island, growing potatoes and fruit, apples and peaches, and rearing cattle and geese. They have abundant fish in the surrounding seas. It may be in the world of today that there is much to be said for life on Tristan da Cunha.

During the Second World War the isolation of Tristan da Cunha was broken and the island became officially a British warship, under the name of *H.M.S. Atlantic Isle,* its function being primarily as a meteorological and radio station.

Réunion

Turning now to the oceanic islands of the Indian Ocean, there are three volcanic islands, Réunion (French), Mauritius (British) and Rodriguez (British), forming a chain sometimes called the Mascarenhas, from the name of their Portuguese discoverer. Like the isolated islands of the Atlantic, they also are volcanic. They lie in the Trade Wind Belt, approximately in latitude 21° to 22° South, with a moderate to heavy rainfall derived from the Southeast Trades and augmented in the summer months by frequent tropical cyclones which are sometimes of a very violent nature. Only on the low-lying sheltered parts of the islands is there any real dry season, but the oceanic position moderates the temperature which at sea level ranges only between 68°F. and 69°F. Prior to their discovery by Europeans, the islands, densely covered with forest, were uninhabited. In the course of time forests have been almost entirely destroyed. Their place has been taken by plantations of sugar cane, the chief economic crop of the islands. The population has been derived mainly from settlers from France and Britain, settlers or imported laborers from India, together with a few Negroes, the descendants of slaves, or natives from Madagascar. A certain number of Chinese have also settled on the islands.

Réunion was occupied by France in the middle of the seventeenth century, and, except for a short period during the Napoleonic Wars when it came into British hands, it has remained French. The quarter of a million people are largely of French descent. With an area a little under 1000 square miles, it rises to 10,000 feet. The range of altitude makes possible the cultivation of a great variety of crops. The earlier ones of coffee, cloves, vanilla and sugar have given place to a greater variety, including tea, cinchona, cocoa, manioc, cassava and rice. Wheat and temperate fruits and vegetables can be grown at higher levels. The principal economic crop is sugar cane so that large quantities of sugar and rum are exported.

It is to be noted that this production is achieved in a tropical island with white labor, or labor of predominantly white descent.

The capital is St. Denis. The only harbor accessible to large vessels is Pointe-des-Galets, which is a partly artificial port.

Mauritius

Mauritius is situated some 500 miles east of Madagascar and almost on the direct line between South Africa and Ceylon and India. It was certainly known to early Arab or Moorish sailors, and, though it was discovered by the Portuguese, the Dutch first settled on the island in 1598. They left, however, in 1710, and it was more than fifty years before the French arrived in 1767 and named the island Île de France. The British occupied the island in 1810; it was formally acknowledged as British by the Treaty of Paris in 1814.

Like Réunion, it is a large island for an oceanic island, having an area of about 720 square miles. It is less elevated than Réunion, the highest point rising to 2711 feet. In consequence there is a much larger proportion of cultivable low ground with rich volcanic soils, and very large numbers of emigrants have crowded into Mauritius from densely peopled India, so that the population approaches half a million. Vegetables and farm crops are grown for home use. Salt is obtained by evaporating sea water in salt pans around the coast. Sandy areas of the coastlands are covered with coconuts and yield copra, but the mainstay of the island is its production of sugar. Mauritius is essentially a sugar island; its prosperity depends on the production and the price of sugar. The porous volcanic soils, the marked seasonal rhythm, the low to moderate rainfall, are just those conditions so well known in the West Indies as eminently suitable for the growth of the sugar cane. By value Réunion and Mauritius have each a higher per capita export trade than any mainland country of Africa except the Rhodesias.

The principal town of Mauritius is Port Louis, situated on the northwestern side of the island and now linked to all parts by the motor roads which have replaced the former island railways. Port Louis is a little too hot and humid for Europeans, who favor the small hill station of Curepipe, 1800 feet above sea level, but only a dozen miles away. In contrast to Réunion, however, there are few pure Europeans in Mauritius. Apart from the Indians, the

Mauritians are largely of mixed blood, together with Negroes and Chinese.

Rodriguez, lying 300 miles northeast of Mauritius, is much smaller. Only 42 square miles in area, it has only a few thousand inhabitants, who engage in fishing and the cultivation of food crops for their own sustenance.

Madagascar

The huge island of Madagascar covers an area of nearly 250,000 square miles. It is not far short of 1000 miles from the extreme northern to the extreme southern point, and in places its breadth reaches 360 miles. It supports a population of at least 4½ million, yet it is true to say that this island remains almost an unknown land to English-speaking peoples. As a French colony nearly 90 per cent of the shipping visiting Madagascar is French; the air services which of recent years have linked it with Paris by three different routes are also French. It comes as a surprise to English readers to realize that there is a very extensive, voluminous and well-informed literature on the geography and resources of Madagascar, but very little published in English. In the *Geographical Review,* XXVII, 1937, Dr. Elizabeth T. Pratt gave a resume of recent literature under the title "Madagascar: Great Isle, Red Isle, a Bibliographical Survey." There are no less than 59 works referred to in footnotes. Special attention is called to the fact that Madagascar is well equipped with both maps and bibliographies covering the description of the country. In the great work of G. Grandidier, brought up-to-date by a later volume covering the period to 1933, more than 8000 items are included. There is a reconnaissance map of the country on the scale of 1:500,000, and various sections of the island have been covered on larger scales, including the important series on 1:100,000.

Although it is only separated from the African continent by the Mozambique channel, some 250 miles wide, and although the basic crystalline complex which occupies the eastern two-thirds of the island does not differ greatly from the crystalline complex of the African continent, Madagascar has had a history entirely its own. Populated from the far side of the Indian Ocean rather than from the continent of Africa, isolated for a very long period previously so that both its fauna and flora have many distinctive characters, Madagascar can claim to be an island continent. In the island there are no large quadrupeds, but a number of distinctive species of lemurs. There are no poisonous snakes, and its flora is equally distinctive.

OUTLINE OF HISTORY. Although some have urged that the peoples of Madagascar may have come at least in part from the African mainland, the general view is that the island was settled by those who traveled across the Indian Ocean, and that this peopling began somewhere about the twentieth century B.C. It is to be noted that the winds blow towards Madagascar from across the Indian Ocean, whereas there are no regular winds *from* the African continent towards Madagascar. The first inhabitants were probably Indonesians of Negro characteristics, whose descendants still constitute one of the important elements of the population. These were reinforced by large incursions of the Hovas, allied to the Malays racially and linguistically. In later times the island became well known to the Arabs, who came from the Persian Gulf as well as from the east coast of Africa and who settled on the northwest and part of the eastern coastlands. Indians also came by sea and populated part of the southeast coast.

There are strong Negro elements, especially on the western side of the island. Some of these may have come as free settlers at a later stage, or may have been mainly brought as slaves. The final Malayan migration to the island seems to have finished actually after the first appearance of European explorers. This was in fact the main invasion by the Hova, who may be said to constitute perhaps one-quarter of the population, and who have profoundly influenced the character of the other island peoples. They offer many points of contrast physically and mentally to the Negroes of Africa.

The mixture of Arab blood in the north has tended to result in peoples who are industrious and frugal and who make both excellent cultivators and good merchants.

The island was definitely sighted by the Portuguese Diego Dias in 1500. At the time when the French were active in the Indian Ocean they had military posts on the east coast for part of the seventeenth century and most of the eighteenth century, but early in the nineteenth century they relinquished them all except the island of Ste. Marie. In 1811 Tamatave was occupied by British troops, and under the Treaty of Paris, 1814, the French settlements in Madagascar were recognized as coming under British control. The British, however, made no attempt to settle on the island and were content to leave it to the control of the Hovas, whose king—Radama I—established friendly relations with the British Government; a British agent was sent to reside at his court. The London Missionary Society established the first Christian missions in 1820, but when Radama was succeeded in 1828 by one of his wives, she persecuted the native Christians to such an extent that most of them lost their lives. In 1836 all missionaries were compelled to leave the island, and for some years all Europeans were excluded from the country. Radama II, though he ruled for only two years before being murdered (1861–1863), re-opened the island to European trade. His wife, who succeeded him, effected treaties in the next five years with British, French and American governments.

Queen Ranavalona II, who ruled from 1868 to 1883, became a Christian, and during her reign much progress was made both in the spread of Christianity and of education. But relations became strained with France because the Hova queen refused to recognize the French claim that certain tracts on the northwest coast had been transferred to them by local chiefs, and in 1883 Tamatave was bombarded and occupied by French marines. In the subsequent peace terms it was agreed that Madagascar's foreign relations should be directed by France, that a French Governor should remain in the capital and that Diégo-Suarez should be ceded to France. In 1890 Britain recognized this French Protectorate over Madagascar. After further disputes, a French expeditionary force in 1895 effected the conquest of the island; consequently, in 1896 the ruling Hova queen was exiled, and Madagascar became a French Colony.

STRUCTURE AND RELIEF. The essential structural element in the island of Madagascar is a high plateau, part of the ancient continent of Gondwanaland, built up basically of crystalline rocks, with a whole range of granites and other igneous rocks which outcrop over vast stretches of the country. Here and there gold-bearing veins have decomposed to give rise to small placer deposits, and there are deposits of graphite which constitute one of the main mineral resources of the island. There are areas where precious stones occur, deposits of radioactive ores of nickel, copper and lead. But over a very large part of the country the ancient rocks are hidden beneath a mantle of laterite or of lateritic decomposition products. The red lands which result are liable to extensive erosion and cause many of the streams draining to the coast to be deep red in color; hence the name sometimes given to the island is "Red Isle."

The crest of the plateau lies nearer the east than the west, and outcrops of volcanic rock give rise to high ground reaching to more than 6000 feet. Around the crystalline plateau, sedimentary rocks have been deposited which are especially important on the western third of the island, and become younger in age as traced towards the Mozambique Channel.

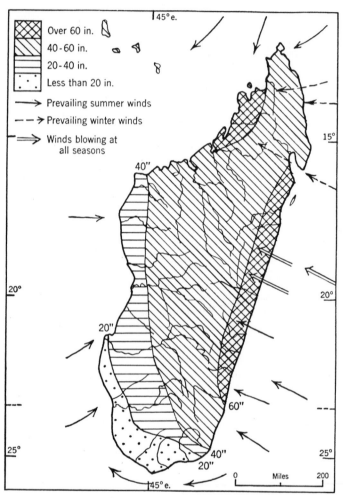

Figure 2. Rainfall and Winds of Madagascar.

The eastern coast tends to be straight, free from indentations, and fringed with coral reefs. There are an onshore wind and a constant swell, and anchorages are very few and far between. From the crest of the plateau the land descends very sharply to the east coast, but to the west the drop is less, though there are some steep scarp faces overlooking the lower territory formed by the sedimentary rocks. Along the east coast is an almost continuous string of lagoons between the coral beaches and the steep rise inland. Linked by cuts this forms a valuable waterway.

CLIMATE. Climatically the island lies within the Trade Wind Belt so that southeasterly winds predominate. They bring a heavy rainfall to the eastern side of the island, comparatively little to the west. Thus four climatic divisions are distinguished:

1. The eastern slopes and the coast, much of which has a rainfall of over 100 inches even at sea level in the rainy period from December to July, but where a considerable fall comes in every month.

2. The plateau, where altitude reduces the temperature from the 70° to 80°F. usual on the coast to a range of 55° to 67°F., typical of Antananarivo, 4600 feet above sea level. Such climatic conditions suggest suitability of the terrain for white settlement.

3. The south and southwest, where the prevailing winds are descending from the plateau and become warm in the process. They deposit little or no rain, so that southward the southwest coasts are really to be described as arid and receive only some 15 inches of rain. For two-thirds of the year the rivers are dry.

4. The northwest. This resembles the southwest but has some northwesterly winds during the midsummer period, with a heavy rainfall and a dry season lasting from about May to November.

VEGETATION. The vegetation corresponds closely with these climatic divisions. It may be hazarded that the original vegetation cover consisted of a continuous evergreen rainforest over the wetter areas of the east and north, giving place to a savanna or perhaps to steppe on the plateau and to semi-arid types in the driest regions. French workers in Madagascar believe, however, that the natural vegetation has been almost completely destroyed throughout the whole island by the process of burning by the inhabitants, so that over at least four-fifths of the whole surface a vegetation resulting from human interference has replaced that which is natural. Many species have been thereby extinguished, and the density of woodland or savanna is much less than it would otherwise be. The map of vegetation reproduced from the work of Professor Maurette shows the distinction which is drawn between the evergreen forests of the east and the deciduous vegetation of the west. The bamboo forests which are common at high altitudes, are probably entirely secondary and the laterite soils found when forests have been cleared are not

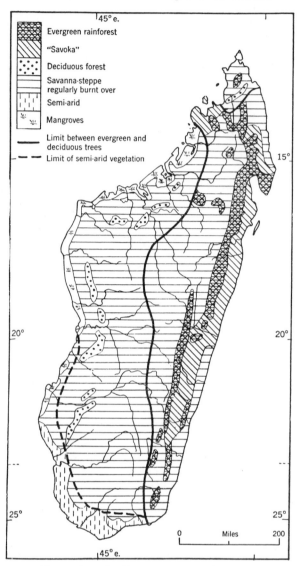

Figure 3. The Vegetation of Madagascar.

very fertile, so that clearings are soon abandoned and allowed to degenerate into bush, locally called "savoka." This is easily burnt, but often as a result there is bare soil with a hard barren crust, rendering the land virtually useless. The French have established a Forestry Service to do what is possible to repair the damage. A small amount of timber, notably ebony, is produced, and products collected from the forests include gum copal.

AGRICULTURE. It will be clear that this island which seems to be favored climatically is far from being as agriculturally rich as might be expected. Little plantation agriculture has been developed. Rice is the principal food crop; many varieties are grown but most of them are rather poor and the yield low. Some upland rice is grown in forest clearings. Manioc is second to rice as a food crop, especially in the wetter regions. Corn (maize) can be grown even in the dry parts during the rainy season, and is therefore of first-class importance in the southwest. Sorghum, yams and beans are other food crops, and sugar cane may be grown where irrigation is possible. Crops which point the way to possible future development include coffee, of *arabica* type grown by villagers and of *liberian* or *robusta* types grown on European plantations in the east. Vanilla, cloves and locally cocoa have been introduced. Cotton, coconuts, sisal and flax have all been tried. The agricultural people of the east have few animals, but on the plateau cattle rearing is a mainstay of the native agricultural economy. Cattle, however, are mainly of the zebu type, and cows give but a minute yield of milk so that hides form the principal product. Fat-tailed sheep and goats are to be found in drier regions, and every Madagascan farm has a few pigs.

HUMAN GEOGRAPHY. The bulk of the African population lives in small villages, usually surrounded by a protective stockade. Most of the towns over part if not the whole owe their development to European influence. Antananarivo, now more usually called Tananarive, is a curious example of a mountain capital situated far from the sea or a river port and with no apparent geographical advantages unless inaccessibility can be claimed as one. A jumble of villages linked by tortuous streets and ancient stairways can scarcely be reached from the more modern sections, and the rugged terrain presents sudden obstacles to building as well as to water supply and drainage. Before the French occupation of Madagascar it was the seat of government of the Merina people, an old trading and once a slave trading center. The French established their rule there in 1895, and the population rapidly increased to make it the commercial and cultural as well as the political capital. It is situated on the edge of the Imerina plains, and in the capital and the surrounding highland plains live possibly one-third of all the people of the island. It

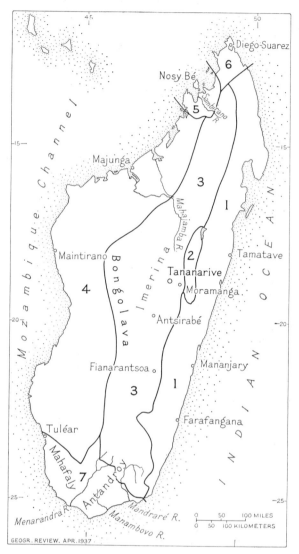

Figure 4. Natural Regions of Madagascar. (1) East: humid mountain region with forested slopes and narrow coastal plain. (2) Alaotra-Mangoro: alluvial depression. (3) Central Plateau: grass-covered. (4) West: rolling plains, grass with scattered woods. (5) Sambirano valley: wet forest no dry seasons. (6) North: forested and steppe covered mountains. (7) South: arid and semi-arid. (From *Geog. Rev.* 1937. Courtesy of the *Geographical Review,* American Geographical Society.)

is connected by railway with Tamatave, the principal port, and a branch from this railway runs northward to Lake Alaotra. Whether the planned extensions of Madagascan railways will ever take place becomes increasingly doubtful, because of the rapid modern development of roads.

Roads suitable for motoring in dry weather cover at least 16,000 miles and are served by an extensive and even elaborate network of motor services although only some 2000 miles can be described as all-weather roads.

In any study of Africa seriously scientific and objective, Madagascar deserves special consideration. It repeats on a smaller scale many of the relief, climate, soil and vegetation features of the tropical parts of the continent itself. It is claimed by many observers that the Madagascan peoples have greater vitality and initiative than characterize the Negro peoples of the continent and that therefore it should prove an easier task to forward development. Yet quite clearly this vast area is far from being an important contributor to world sources of foodstuffs. The bulk of the trade is with France.

The completion of half a century of effective French occupation in Madagascar (1896–1946) was the signal for a stock taking of the island's agricultural economy.[1] The total area of cultivated land is given at 3,310,000 acres, of which rice occupies 40 per cent, other subsistence crops rather more and commercial crops about 18 per cent. The last are now characterized by the great variety of products for export. Coffee holds first rank and accounts for one-third the total value of exports. But more than half the production is in one district, the Fianarantsoa district. Although rice is the basic subsistence crop, the amount exported accounts for less than 4 per cent of the total. About 11 per cent of the ricelands of Madagascar are irrigated. The other commercial crops grown for export include cocoa, vanilla, cloves, pepper, cinnamon and other spices, copra, raffia, tobacco, sugar cane (sugar and rum), manioc (for flour) and tapioca. Reference is made to the marked development of the livestock industry, which at the time of the survey boasted 6 million cattle, 420,000 pigs and 300,000 sheep and goats, with an export in 1945 of 12,500 tons of meat and meat products (including canned meat) and about 400,000 hides. Cut off as it was during the years of the Second World War agricultural production dropped, and when

[1] Cinquantenaire de Madagascar, *Rev. int. de botanique appliquée,* XXVI, 1946, 333–504. Summarized briefly in *Geog. Rev.,* XXVII, 1947, 495–496.

the foregoing figures are viewed against the background of the enormous area of the island, Madagascar must still be regarded as an underdeveloped land.   As pointed out in the conclusions, however, it is necessary first of all to raise the standard of life of the indigenous peoples, four-fifths of whom are cultivators.

PART
3

Africa Today

African Problems
Past, Present and Future

In the two preceding parts of this book I have endeavored to describe the geographical background of the African continent and its constituent countries. I have endeavored also to trace in outline the history and development of the continent and its countries up to the time of the Second World War. We may regard this geographical and historical study as an essential foundation or as a background against which it becomes possible to view present happenings in Africa, impending and future developments.

There is perhaps no part of the world where rapid change is so apparent in the middle of the twentieth century as throughout Africa, and particularly in tropical Africa. The changes which are taking place are so marked, so fundamental and so rapid that we may properly use the word kaleidoscopic. A very interesting general view was given by Dr. G. H. T. Kimble, Director of the American Geographical Society and Secretary-Treasurer of the International Geographical Union, after a rapid tour which he carried out in the winter of 1950–1951. Traveling from Egypt through East Africa, flying across the Belgian Congo to West Africa, he has recorded his impressions in the pages of the *Canadian Geographical Journal*.[1]

"Not the least remarkable thing about tropical Africa," he says, "is that you can find there almost everything you expect to find." He instances the wild life, saying that it would not be the first time if a pride of lions, strolling from a near-by National Park, hindered the landing of an international plane on one of the Kenya airports.

What has in fact changed the whole African scene so rapidly is the development of transportation. At the opening of the present

[1] G. H. T. Kimble, "Focus on Tropical Africa," *Canadian Geographical Journal*, XLIII, July 1951, 2–15.

century very few Africans had ever been outside their tribal limits. Tribal organization was so strict that, even had opportunity offered, permission would not have been granted by tribal chiefs. Today the University Colleges which have been established in East and West Africa draw students from so far away that they may spend 3 months out of their 4-month-long vacation getting to and from their homes. It is recorded that in the year 1951 there were no less than 50,000 Africans from tropical Africa studying, visiting, or working in England. The labor in the Katanga copper mines, or the gold mines of the Rand, is drawn from a very large radius, and it is common to find West Coast Africans who have received a missionary education working as clerks in the offices of Elisabethville in the heart of the Belgian Congo.

It is this increased mobility which has been mainly instrumental in disrupting the old tribal system of life, of depriving the chiefs of much of their authority and of creating a class of African having no real roots in the soil. They tend to drift to towns, and as happens in so many parts of the world social adjustment fails to keep pace. Bad housing conditions, inadequate sanitation and the spread of the diseases of civilization, especially of venereal disease, result in an inevitable sense of frustration among these foot-loose Africans. The dignity of tribal life has been lost, and modern concepts of democracy have not yet taken its place.

On the other hand, increased mobility has made possible immensely rapid and beneficial economic development. As we have mentioned elsewhere, first the bicycle, later the automobile, especially the bus, have made the jungle African free to get about his country much more easily than ever before, and much faster. The bush farmer is able to get his surplus crops to a city market, where he has quickly learned to understand and appreciate the products of overseas factories.

There are perhaps two particular aspects of this increased mobility which may be mentioned. The first is the growth everywhere of the village shop or store, now to be found in practically every settlement, where it is possible to buy not only local produce but such universally used imported goods as soaps, patent medicines, cigarettes, cotton and rayon cloth, razor blades and umbrellas. The shopkeeper not infrequently runs his own car and obtains regular supplies, and as soon as a settlement has become sufficiently large to have a village shop it is almost certain that a taxicab or a motor bus will link it with some larger center.

In the second place the agents of government can reach with ease all parts of their districts. District Commissioners, for example, now cover in a single day distances which would formerly have taken

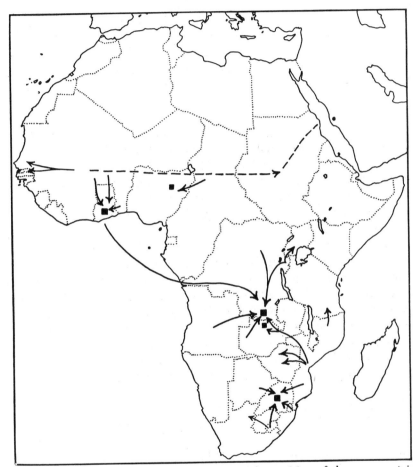

Figure 1. Main Lines of Labor Movement in Africa. Most of the movement is towards the modern mining centers—the Rand, Katanga and Jos Plateau of Nigeria. The important movement from the Rhodesias and Nyasaland should be added.

at the average rate of travel of 15 miles per day a matter of weeks. So the great octopus of modern administration spreads its tentacles to the farthest corners of African lands, and along the same channels as law and order come education, social and medical services. In the opposite direction there comes an ever-increasing stream of surplus products available for export.

With this increased mobility we can connect what is broadly to be described as a rise in the standard of living, which is evidenced in particular by the increasing variety of food which enters into the daily diet. In due course the old "hungry season" will have been forgotten. Kimble instances the typical case where twenty years ago the West African fishing village with more than sufficient for its own needs would perhaps be able to export a few miles inland a little dried fish. Today there are villages along the Gold Coast near Accra which between them need a fleet of forty trucks to handle their business, and some of their fresh fish is marketed as far as 300 miles upcountry. Thanks to the use of the airplane for commodities of high value, those who enjoy the amenities of higher incomes at such places as Leopoldville may enjoy fresh strawberries, picked at dawn on the eastern highlands of the Belgian Congo a thousand miles away. The administrator, the trader and others who can pay the price need no longer fear the dangers of isolation. When expert medical advice is needed, or hospital treatment is urgent, the helicopter is the answer.

With this increased mobility and the breakdown of old isolation it is becoming increasingly difficult to find even a small group of native Africans untouched by contact with Western peoples and Western ideas. The pygmies of the Congo, the headhunters of the remote interior, the warring feudal tribes of the east, are scarcely to be found any longer. War dances may be remembered and are produced as a show for the visiting tourist. Kimble mentions his visit to a lake in which a former king of the Baganda people in Uganda threw his enemies to be devoured by his pet crocodiles. Today it is used as a swimming pool by his grandson, a graduate of the University of Cambridge in England.

Yet some of the old African customs are being incorporated with suitable modifications into modern life. The bush telegraph, or talking drum, about which so much has been written by travelers and explorers, is still used. Indeed it has been used to such effect for signaling along some of the tropical African railways that those lines have a better accident record than the finest equipped lines in Europe and America.

It was one of the surprises of my own studies in West Africa to see in the bazaar at Lagos a druggist's stall selling all the well-known brands of patent medicine from Europe and America side by side with the stall of the witch doctor where mysterious charms in dried skin and bone and hair, and mysterious preparations of roots and stems and seeds, or charms of bone and ivory, were in equal demand.   In a secluded grove in thick bush one may stumble accidentally upon, rather than be conducted to, a shrine of the fetish worshippers, perhaps to find a very life-like image of the local Commissioner skillfully made from cow dung and mud and painted in life-like colors either to be revered or, as the case may be, to have symbolical needles and pins stuck into it.   If one makes one's way

Figure 2. A Typical Roadside Store, Gold Coast. The coming of the village store, roofed with corrugated iron, and with sheets of corrugated iron for sale is a sure sign that Western civilization has reached an African village. (Copyright L. Dudley Stamp.)

into a village hut, there are the same uncertainties as to what one may find.   It may be that the mud hut is almost devoid of furniture.   On the other hand, it is equally likely to include a modern radio set run by dry battery, or a phonograph complete with latest American records.   In either case it is more than probable that a thoroughly efficient and modern three-speed bicycle will be in the possession of the owner of the hut.

As in other parts of the world, increased mobility and accessibility have resulted or are resulting in a decline of rural arts and crafts.   The two-gallon gasoline container proves itself a far lighter, more efficient and less easily damaged receptacle for water than an earthenware jar, and a discarded can the most efficient of dippers to be associated with it.   Thus the old trade of making earthenware pitchers no longer exists.   The same is true of wood working, and even of metal working, so that already government-sponsored or mission-sponsored schools are being established to keep alive the old arts and crafts. With house building the same is true. The great desire is for that curse of the tropics, corrugated or galvanized iron. The sheets which rust so readily in wet tropical climates are to be found everywhere, but even without attention they last longer than straw for the roofs. They are not inflammable and they keep out the wet, though anyone who has suffered through a night of heavy rainfall in a hut roofed with galvanized iron or has felt the heat which develops in the interior under the high sun of noon must be forced to doubt whether this modern progress is really progress.

The inevitable change everywhere is of course affecting clothing. The general tendency is for more clothing—incidentally a greater demand on the world's factories; and there are those medical men who link the increase of certain diseases with this increase in the amount of clothing worn. The human skin does not suffer from being wet by heavy tropical downpours, but cotton clothing soaked through by a similar downpour and left to dry on the body may well be responsible for the growth in tuberculosis and other diseases of the lung which are indeed so serious in the wetter parts of tropical Africa.

African womenfolk, notably in West Africa, have tended to develop flowing styles in brightly colored and broadly patterned cottons and rayon which have now become characteristic. African men, on the other hand, away from the Mohammedan districts, tend to adopt the inevitable trousers and shirt of European pattern, wearing full European costume only on important occasions, or according to the dignity and importance of the position of the wearer.

For centuries the outside world has had an interest in African products. In the early days it was ivory, black ivory, and gold. Later came an appreciation of a wider range of African products of mahogany and wild rubber, of gums from the bush country, or leather, such as the so-called Morocco leather from West Africa. Then there were the search for minerals and the realization that hidden away in the heart of Africa were vast deposits of copper, so much needed by the Western world, or gold, or diamonds. So by the middle of the twentieth century we find the Congo-Rhodesian copper area producing nearly 20 per cent of the world's total and other fields in prospect of development. The largest diamond mines in the world, formerly claimed by Kimberley in South Africa, are now to be found in Tanganyika. The enormous deposits now proved of iron ore, of bauxite for the production of aluminum, and the important, if not outstanding, deposits of tin ore—the Belgian Congo and Nigeria producing approximately 20 per cent of the world's total—chromium, manganese and cobalt are all indications of Africa's mineral wealth. Of oil there is little and little likelihood of any. Of coal, except in South Africa and limited fields in Tanganyika, Nigeria and Rhodesia, it is doubtful whether Africa has any great riches. On the other hand, there is general agreement that the potential hydroelectric power far exceeds that of any other continent; possibly Africa has one-third of the total water power potential of the entire world.

If mineral deposits are expendable resources, this water power is not, and is a permanent asset of the continent. But the greatest of all the present and future problems of Africa is the development of the food-producing capabilities of the land.

In 1951 the Committee on Economic Affairs of the United Nations published a *Review of the Economic Conditions in Africa*, which summarizes in a very convenient way and in a short space the economic development which had been reached by 1948 or 1949. The summary statement which follows is based essentially upon this publication.

The population of the whole continent is given as 198 millions, representing 8 per cent of the world's population, living on 23 per cent of the world's land area. Ninety-seven per cent of the people are indigenous or long resident in the continent. Those of European origin number on the whole about 5 million, half of them living in the Union of South Africa, 320,000 in East and Central Africa, 80,000 in West Africa, and the remainder mainly in the northwest. About half a million people are recent immigrants from Asia.

In 1949 the only four independent countries were Egypt, Ethiopia, Liberia and the Union of South Africa, including in all about 50 million people, or one-quarter of the total population and about 11 per cent of the total area. The territories under the control of the United Kingdom were estimated to have a total population of 57 million, those under French Union about 42 million and under Belgium about 15 million. In Portuguese territories the figures are given as 11½ million people, in Spanish 1.6 million. It is noted that the seven United Nations Trust Territories had in all about 17.6 million people or nearly 9 per cent of the total population of the continent. This is excluding Southwest Africa.

The overwhelming position in foreign trade occupied by the Union of South Africa is noteworthy. Including gold, its trade represented nearly two-thirds of that of the whole continent. Merchandise alone accounted for one-quarter of the continent's foreign trade.

It is admittedly extremely difficult to estimate agricultural production in countries where the bulk is grown for immediate home consumption. But if we take the eight crops which supply 85 per cent of the world's food intake, namely, wheat, rye, oats, barley, rice, maize, sugar and potatoes, whether we measure per unit of area or per capita, outputs were very low—per unit area probably only a little over half the world average. It is to be noted, however, that a large part of the sustenance of African peoples is not in the crops mentioned, but in others such as millets and sorghums, sweet potatoes, yams, beans and groundnuts. Africa, excluding Egypt, in 1949 accounted for only about 8 per cent of the value of total world imports and 9.9 per cent of the total world exports. Expressed in per capita terms, however, Africa's share in world trade is higher than in the Far East, though somewhat below Latin America.

In certain commodities, however, Africa's output is very great. In 1948 the continent produced 98.4 per cent of the world's diamonds, 80 per cent of the world's cobalt, 60 per cent of the world's gold, 35.5 per cent of the world's phosphates, 30 per cent of chromium ore and manganese ore, 18 per cent of copper. On the other hand, African production of iron ore and coal, the basic materials of heavy industry, was very small and the same is true of oil—less than 3 per cent in each case.

As regards agricultural production, in 1948 Africa produced 68 per cent of the world's cocoa, 69.5 per cent of palm oil, 75 per cent of sisal and 15 per cent of coffee.

In assessing possibilities for development, the United Nations deals with the difficulties stressed in their book, and notes the low average density of population, about 16 per square mile. Only Australia and South America have lower densities, and any development in the continent is likely to be hindered by the problems of labor shortage. It is largely for this reason that the increase in output of such important export crops as cocoa, groundnuts, other vegetable oils and cotton has come not from large-scale plantations, which so many seem to imagine, but from the African small holder. Only in a few areas of the continent, mainly in East Africa, are plantation crops grown on estates owned mainly by non-Africans. These estates produce sisal, sugar, tea and coffee.

The labor shortage led the Dutch East India Company as early as the seventeenth century to introduce laborers from the Far East. The process continued and at a much later stage was followed by successive importations of Indian labor into Natal, Chinese labor into the Transvaal gold mines and even labor from India, China and Cuba for railway construction in the Congo. Apart from the fact that Africans had little reason to trust a prospective European employer, they had little or no incentive to exchange labor for wages. The position is now different. Such incentives are developing rapidly. The African naturally desires the products of modern industry, and the development of taxation makes it essential to earn money wages. It is interesting that the native reserves which have been set up, being maintained as areas of tribal life, are to a large extent cut off from the direct effects of development taking place outside. They have no internal capital resources, they become increasingly unable to support their growing populations and they become exporters of labor.

In Africa as elsewhere in the world there is a drift of population from the country to the towns. Both the Gold Coast and Kenya have reported a shortage of labor on the farms but unemployment in the towns. The migrant labor which has thus become a feature—for example, in the mining areas of Africa—is in fact relatively inefficient. Much time is lost in traveling, much of it being done on foot over great distances in conditions which have bad effects on health. The womenfolk remain behind, with serious social results. There is thus an ever-increasing attempt, as at the steel works at Vereeniging, to retain a stable labor force of both Europeans and Africans.

The United Nations Review summarizes the position by saying that Africa as a whole is economically among the least-developed areas of the world, with very low levels of production and consumption. Only two mainland countries had in 1948 a per capita export exceeding 50 dollars per year; they were Northern and Southern Rhodesia. Only two countries had a government revenue of over 40 dollars per head; they were Tunisia and the Union of South Africa. The vast bulk of the continent had a per capita export of less than 20 dollars and a government revenue of less than 10 dollars per head.

Turning to other aspects of development, we find the growth of roads interesting, but when expressed in terms of number of people per mile of road, or area per mile of road, the sparseness of the network is still very clear. Despite the existence in the Union of South Africa of nearly half a million motor vehicles, representing one for every 26 persons, the average number in Africa as a whole, excluding Egypt, was very low. The Union of South Africa had in fact nearly two-thirds of all the motor vehicles in the continent, excluding Egypt, and in territories like Sierra Leone and Liberia—very wet areas—there was less than one vehicle for every 2000 people. The figures would look very different if one took a census of bicycles.

Among other interesting figures is the low proportion of wage earners throughout Africa. In the prosperous cocoa-producing territory of the Gold Coast, the number of wage earners is still very small, because the cocoa producers are working on their own account.

All these facts go to show how very different is the pattern of life over nearly the whole of Africa, especially tropical Africa, from that to which we are accustomed in temperate latitudes. Indeed we may read with profit that charming book, far more than an adventure story, by Laurens Van der Post, *Venture to the Interior*,[1] in which he gives a snapshot picture of the amazing contrasts in East Africa of 1950, and recounts the difficulties which he had in exploring two little-known lofty plateaus in the heart of Nyasaland.

A very important aspect of the economic and social development of Africa since the end of the Second World War has been the large part played by American agencies and individual experts in many fields. The development of dependent overseas territories was from the first an integral part of the Marshall Plan, and by the end of 1950 the Economic Cooperation Administration had financed in whole or in part projects in nearly every country of tropical Africa. Road work took a high place but geological surveys and mineral development were undertaken in many areas with soil conservation, reservoir construction, locust control and port development more locally. Professor J. E. Orchard has reviewed the work to the end of 1950[2] and has analyzed critically the difficulties faced in Africa.

The Technical Cooperation Program, popularly known as "Point IV," has by contrast been concerned with the independent countries of Africa—Egypt, Libya, Ethiopia and Liberia. In particular there has been full participation in the five-year development plan for Liberia from 1951–1952. The Technical Cooperation Administration has sponsored and published a *Reconnaissance Soil Survey of Liberia* and a survey of *Forest Resources*.

[1] Toronto, 1952.
[2] ECA and the Dependent Territories, *Geog. Rev.*, XLI, 1951, 66–87.

It will have become clear that Africa of today is a continent of change. Even since the preceding pages were written and the typescript sent to the printers, far-reaching changes have taken place and the reawakened interest of the Western world in African affairs is producing a stream of literature which threatens to become a flood.

A valuable work of reference prepared by a study group of the South African Institute of International Affairs under the title *Africa South of the Sahara* was published by the Oxford University Press (Cape Town, New York, and London) in 1951. The monumental and graphically illustrated work entitled *The Sterling Area: An American Analysis,* prepared under the direction of John M. Cassels for the Economic Cooperation Administration, published by the U.S. Government Printing Office (1952), and sold at the incredibly low price of three dollars, devotes two valuable chapters to the British areas in Africa. The American Geographical Society's *Atlas of Diseases* is being published in single plates, each giving a wealth of information, with the quarterly parts of the *Geographical Review.* Detailed maps of helminthiasis, yellow fever and dengue, and plague are now available.

The French have continued the publication of the great *Encyclopédie coloniale et maritime* begun in 1942, and two volumes dealing with *Afrique occidentale française* edited by E. Guernier have appeared.

Seventy-five years of activity by the Royal Geographical Society of Egypt were marked by celebrations in Cairo in January 1951, and the growth of geographical studies in the universities of Egypt should be stressed. Egyptians have a live interest in their own natural resources. A useful summary from an outside point of view has been given by Alan B. Mountjoy on the "Development of Industry in Egypt" (*Economic Geography,* July 1952).

Two valuable recent papers on Nigeria are K. M. Buchanan's "Nigeria—Largest Remaining British Colony" (*Economic Geography,* October 1952) and Ronald Miller's "The Climate of Nigeria" (*Geography,* XXXVII, November 1952). Those who are interested in the scenery of the southern half of the continent and its origin have welcomed the second edition of L. C. King's *South African Scenery* (Edinburgh, 1951). Benjamin E. Thomas has given an account of "Modern Trans-Saharan Routes" (*Geographical Review,* April 1952), which may be used to supplement the details given in Chapter 12.

The material progress of Africa continues, with special emphasis on development of communications to open up new mining and food-producing lands. The need for improving export facilities is being met by harbor works, including reconstruction of Takoradi harbor (and plans for a new Gold Coast port at Tema), new deep-water quays at Freetown, Kilindini, and Dar-es-Salaam.

Recent events have served to emphasize the conflicting currents in African political development and the clash of cultures. Reference has been made in the pages of this book to the continuing hold which belief in witchcraft and magic has upon the African in many areas. This hold is strengthened by the existence of secret societies. Opinions differ as to the wisdom of Europeans attending such ceremonies as those for the propitiation of the rain-gods, and the question came to the fore in 1952. Members of the Kikuyu tribe in Kenya resuscitated the strongly anti-Christian and anti-European Mau-Mau society for political ends, and a wave of terrorism resulted. Representatives of law and order both African and European fought the reactionary outbreak, and repentant Africans who had taken Mau-Mau oaths were "cleansed" by counter ceremonies.

The countries of Africa are moving by different paths towards independence, helped in different ways by the controlling Colonial powers. How far the United Nations has a right to interfere with "internal" affairs was brought into the limelight in 1952 by the racial policy of the South African government, the policy of France in Tunisia, and the attempt of the British in Tanganyika to develop agricultural production, which had involved moving members of the Meru tribe to other areas.

The year 1952 witnessed the abdication of King Farouk of Egypt, and the installation of a government with a military leader and a regency during the minority of King Fuad II. The dropping of the title King of Egypt and of the Sudan helped to clear the way for Sudanese independence, with good will from both Britain and Egypt. A republic was declared in 1953.

In North Africa some contrasts between Algeria, an integral part of France, and the French protectorates of Tunisia and Morocco have become apparent. All have Moslem majorities, but the large resident French populations have acquired rights quite different from those of the handfuls of European administrators found in most of the countries of tropical Africa.

So the kaleidoscopic pattern of the life of a continent changes, but it is against a background where the limitations of natural resources and physical conditions, still imperfectly understood and still needing much careful study, play a major part.

Statistical Summary

EGYPT (MISR)

An independent republic: King Farouk I succeeded 1936, abdicated 1952; King Fuad II, Farouk's infant son (ruling under a regency), succeeded in 1952. A republic was proclaimed in 1953.

Area. 386,198 square miles (settled area 13,500 square miles).

Population. 19,087,304 (1947 census); 15,932,694 (1937 census). Density: 1398 per square mile (1947) over settled area.

Towns in 1947: Cairo (capital), 2,100,506; Alexandria, 925,081; Port Said, 178,432; Tanta, 139,965; Mahalla el Kubra, 115,509; Suez, 108,250; Mansura, 102,709.

Religion: In 1937 Moslems; 91.4%; Christians, 8.19%; Jews, 0.4%.

Land Use, 1946–1947

Cultivable	8,451,874 acres
Cultivated	6,311,040
Public utilities	669,281
To be reclaimed	2,471,553

Land Use, 1949–1950

Cotton	2,049,592 acres
Corn (maize)	1,506,563
Wheat	1,424,133
Rice	726,868

Land Use, 1947

Horses, 27,747; donkeys, 1,125,945; mules, 12,225; cows, 1,321,052; buffaloes, 1,240,196; sheep, 1,875,338; goats, 1,475,831; camels, 196,721; pigs, 50,343.

Minerals, 1949. Phosphate rock, 350,480 metric tons; petroleum, 2,288,972 tons.

Trade, 1950

Exports: £E172,959,011.

Imports: £E212,682,206.

Trade, 1946–1948. Exports: Cotton (raw), 69%; tobacco, 12%; rice, 7%.

Currency. £E1 (one Egyptian pound)

= £1 sterling = $2.80 (1951–1952).

= 100 piastres or 1000 mils.

MOROCCO (MAGHREB-EL AKSA)

An Empire, in principle an absolute monarchy, in which the Sultan exercises supreme civil and religious authority. Sultan Sidi-Mohammed, 1927. The country is actually divided into three zones (since 1912, modified 1923) under different forms of protectorate. The Sultan resides in the French Zone.

Area

French Zone	153,870 square miles
Spanish Zone (Northern, Ifni and Southern)	18,009
Tangier International Zone (France, Spain, Britain)	225
Total	172,104

Population

French Zone: 360,000 Europeans; 7,980,000 Moslems; 200,000 Jews. (Estimated January 1, 1950—total 8,540,000.)

Spanish Zone: 72,184 Europeans; 995,329 Moslems; 14,196 Jews. (Census of 1945—total 1,082,009.)

Tangier Zone: 16,500 Europeans; 36,500 native Moslems; 7000 Jews. (Estimated 1941—total about 100,000, including non-native Moslems.)

French Zone towns in 1949: Casablanca, 569,500 Marrakesh, 239,-200; Fez, 202,000; Meknes, 162,400; Rabat, 161,600.

Spanish Zone towns in 1945: Tetuan, 93,658; Larache, 41,286.

Land Use (French Zone). Cultivable, 38,500,000 acres; forest, 8,800,-000 acres.

Chief crops: barley, wheat, maize.

1949: Horses, 103,000; asses, 615,000; mules, 144,000; cattle, 1,762,-000; sheep 9,149,000; goats, 6,805,000; pigs, 103,000; camels, 183,-000.

Minerals (French Zone), 1949. Phosphates, 3,692,952 metric tons; anthracite, 341,400 tons; iron ore, 356,818 tons; manganese, 221,877 tons.

Trade (French Zone)

1949: Exports, 53,516,000,000 francs.

Imports, 103,321,000,000 francs.

1949: Exports: Cereals, 15%; canned fish, 15%; phosphates, 12%.

Currency

French Zone (as in France): 350 francs = $1.00 U.S.

Spanish Zone (as in Spain): 11 pesetas = $1.00 U.S.

ALGERIA (L'ALGÉRIE)

A Government-General of the French Union divided into Northern Algeria, with three departments (Oran, Algiers and Constantine), and Southern Algeria, with four territories.

Area

Northern Algeria: 80,117 square miles }
Southern Algeria: 767,435 square miles } 847,552 square miles.

Population

Northern Algeria: 7,859,023 }
Southern Algeria: 816,993 } 8,876,016 (census of 1948).

Towns in 1948: Algiers (capital), 315,210; Oran, 256,661; Constantine, 118,774; Bône, 102,823.

Land Use, 1949

Cultivated	15,600,000 acres
European owned	5,000,000
State forests	5,260,000

Chief crops: wheat and barley.

Vineyards: 835,000 acres.

Tobacco: 77,000 acres.

Horses, 201,000; donkeys, 309,000; mules, 229,000; cattle, 797,000; sheep, 3,839,000; goats, 2,596,000; pigs, 160,000; camels, 140,000.

Minerals, 1949. Iron ore, 2,536,872 metric tons; phosphates, 645,000 tons.

Trade, 1949

Exports: 88,709,200,000 francs.

Imports: 127,521,000,000 francs.

Exports: Wine, 48%; fruits, 8%; cereals, 7%.

Currency. As in France: 350 francs = $1.00 (1951–1952).

TUNISIA (AFRIKIYA: TUNISIE)

A French Protectorate. The ruler is the Bey of Tunisia, Sidi Mohammed al-Amin. There is a French Resident-General.

Area. 48,195 square miles.

Population. 3,143,498 (census of 1946): French, 143,977; Italians, 84,935; Maltese, 6,459; total European, 239,549. Arabs and Bedouins, 2,832,978; Tunisian Jews, 70,971.

Towns in 1946: Tunis, 364,593; Sfax, 54,637.

Land Use

Total area: 31,000,000 acres.

Productive: 22,250,000 acres.

Arable, 33%; forests, 11.2%; orchards and vineyards, 9%; meadow, 1.1%; common and uncultivated, 45.7% (percentage of the productive land).

1949: Horses, asses and mules, 222,000; cattle, 359,000; sheep, 1,-885,000; goats, 1,315,000; camels, 156,000; pigs, 41,700.

Minerals, 1949. Phosphates, 1,442,000 metric tons; iron ore, 679,000 tons.

Trade, 1949

Exports: 27,396,000,000 francs.

Imports: 42,368,000,000 francs.

Exports: Phosphates, 15%; olive oil, 11%; cereals, 10%.

Currency. As in France: 350 francs = $1.00 (1951–1952).

LIBYA

An independent Kingdom, formerly an Italian Colony, proclaimed 1950, came into effective existence 1952, under Mohammed Idris el Senussi as King.

Area. 679,358 square miles.

Population. 888,401 (Italian cenus of 1938, probably incomplete; including 89,098 Italians and 30,046 Jews).

Tripolitania	796,900 (1950)	
Fezzan	49,950 (1950)	} 1,173,850 (1950).
Cyrenaica	327,000 (1950)	

Towns in 1950 (estimated): Tripoli, 92,000; Benghazi, 60,000; Derna, 15,000.

Religion: Moslems, 90% (estimated), of whom a third are of Negro stock.

SPANISH SAHARA
(A Spanish Colony)

Area. 105,409 square miles.

Population. 40,000 (exclusive of 30,000 nomads who enter in the rainy season).

FRENCH WEST AFRICA (AFRIQUE OCCIDENTALE FRANÇAISE)

Part of Overseas France (France d'Outremer) under a Governor-General at Dakar; divided since 1946 into eight territories.

Area

Senegal	81,050	square miles
French Guinea	108,400	
Ivory Coast	129,800	
Upper Volta	122,900	
Dahomey	44,650	
French Sudan	461,300	
Mauritania	364,000	
Niger	494,700	
Total	1,806,000	

Population, 1949

Senegal	1,992,000
French Guinea	2,180,000
Ivory Coast	2,065,000
Upper Volta	3,069,000
Dahomey	1,505,000
French Sudan	3,177,000
Mauritania	518,000
Niger	2,029,000
Total	16,535,000

Europeans numbered 52,000 (40,000 French).

Towns (1949–1951). Dakar (capital), 228,000; St. Louis (Senegal), 63,000; Conakry (Guinea), 43,423; Bamako (Sudan), 84,600; Abidjan (1948: 45,735); Porto Novo (Dahomey), 30,827; Bobo-Dioulasso (Upper Volta), 37,500.

Trade, 1949

Exports: 27,400,734,000 francs C.F.A.

Imports: 34,479,740,000 francs C.F.A.
Exports: Groundnuts and oil, 42%; coffee, 15%; cocoa, 15%.
Currency. West African francs (francs C.F.A.), double the value of French francs.

FRENCH TOGOLAND

Trusteeship Territory under United Nations (formerly part of German Togoland).
Area. 21,893 square miles.
Population, 1949. 970,983 African and 841 Europeans. Lomé, 30,000.
Trade, 1949
    Exports: 844,700,000 francs C.F.A.
    Imports: 1,454,400,000 francs C.F.A.
    Exports: Cocoa, 23%; coffee, 15%; palm oil and kernels, 12%.

LIBERIA
(An Independent Republic)

Area. 43,000 square miles, estimated.
Population. Estimated 1,500,000, including 12,000 to 20,000 Americo-Liberians.
    Towns: Monrovia (capital), estimated 20,000.
Trade
    1949: Exports: $14,327,865.
    1947: Imports: $8,762,728.
    Exports: Rubber, palm kernels, gold.
Currency. Liberian dollar was raised to parity with the U.S. dollar in 1944.

GAMBIA
(A British Colony and Protectorate in British West Africa)

Area. 4,101 square miles.
Population. 250,000 (Bathurst [capital], in 1944: 21,152; Protectorate [in 1948 census], 229,284).
Trade, 1949
    Exports: £1,753,915.
    Imports: £2,356,300.
    Exports mainly groundnuts.
Currency. As in Britain, pound sterling.

SIERRA LEONE
(A British Colony and Protectorate in British West Africa)

Area. 30,169 square miles.
Population. 1,858,000 (1948 estimate). Capital, Freetown, 86,000.
Trade, 1949
    Exports: £4,243,099.

Imports: £6,171,910.
Exports: Palm kernels and palm oil, iron ore, kola nuts, ginver, pissava.
Currency. As in Britain, pound sterling.

GOLD COAST
(A British Colony and Protectorate in West Africa)

Area. 91,843 square miles (including 13,041 square miles of Togoland).
Population. 4,111,680, including 6770 non-Africans (census of 1948), including 382,717 in Togoland.
Towns 1948: Accra, 135,926; Kumasi, 68,483; Sekondi-Takoradi, 44,557.
Trade, 1949
Exports: £48,246,334.
Imports: £52,942,041.
Exports: Cocoa, 68%; gold, 14%; manganese, 9%; timber, diamonds.
Currency (as in Britain), pound sterling.

NIGERIA
(A British Colony and Protectorate in West Africa)

Area. 372,674 square miles (including 34,081 square miles of Cameroons).
Population. 25,000,000 (1949 estimate).
Towns (1948 estimates): Ibadan, 335,500; Lagos, 230,000; Kano, 102,000; Iwo, 86,000; Ogbomosho, 84,500.
Trade, 1948
Exports: £37,527,112.
Imports: £44,897,309.
Exports (1949): Palm oil and kernels, 34%; cocoa, 23%; groundnuts, 21%; tin, cotton, timber.
Currency. As in Britain, pound sterling.

TOGOLAND (BRITISH)
(United Nations Trusteeship under Britain, Administered by Gold Coast)

Area. 13,041 square miles.
Population. 382,717 (census of 1948).

CAMEROONS (BRITISH)
(United Nations Trusteeship under Britain, Administered by Nigeria)

Area. 34,081 square miles.
Population. 1,032,700 (1949 estimate).

SUDAN

Until 1951 a condominium ruled jointly by Britain and Egypt under the title Anglo-Egyptian Sudan. When Egypt abrogated the treaty the King

of Egypt was declared King of the Sudan, but effective administration remained in British hands.
Area. 967,500 square miles.
Population. 8,309,663 (1949 estimate), including 301,030 non-native.
Towns: Omdurman, 117,650; Khartoum (capital), 30,850; Port Sudan, 47,000; Atbara, 42,000.
Trade, 1949
   Exports: £E26,435,396.
   Imports: £E23,869,569.
   Exports: Cotton, 72%; cottonseed, 8%; gum, 6%.
Currency. The Egyptian pound (£E) of 100 piastres or 1000 mils.

ERITREA
(Autonomous Province under Ethiopian Empire, Former Italian Colony)

Area. 40,020 square miles.
Population. 1,86,000 (estimated), including 21,000 Italians (1949). Asmara 117,000.

FRENCH SOMALILAND (COTE FRANÇAISE DES SOMALIS)
(French Colony)

Area. 9,071 square miles.
Population. 48,210 (estimated 1949), Europeans 2,034.

BRITISH SOMALILAND
(A British Protectorate)

Area. 68,000 square miles (estimated).
Population. 700,000 (estimated).
Trade, 1949
   Exports: £660,075
   Imports: £844,334.
   Exports: Skins, 64%; sheep and goats, 33%; gum, 2%.

ITALIAN SOMALILAND (SOMALIA)

Area. 189,000 square miles (estimated).
Population. 1,000,000 (estimated 1950), including 4500 Italians. Mogadiscio, 70,000 (estimated).

ETHIOPIA (ABYSSINIA)

A sovereign independent state or empire. Emperor Haile Selassie I, re-entered after Italian occupation, 1942.
Area. 350,000 square miles (estimated).
Population. 15,000,000. (1947 official estimate but believed to be an exaggeration. Unofficial estimate 8 to 10 million.)

Leading race Amhara (2,000,000) and official language Amharic.
Towns: Addis Ababa (capital), 300,000; Dire Dawa, 30,000; Harar, 25,000.
Trade, 1949
Exports: $Eth.99,555,060.
Imports: $Eth.106,642,680.
Exports: Coffee, 27%; hides and skins, 24%; cereals and pulses, 24%.
Currency. Ethiopian dollar of 100 cents ($Eth.)
= 2 shillings East African.
= £0.1 or 28 cents U.S. (1951–1952).

FRENCH EQUATORIAL AFRICA (AFRIQUE EQUATORIALE FRANÇAISE)

A French colony under a Governor-General divided into four territories, each under a governor.

Area

Gabun (Gabon), capital Libreville	104,000 square miles
Middle Congo (Moyen Congo), capital Pointe Noire	172,000
Ubangi-Shari (Oubangi-Chari), capital Bangui	236,000
Chad (Chad), capital Fort Lamy	400,000
Total	912,000

Population (estimated January 1, 1950)

	European	African
Gabun	3,378	405,400
Middle Congo	9,050	675,400
Ubangi-Shari	4,391	1,067,400
Chad	3,301	2,238,200
Total	20,120	4,386,400

Brazzaville had 6505 Europeans on January 1, 1951.

Land Use, 1944. Horses, 125,000; asses, 175,000; cattle, 4,000,000; sheep and goats, 5,000,000; camels, 200,000.

Trade, 1949
Exports: 7,253,800,000 francs (C.F.A.).
Imports: 13,393,600,000 francs (C.F.A.).
Exports: Cotton, 36%; wood, 24%; gold, 12%; palm oil, rubber.
Currency
Francs C.F.A.   = 2 French francs.
175 francs C.F.A. = $1.00 U.S.

FRENCH CAMEROONS

Trusteeship territory (formerly German Kamerun) held from United Nations.
Area. 166,489 square miles.

Population. 8998 Europèans; 2,997,164 Africans (1950).
Towns: Yaounde (capital), 50,000; Douala.
Trade, 1949
Exports: 6,661,000,000 francs (C.F.A.).
Imports: 8,776,100,000 francs (C.F.A.).
Exports: Cocoa, 47%; bananas, 15%; palm oil and kernels, 15%.
Currency. Francs C.F.A.

BELGIAN CONGO (CONGO BELGE, BELGISCH CONGO)
(A Belgian Colony under a Governor-General)

Area. 904,750 square miles (estimated).
Population. 11,073,311 Africans; 53,176 Europeans; 1063 Asiatics.
(Census of December 31, 1949).
Towns, 1949: Leopoldville (capital), 160,304; Elisabethville, 48,734.
Minerals, 1949. Copper, 176,000 metric tons (1950); gold, 10,504 kilos; diamonds, 9,700,000 carats (1950); cobalt, tin, zinc, cadmium.
Trade, 1949
Exports: 10,967,943,000 francs.
Imports: 10,346,272,000 francs.
Exports: Copper, 25%; palm oil and kernels, 17%; cotton, 13%; other metals, rubber.
Currency. Congolese franc.

RUANDA-URUNDI

(United Nations Trusteeship territory, administered as part of Belgian Congo, formerly part of German East Africa)
Area. 20,900 square miles.
Population. 3,882,392 Africans; 3407 Europeans; 2894 Asiatics (census of 1949).
Trade included under Belgian Congo.

SPANISH GUINEA

(A Spanish colony in West Africa comprising a mainland tract and the islands of Fernando Po, Annobón, Corisco and Elobey)
Area. 10,852 square miles, including Fernando Po, 800, and Annobón, 7.
Population. 170,582, including Fernando Po, 39,980 (1945).

SÃO TOMÉ AND PRÍNCIPE
(Two Portuguese Islands in the Gulf of Guinea)

Area. 372 square miles.
Population. 60,490 (1940).

UGANDA

(A British Protectorate in East Africa over Buganda and Other Kingdoms)

Area. 93,981 square miles, but including 13,690 square miles of water.
Population. 4,993,965 (census of 1948). 4,953,000 Africans; 3448
Europeans; 37,517 Asians. Capital: Kampala.
Trade, 1949
  Exports: £ 23,433,182.
  Imports: 12,817,633.
  Exports: Cotton, 74%; coffee, 12%; cottonseed, 5%.
Currency. East African shilling divided into 100 cents. 20 shillings =
one pound sterling.

KENYA

(A British Colony and Protectorate in East Africa)

Area. 219,730 square miles.
Population. 5,379,966 (census of 1948). 5,225,120 Africans; 29,660
Europeans; 97,687 Indians and Goans; 24,174 Arabs. Capital: Nairobi.
Trade, 1949
  Exports: £ 29,173,704 (including £ 18,209,570 re-exports).
  Imports: £ 54,123,277.
  Exports: Sisal, 26%; coffee, 14%; hides and skins, 11%.
There is a customs union between Uganda, Kenya and Tanganyika so
that it is difficult to separate the trade of the three countries. Many of
the exports of Kenya are destined for Uganda, most of the exports of
Uganda pass through Kenya.
Currency. As in Uganda.

TANGANYIKA

(United Nations Trusteeship Held by Britain, Formerly German
East Africa [part])

Area. 362,000 square miles approximately, including 20,000 water.
Population. 7,487,305 (census of 1948). 7,410,269 Africans; 16,299
Europeans (including 5397 Polish refugees); 60,737 Asiatics. Dar-es-
Salaam (capital), 70,000 estimated, 1950.
Trade, 1949
  Exports: £ 20,124,985.
  Imports: £ 27,576,110.
  Exports: Sisal, 58%; cotton, 11%; coffee, 8%; diamonds, 6%; gold, hides
and skins.
Currency. As in Uganda.

ZANZIBAR

(A British Protectorate, now consisting of two islands off the east coast of
Africa. .Sultan, Seyyid Sir Khalifa bin Harub, succeeded 1911)

Area. Zanzibar island, 640 square miles; Pemba, 380.
Population. 264,162 (census of 1948). Zanzibar, 149,575; Pemba,

114,587.   199,608 Africans; 44,560 Arabs; 15,892 Indians; 296 Europeans; 3554 others. Zanzibar town, 45,284.
Trade, 1949
  Exports: £ 2,823,336.
  Imports: £ 2,979,874.
  Exports: Cloves and clove-oil, 33%; coconut oil, 21%; copra, 15%.
Currency.. As in Uganda.

PORTUGUESE EAST AFRICA (MOÇAMBIQUE
(A Portuguese Colony under a Governor-General)

Area.   297,731 square miles.
Population.   5,085,630 (census of 1940).   5,031,955 Africans; 27,438 Europeans; 15,641 mixed; 1449 yellow races; 9147 Indians.
  Towns 1940: Lourenço Marques (capital), 69,861; Beira, 12,988.
Trade, 1949
  Exports: 965,599,000 escudos.
  Imports: 1,750,563,893 escudos.
  Exports: Cotton, 27%; copra, 18%; sisal, 13%.
Currency (as in Portugal): 80.65 escudos, one pound sterling. Approximately 29 escudos to $1.00.

ANGOLA (PORTUGUESE WEST AFRICA)
(A Portuguese Colony under a Governor-General)

Area.   481,351 square miles, including the detached tract of Cabinda.
Population.   3,738,010 (census of 1940).   3,665,829 Africans; 44,-083 Europeans; 28,035 mixed; 63 others. Capital: S. Paulo de Luanda.
Trade, 1949
  Exports: 1,793,012,000 angolars or Portuguese escudos.
  Imports: 1,337,024,000.
  Exports: Coffee, 31%; diamonds, 14%; maize, 9%.
Currency. See Portuguese East Africa.

SOUTHERN RHODESIA
(A Self-Governing Colony of the British Commonwealth)

Area.   150,333 square miles.
Population.   1,794,000 (1946 estimate); 2,095,000 (1950 provisional estimate).   1946: 1,704,000 Africans; 82,386 Europeans; 7470 Asiatic and colored.   1950: 1,957,000 Africans; 129,000 Europeans; 8800 Asiatic and colored. Capital: Salisbury (39,000 Europeans); Bulawayo (33,000 Europeans).
Land Use

Tribal settlements (native reserves)	21,127,040 acres
Native purchase areas	7,859,942
Crown lands available for settlers	32,685,659

Livestock, European-owned: 1,188,101 cattle; 108,064 sheep; 37,155 pigs; 18,431 goats (1949). African-owned: 1,815,733 cattle; 207,113 sheep; 69,583 pigs; 524,029 goats (1949).

Trade, 1949
Exports: (domestic) £29,621,299.
Imports: £54,585,817.
Re-exports: £4,901,490.
Exports: Tobacco, 39%; gold, 18%; asbestos, 13%; chrome ore.
Currency. As in Britain, pounds, shillings and pence.

NORTHERN RHODESIA
(A British Colony in South-Central Africa)

Area. 287,640 square miles.
Population. 1,740,000 (estimate of 1950); 21,907 Europeans; 1117 Asiatics; 804 colored (census of 1946); 36,000 Europeans; 3100 Asiatics and colored (estimate of 1950). Capital: Lusaka.
Trade, 1948
Exports: £28,129,623.
Imports: £16,098,874.
Re-exports: £339,657.
Exports (1949): Copper, 85%; zinc, 6%; lead, 4%.
Currency. As in Southern Rhodesia.

NYASALAND
(A British Protectorate)

Area. 37,374 square miles (land).
Population. 2,400,000 (1950 estimate). About 3000 Europeans and 4000 Asiatics. Capital: Zomba.
Trade, 1949
Exports: £4,689,733.
Imports: £5,041,627.
Exports: Tobacco, 67%; tea, 25%; cotton, 5%.
Currency. As in Rhodesia.

UNION OF SOUTH AFRICA
(A Self-Governing Dominion of the British Commonwealth)

Area

Cape of Good Hope	277,113 square miles
Natal	35,284
Transvaal	110,450
Orange Free State	49,647
Total	472,494

Population

Europeans	2,372,690 (census of 1946)
Non-Europeans	9,045,659
Total	11,418,349

Non-Europeans include 7,831,915 Bantus; 285,260 Asians; 928,484 others.

Towns (1946), European population *only:* Johannesburg, 260,747; Cape Town, 173,412; Durban, 96,804; Pretoria, 78,028; Port Elisabeth, 53,461; Germiston, 34,394; East London, 31,311; Bloemfontein, 30,291; Pietermaritzburg, 22,446.

Pretoria is the seat of government, Cape Town the seat of legislature.

Land Use, 1949

Land in farms: 214,777,497 acres
Number of farms: 177,242

Crops: Maize, wheat, potatoes, kaffir corn, oats, barley, fruits, sugar cane, tobacco.

Animals: Horses, 346,594; cattle, 12,241,925; sheep, 31,907,749; goats, 5,528,820.

Minerals, 1949. Coal, 27,600,000 tons; asbestos, 70,917 short tons; manganese ore, 644,831 long tons; gold, 11,705,048 ounces; diamonds, 1,494,527 metric carats; copper, platinum, chrome ore.

Trade, 1949

Exports, excluding gold: £153,624,896.
Imports, excluding gold: 314,579,015.
Exports: Gold, 44%; wool, 14%; diamonds, 4%.

Currency. South African pounds, shillings and pence.

SOUTHWEST AFRICA

(A territory administered by the Union of South Africa. The old Mandate from the League of Nations was a Class III Mandate which laid down that the territory should be governed as an integral part of the territory of the Mandatory power)

Area. 317,725 square miles.

Population (1946 census): 37,858 Europeans; 53,172 colored; 269,569 Africans. Capital: Windhoek, 23,492 (1946).

Trade, 1949

Exports: £14,863,702.
Imports: 13,069,816.

BASUTOLAND

(A British Protectorate)

Regent: Ma'Ntsebo, widow of the late Paramount Chief, acting for Bereng, a minor.

Area. 11,716 square miles.

Population (census of 1946). 563,854, including 1689 Europeans, 274 Asiatics, and 602 colored. In addition about 35,000 Basutos were working in the Rand mines and 75,000 elsewhere.

BECHUANALAND PROTECTORATE
(A British Protectorate)

Each group of tribes is ruled by its chief.
Area. About 275,000 square miles.
Population (census of 1946). 2325 Europeans; 1804 Asians and colored; 292,754 Africans.

SWAZILAND
(A British Protectorate)

Chief: Mswazi II succeeded 1939.
Area. 6705 square miles.
Population (census of 1946). 3204 Europeans; 6 Asians; 735 colored; 181,269 Africans.

MADAGASCAR AND DEPENDENCIES
(A French Colony under a High Commissioner)

Area. 227,500 squares miles approximately.
Population. 4,350,700 (estimate of 1950, including the Mayotte and Comoro Islands) and including 44,517 French and 19,912 other Europeans. Capital: Tananarive, 174,153 (1950); Tamatave, 28,747; Majunga, 32,163.
   Trade, 1949
      Exports: 7,369,500,000 francs.
      Imports: 11,789,400,000 francs.
      Exports: Coffee, 23%; meat, 18%; hides, 10%; vanilla, cloves.
   Currency. Madagascan francs (francs C.F.A.) = 2 French francs.

RÉUNION (ÎLE DE LA RÉUNION)
(An "Overseas Department" of France)

Area. 970 square miles.
Population. 242,343 (1946). Capital: St. Denis: 36,096.
Trade, 1949
   Exports: 2,248,000,000 francs C.F.A.
   Imports: 2,873,000,000 francs.
   Exports: Sugar, 77%; rum, 11%; vegetable oils, 9%.
Currency. One franc C.F.A. = 2 French francs.

MAURITIUS
(A British Colony under a Governor)

Dependencies: Rodrigues, 42 square miles; also other small islands.

Area. 720 square miles.

Population. 419,185; dependencies 13,468 (1944). Capital: Port Louis, 70,941 (1949).

Trade, 1949

    Exports: 163,075,201, Mauritius rupees.

    Imports: 153,139,958, Mauritius rupees.

    Exports: Sugar, 96%; rum, 3%.

Currency. The Mauritius rupee, like the Ceylon rupee, is divided into 100 cents. Linked with sterling at one shilling and sixpence per rupee. One rupee approximately 21 cents U.S.

ATLANTIC ISLANDS

St. Helena. British Colony, 47 square miles; 4700 people (1949).

Ascension. Dependency of St. Helena, 34 square miles; 162 people (1949).

Tristan da Cunha. British, habitable area 12 square miles; 248 people (1949).

Cape Verde Islands. Portuguese, 1557 square miles; 181,286 people (1940).

Madeira. Administered as districts of Portugal.

Canary Islands. Administered as part of Spain.

Index

Index